APPLIED MATRIX
MODELS

APPLIED MATRIX MODELS

MODELS

A Second Course in Linear Algebra
with Computer Applications

ANDY R. MAGID

A WILEY-INTERSCIENCE PUBLICATION

JOHN WILEY & SONS

New York • Chichester • Brisbane • Toronto • Singapore

Library of Congress Cataloging in Publication Data

Magid, Andy R.
    Applied matrix models.

    "A Wiley-Interscience publication."
    Includes index.
    1. Matrices.   2. Matrices—Data processing.   I. Title.
QA188.M34   1985   512.9′434   84-19668
ISBN 0-471-88865-6

Printed in the United States of America

10 9 8 7 6 5 4 3 2 1

PREFACE

This book had its origins in a course I introduced at the University of Oklahoma in the spring semester of 1982. This was to be a second course in linear algebra with computer applications. I wanted to teach students who, in their first course in linear algebra, had learned the basics of vector and matrix algebra and how to set up and solve the primary problems of linear algebra—solving systems of linear equations and obtaining eigenvalues and eigenvectors of matrices—in the way such problems arise in actual applications. That is, I intended to teach them how to recognize the linear problem in the context of the application, how to use available computer packages to solve the linear problem, and also how to have a feeling for the linear algebra the package performs. I also had some definite ideas about what I did *not* want to teach them: I was not trying to create either a course in numerical linear algebra or a course in the programming of linear algebra algorithms—both courses are already available in the standard curriculum, and neither is really suitable for the audience I intended to reach.

Because there was no single text available which covered the contents of the course as I envisioned it, I began to assemble and integrate a number of ideas from various sources to create my lecture notes. (Foremost among these sources were *Linear Algebra and Its Applications*, by G. Strang, *Applications of Linear Algebra*, by C. Rorres and H. Anton, and *LINPACK User's Guide*, by J. Dongarra et al., and the debt the present volume owes to those works is considerable.) As with all such ventures, there was a mixture of success and failure, but with the help (and patience!) of an enthusiastic group of students the course ultimately had more of the former than the latter. So I gave some thought to turning my lecture notes into a book. A conversation with David Kaplan, ultimately my editor, and some helpful encouragement from him then helped convert these thoughts into a commitment, and this book is the result.

There are a couple of features of this book about which the reader should be warned. One such feature concerns the approach taken to using a computer to solve linear algebra problems. This is done here by using library procedures to do the linear algebra (these need to be put into simple FORTRAN calling programs to handle input and output, of course). Programming purists will object, and rightly so, that this teaches the reader nothing about converting linear algebra methods into computer code. Such coding has all sorts of pedagogic and therapeutic value for teaching programming, but, in my view, has as little place in a course in applications of linear algebra as, say, requiring students to write their own procedure to compute cosine would have in a course in calculus. Of course, calculus students need to learn about Taylor-series expansions, and they should understand that such ideas are in principle behind the cosine routines in the computers they are using, but there is no need to postpone their using the FORTRAN function COS(X) until they have studied enough numerical analysis to understand why the particular rational function approximation (which is not the Taylor series) was chosen to code this function. Similarly, students who can understand the Q-R factorization of a matrix, say, in terms of the Gram–Schmidt orthogonalization process, should be entitled to use the LINPACK routine that accomplishes this factorization and to solve least-squares problems with it, even if they are in no position to code such a routine themselves. Briefly put, this book is aimed at the user of linear algebra who wishes to intelligently employ available library routines to solve his or her problems, and is willing to employ mathematical technology (in the form of computer routines) that he or she may not be able to recreate.

Another feature that the reader needs to be warned about is the author's willingness to freely use determinants in theoretical arguments. This is not currently very fashionable; much of the modern trend in the theory of linear equations has led to the elimination of determinants from that theory. The reason, of course, is that a determinant is a hard thing to compute—at least by serial processing on a large general matrix—and so most modern linear algebra texts try to avoid their use as much as possible. Since computations of this type are not at issue here, determinants have been used in a number of places, in their essential algebraic sense as the basic invariants of matrices under elementary operations. Indeed, as the theory of matrix invariants in higher algebra shows, any invariants of matrices under such operations must be polynomials in determinants. So it is not surprising that determinants arise naturally in the theory of systems of linear equations, since the solutions of such systems are obtained by operations on matrices, and when they do arise, they appear in our discussions.

Finally, I am happy to be able to acknowledge the help of Rhonda Peterson, who typed the manuscript, the suggestions of the University of Oklahoma students, who have taken the course on which this book is based, and the encouragement of my family.

ANDY R. MAGID

Norman, Oklahoma
October 1984

CONTENTS

PART 2   DYNAMIC MODELS

APPLIED MATRIX
MODELS

1

INTRODUCTION

1.1 THE BOOK AND HOW TO USE IT

This book is intended for readers who have learned some basic linear algebra, who have a little computing experience, and who are now ready to learn about the applications of linear algebra, perhaps with a view to using such applications in their own work. Even with small-scale applications, such as those considered in this book, the arithmetic involved with linear algebra becomes lengthy, and so the use of the computer to perform computations is stressed throughout the book. Not every, in fact not even most, users of linear algebra will have the inclination or training to do their own computer coding of linear algebra computations. Fortunately, excellent program libraries of linear algebra routines are available, and the computational sections of this book explain how to use them. There are various levels of understanding that a user of a library routine may achieve; the explanations in this book are designed to help the reader understand the theoretical ideas a routine is intended to implement. It is these three themes —applications, computations, and the background necessary to understand the computations—that form the organizing principles of this book.

1

Readers of this book are expected to know basic linear algebra. That is, they should know the algebra of matrices and vectors, how to solve systems of linear equations, and know about eigenvectors and eigenvalues. In fact, the actual number of prerequisites is rather small: readers who feel comfortable with the review section 1.2 on matrix and vector algebra are adequately prepared for the rest of the book; the remainder of the chapters are self-contained mathematically, although some additional theory is developed in the exercises. Readers are also expected to have some computing experience. Here again, the assumed number of prerequisites is fairly small: it is more important to have had the experience of entering programs and data and seeing the results of computation than to have had any particular programming or operating training. The language used for the programs in this book is FORTRAN. Readers without previous experience in FORTRAN will find in Section 1.4 an explanation of the language sufficient to deal with programs of subsequent chapters.

The FORTRAN language is used for two reasons: (1) because of the ease in dealing with matrices as vectors in that language; and (2) because the linear algebra program libraries used here are in that language. The most important of these libraries is LINPACK, written at Argonne National Laboratories. All of the methods in Chapters 2, 3, and 4 of this book use the LINPACK routines exclusively, and they are used in Chapter 5 as well. There is an excellent manual documenting LINPACK, complete with program listings—the *LINPACK User's Guide*[†]—which many readers will want to consult. The aspects of LINPACK that are needed in this book, however, are explained as they are required.

LINPACK does not contain eigenvalue/eigenvector routines. When such routines are needed, we use the procedure EISPAC,[‡] and the procedure EIGRF (the latter is in the IMSL[§] program library). To be able to use the programs in this book, then, the reader must have access to a computing facility on which the LINPACK and IMSL libraries, and the EISPAC procedure, have been installed.

The book is organized so that the methods discussed are introduced in the order of their logical complexity. Chapter 1 is a review chapter; Chapter 2 addresses the problem of systems of equations with a unique solution. Chapter 3 takes up the problem of systems with possibly infinitely many solutions, and Chapter 4 the problem of systems with possibly no solutions.

[†]J. Dongarra et al., *LINPACK User's Guide*, SIAM, Philadelphia, 1979.
[‡]A control program for EISPACK. See B. Smith et al., *Matrix Eigensystems Routines—EISPACK Guide* (2nd ed.), Lecture Notes in Computer Science, Springer-Verlag, Heidelberg, 1976.
[§]Published by IMSL, Inc. Houston. Library Reference Manual provided to subscribers.

As a group, these last three chapters constitute a study of the linear algebra used to deal with static and steady-state applications. Chapters 5 and 6 deal with eigenvector and eigenvalue problems associated with discrete and continuous time (respectively) models. These two chapters are grouped together as the study of dynamic models. A more detailed summary now follows.

The problem dealt with in Chapter 2 is a system of n linear equations in n unknowns whose unique solution is sought. In the theoretical sections of the chapter, the solution process is explained by means of transforming the system (Gaussian elimination) and by writing the system in matrix form and factoring the matrix of coefficients (L-U decomposition). Among the applications lending to such systems, the chapter considers electrical networks, production economic models, and static distributions. The computational sections cover solution using LINPACK to perform L-U decomposition, and also solutions by iteration.

In Chapter 3 systems of m equations in n unknowns are examined. In the theoretical sections the nature of the set of solutions of such a system is covered, along with the concept of rank and row reduction. The applications considered are network flow, resource allocation, and economic exchange models. There is no row-reduction routine in the program libraries, so in the computational section one is developed, using the basic linear algebra subroutines attached to LINPACK.

Chapter 4 also deals with systems of m equations in n unknowns, but now the emphasis is on possibly inconsistent systems. With such a system, the object is to find the best approximate solution. The notion of "best" requires a discussion of vector geometry in the theoretical sections, which then leads into the various solution methods: the normal equations for least squares, the Gram–Schmidt process, and its matrix form (Q-R decomposition). The applications sections deal with fitting equations to data in various contexts. The computational sections explain how to implement the solution methods, either via the normal equations or using the Q-R decomposition.

Chapter 5 begins the study of problems for which the desired solution requires computation of eigenvectors and eigenvalues of a matrix. The theoretical sections present the theory of eigenvectors and eigenvalues, and a slight discussion of the algorithms used in their computation, as well as a more extensive discussion of their interpretation. The applications deal with models for which powers of a matrix, or powers of a matrix times a vector, need to be computed, including population growth and Markov chains. The computational sections cover using the EISPAC and IMSL eigenvalue/eigenvector procedures.

Chapter 6 applies eigenvalue/eigenvector methods to the solution of systems of differential equations. The theoretical sections discuss how such solutions are found using eigenvalues and eigenvectors to obtain the solution functions, while the applications sections focus on sources of such problems in such areas as chemical reactions and mechanical systems. (The computations necessary to solve these problems are already treated in Chapter 5.)

1.2   REVIEW OF VECTOR AND MATRIX ALGEBRA

n-vectors are column *n*-tuples of numbers:[†]

$$
v = \begin{bmatrix} v_1 \\ \vdots \\ v_n \end{bmatrix} \qquad w = \begin{bmatrix} w_1 \\ \vdots \\ w_n \end{bmatrix}
$$

The entries $v_1, \ldots, v_n$ of the vector v are its *components*. Vectors are added by adding corresponding components and we can multiply a vector by a *scalar*[†] (number) by multiplying each component by the scalar:

$$
v + w = \begin{bmatrix} v_1 + w_1 \\ \vdots \\ v_n + w_n \end{bmatrix} \qquad av = \begin{bmatrix} av_1 \\ \vdots \\ av_n \end{bmatrix}
$$

The 0 *n*-vector has all its components zero, and $-v$ is the vector $(-1)v$. A *linear combination* of the *n*-vectors $v_1, \ldots, v_m$ is a vector w of the form

$$
w = a_1 v_1 + \cdots + a_m v_m
$$

If all the a_i are zero, then w is zero; this is called the trivial linear combination. If $v_1, \ldots, v_m$ are *linearly dependent* if some nontrivial linear combination of them is 0; otherwise, they are *linearly independent*.

The collection of all linear combinations of a set of vectors is called their *span*. Since a sum of linear combinations, or a scalar multiple of linear combinations, is again a linear combination, the span of a set of vectors is closed under vector addition and scalar multiplication.

A set of *n*-vectors closed under vector addition and scalar multiplication is called a *vector subspace*. Every vector subspace is the span of a set of vectors; a linearly independent such spanning set is called a *basis* for the subspace. Every vector subspace, including the space of all *n*-vectors, has a basis. The number of vectors in all bases of a given subspace is the same

---

[†] These may be real or complex. The latter are required only in Chapters 5 and 6. Unless otherwise specified, we usually mean just real numbers.

and is called the *dimension* of the subspace. For the space of all n-vectors, this dimension is n. In any subspace, a minimal spanning set or maximal linearly independent set is a basis. If the subspace has dimension m, then a spanning set, or linearly independent set, of m elements is a basis.

An m by n (or $m \times n$) *matrix* is a rectangular array of mn numbers into m rows of n elements or n columns of m elements:

$$A = \begin{bmatrix} a_{11} & \cdots & a_{1n} \\ \vdots & & \vdots \\ a_{m1} & \cdots & a_{mn} \end{bmatrix}$$

The entry in row i and column j, a_{ij}, is called the (i, j) entry. A column n-vector is then just an $n \times 1$ matrix.

Pairs of m by n matrices can be added by adding corresponding entries, and a matrix can be multiplied by a scalar by multiplying all the entries by that scalar:

$$\begin{bmatrix} a_{11} & \cdots & a_{1n} \\ \vdots & & \vdots \\ a_{m1} & \cdots & a_{mn} \end{bmatrix} + \begin{bmatrix} b_{11} & \cdots & b_{1n} \\ \vdots & & \vdots \\ b_{m1} & \cdots & b_{mn} \end{bmatrix}$$

$$= \begin{bmatrix} a_{11} + b_{11} & \cdots & a_{1n} + b_{1n} \\ \vdots & & \vdots \\ a_{m1} + b_{m1} & \cdots & a_{mn} + b_{mn} \end{bmatrix}$$

$$c \begin{bmatrix} a_{11} & \cdots & a_{1n} \\ \vdots & & \vdots \\ a_{m1} & \cdots & a_{mn} \end{bmatrix} = \begin{bmatrix} ca_{11} & \cdots & ca_{1n} \\ \vdots & & \vdots \\ ca_{m1} & \cdots & ca_{mn} \end{bmatrix}$$

The *transpose* of the $m \times n$ matrix A is the $n \times m$ matrix A^T whose (i, j) entry is the (j, i) entry of A:

$$A = \begin{bmatrix} a_{11} & \cdots & a_{1n} \\ \vdots & & \vdots \\ a_{m1} & \cdots & a_{mn} \end{bmatrix} \qquad A^T = \begin{bmatrix} a_{11} & \cdots & a_{m1} \\ \vdots & & \vdots \\ a_{1n} & \cdots & a_{mn} \end{bmatrix}$$

An $m \times n$ matrix A and an $n \times p$ matrix B can be multiplied to obtain an

$m \times p$ matrix:

$$A = \begin{bmatrix} a_{11} & \cdots & a_{1n} \\ \vdots & & \vdots \\ a_{m1} & \cdots & a_{mn} \end{bmatrix} \qquad B = \begin{bmatrix} b_{11} & \cdots & b_{1p} \\ \vdots & & \vdots \\ b_{n1} & \cdots & b_{np} \end{bmatrix}$$

$$AB = \begin{bmatrix} c_{11} & \cdots & c_{1p} \\ \vdots & & \vdots \\ c_{n1} & \cdots & c_{np} \end{bmatrix}$$

where

$$c_{ij} = a_{i1}b_{ij} + a_{i2}b_{2j} + \cdots + a_{in}b_{nj}$$

In particular, we have defined Ax where A is an $m \times n$ matrix and x an n-vector ($= n \times 1$ matrix). When the relevant products and sums can be formed matrix multiplication is associative, $A(BC) = (AB)C$, distributive over addition, $A(B + C) = (AB) + (AC)$, but not always commutative, $AB \neq BA$ for some A, B. With respect to the transpose, matrix multiplication gets reversed:

$$(AB)^T = B^T A^T$$

There are several alternative formulations of matrix multiplication. To explain these simply, we introduce some notation:

(1.2.1)   Rows and Columns of A Matrix.   Let A be an $m \times n$ matrix. Then A_i, $i = 1, \ldots, n$, denotes the ith column of A (an $m \times 1$ matrix) and A^i, $i = 1, \ldots, m$, denotes the ith row of A (a $1 \times n$ matrix). Symbolically, we have

$$A = \begin{bmatrix} A^1 \\ \vdots \\ A^m \end{bmatrix} = [A_1 \cdots A_n]$$

(1.2.2)   Matrix Multiplication Formulas.   Let A be an $m \times n$ matrix and B an $n \times p$ matrix, and let a_{ij} denote the (i, j) entry of A and b_{ij} the (i, j) entry of B. Then in terms of (1.2.1):

1. The jth column $(AB)_j$ of the product AB is given by the linear combination

$$(AB)_j = A(B_j) = b_{1j}A_1 + \cdots + b_{nj}A_n \qquad \text{for } 1 \leq j \leq p$$

2. The ith row $(AB)^i$ of the product AB is given by the matrix combination

$$(AB)^i = A^i B = a_{i1} B^1 + \cdots + a_{in} B^n \qquad \text{for } 1 \le i \le m$$

3. The (i, j) entry $(AB)_{ij}$ of the product AB is given by the matrix product

$$(AB)_{ij} = A^i B_j \qquad \text{for } 1 \le i \le m \quad \text{and} \quad 1 \le j \le p$$

Matrix products of square $(n \times n)$ matrices are always formable. The *identity* $n \times n$ matrix I_n is the matrix[†]

$$I_n = \begin{bmatrix} 1 & & & \\ & 1 & & \\ & & \ddots & \\ & & & 1 \end{bmatrix}$$

[The (i, j) entry of I_n is zero if $i \ne j$ and 1 if $i = j$.] If A is any other $(n \times n)$ matrix then $AI_n = I_n A = A$. A $(n \times n)$ matrix A is *invertible* if some $n \times n$ matrix multiplies it to the identity. If A is invertible the unique matrix multiplying it to the identity is denoted A^{-1} and we have $AA^{-1} = A^{-1}A = I_n$. A^{-1} is called the *inverse* of A.

Powers of the $n \times n$ matrix A are defined by

$$A^0 = I^n, \qquad A^1 = A, \qquad A^2 = AA, \ldots, A^{k+1} = AA^k$$

If A is invertible, the negative powers of A are defined by $A^{-k} = (A^{-1})^k$. With these definitions, the usual laws of exponents apply:

$$A^p A^q = A^{p+q} \qquad (A^p)^q = A^{pq}$$

(1.2.3) Determinants. There is a number, called the determinant, associated to any $n \times n$ matrix A, and denoted $\det(A)$. Among its properties are:

1. If the matrix A' is obtained from A by adding a multiple of a row to another row, or a multiple of a column to another column, then $\det(A') = \det(A)$.

2. If A' results from A by interchanging two rows, or by interchanging two columns, then $\det(A') = -\det(A)$.

[†]Zero entries of a matrix are usually denoted by blanks in this book.

3. $\det(aA) = a^n \det(A)$.
4. $\det(AB) = \det(A)\det(B)$.
5. $\det(I_n) = 1$.
6. If $(A)_{ij}$ denotes the $(n-1) \times (n-1)$ matrix obtained from A by discarding row i and column j, and a_{ij} denotes the (i, j) entry of A then for any $k = 1, 2, \ldots, n$ we have
   (a) $\det(A) = \Sigma_i(-1)^{i+k}a_{ik}\det((A)_{ik})$ (cofactor expansion down column k);
   and
   (b) $\det(A) = \Sigma_j(-1)^{k+j}a_{kj}\det((A)_{kj})$ (cofactor expansion along row k).
7. If A is a 2×2 matrix then $\det(A)$ is calculated as follows:

$$A = \begin{bmatrix} a & b \\ c & c \end{bmatrix} \qquad \det(A) = ad - bc$$

8. If A has zeros below the diagonal (a lower triangular matrix), above the diagonal (an upper triangular matrix), or both (a diagonal matrix) then $\det(A)$ is the product of the diagonal entries of A.
9. $\det(A^T) = \det(A)$.

Determinants determine if matrices are invertible. We record this along with other criteria for invertibility:

(1.2.4) Invertibility Criteria. The $n \times n$ matrix A is invertible if any of the following hold, and conversely:

1. $\det(A) \neq 0$.
2. $Ax = 0$ implies $x = 0$ for any n-vector x.
3. The columns of A are linearly independent.
4. The columns of A span the space of n-vectors.

These criteria can be expressed in terms of the equation

$$Ax = b$$

for b a given n-vector, to be solved for x: criterion number 2 can be interpreted as saying there is a unique solution, and number 4 as saying that for any b there is at least one solution. If A is invertible, the unique solution for any given b is

$$x = A^{-1}b.$$

EXERCISES 1.2

1. Let $v = \begin{bmatrix} 1 \\ 1 \\ 3 \end{bmatrix}$, $w = \begin{bmatrix} -1 \\ 3 \\ -1 \end{bmatrix}$, $u = \begin{bmatrix} a \\ b \\ c \end{bmatrix}$

   (a) Show that v and w are linearly independent.

   (b) Show that u is a linear combination of v and w if and only if $2a + b - c = 0$.

   (c) Let V be the set of all 3-vectors x such that $[2 \quad 1 \quad -1]x = [0]$. Show that V is a vector subspace.

   (d) Show that v, w form a basis of V.

2. Let $v_1 = \begin{bmatrix} 1 \\ 1 \\ -1 \end{bmatrix}$, $v_2 = \begin{bmatrix} 1 \\ 2 \\ 1 \end{bmatrix}$, $v_3 = \begin{bmatrix} 3 \\ 5 \\ 1 \end{bmatrix}$, $v_4 = \begin{bmatrix} 5 \\ 8 \\ 1 \end{bmatrix}$

   (a) Show that v_3 and v_4 are linear combinations of v_1 and v_2.

   (b) Show that v_1 and v_2 are linearly independent.

   (c) Show that v_1, v_2 form a basis for the vector subspace V spanned by v_1, v_2, v_3, v_4.

   (d) Find a 1×3 matrix A such that V is the set of all 3-vectors x with $Ax = [0]$.

3. Let A be an $n \times n$ matrix with (i, j) entry a_{ij}. Let A_{ij} be the matrix obtained from A by deleting row i and column j. Let B be the $n \times n$ matrix whose (i, j) entry is $(-1)^{i+j}\det(A_{ji})$. Prove that $AB = \det(A)I_n$ [like property 6 of (1.2.3)]. The matrix B is called the *classical adjoint* of A.

4. Assume A is an invertible $n \times n$ matrix and that $Ax = b$ for n-vectors x and b, with ith entries x_i and b_i, respectively. Let B be the classical adjoint of A from problem 3.

   (a) Show that $A^{-1} = \det(A)^{-1}B$.

   (b) From $x = A^{-1}b$ show that

   $$x_i = (\det A)^{-1}(b_{i1}b_1 + \cdots + b_{in}b_n)$$

   where b_{ij} are as in problem 3.

   (c) Let C_i, $i = 1, \ldots, n$, be the matrix obtained from A by replacing column i by b. Using this and property 6 of (1.2.3) show that

   $$x_i = (\det A)^{-1}\det(C)$$

   (This formula is known as Cramer's rule).

1.3 WHY MOST MATRICES ARE GOOD

It is usually a safe assumption in computational linear algebra to assume that a square matrix is invertible, or that a matrix has distinct eigenvalues. This section explains why. This is basically a probabilistic issue, so we have to start with a discussion of a related probabilistic issue.

If an event has n possible outcomes which happen randomly and equally likely then it is customary to say that each happens with probability $1/n$: a toss of a fair coin turns up heads with probability $\frac{1}{2}$; a toss of a fair die turns up three with probability $\frac{1}{6}$, and so on. The situation is more complicated when infinitely many random, equally likely, outcomes are possible. For example, suppose that in each 1-minute period a certain event, such as the arrival of a photon at a detector, happens at random. This could be modeled by the event of selecting a point t at random in a unit interval [see Fig. (1.3.1)]. It is difficult to say what the probability of the selection of a particular point is. However, it is not difficult to see that the probability of selecting a point in the left-half interval is $\frac{1}{2}$, the probability of selecting a point in the middle-third subinterval is $\frac{1}{3}$, and in general that selecting a point in the subinterval between a and b is $b - a$ [see Fig. (1.3.2)]. Now suppose we consider an infinite sequence of intervals of shorter and shorter length condensing down to the point t_0 [see Fig. (1.3.3)]. The probability of selecting t_0 is certainly no more than that of landing in each of the intervals in the sequence; since these probabilities decrease to 0, the probability of selecting the specific point t_0 is zero. That is some point must be selected, but the only sensible probability to assign to the selection of a particular point is zero.

This phenomenon is a special case of something that happens in higher dimensions also: The key fact is that the probability of landing on a particular point is zero because there is no interval inside a point.

Figure (1.3.1).

Figure (1.3.2).

Figure (1.3.3).

Now suppose we imagine an "n-dimensional unit cube"

$$C = \{(x_1, \ldots, x_n) \mid 0 \le x_i \le 1 \quad (i = 1, 2, \ldots, n)\}$$

whose "volume" is 1. An "n-box" inside C would be a set of the form

$$B = \{(x_1, \ldots, x_n) \mid a_i \le x_i \le b_i \quad (i = 1, 2, \ldots, n)\}$$

whose "volume" is defined to be $(b_1 - a_1)(b_2 - a_2) \cdots (b_n - a_n)$. As before, we define the probability of landing inside B when a point in C is chosen at random as the fraction of the volume of C contained in B, namely, the volume of B. And if S is some subset of C which contains no boxes in its interior, then the probability of choosing a point in S is zero. [The two-dimensional case is illustrated in Fig. (1.3.4).]

Figure (1.3.4).

```
┌─────────────────────────┐
│                         │
│              ___        │
│            /    S       │
│           /             │
│   ___   /               │
│  (   \_/                │
│   \__                   │
│      \                  │
│       \              C  │
└─────────────────────────┘
```

The type of set S we will need to consider is a zero set of a polynomial function. The relevant fact here is the following:

(1.3.5) Polynomial Zero Sets Have No Interior Boxes. Let $f = f(X_1, \ldots, X_n)$ be a polynomial function and $S = \{(y_1, \ldots, y_n) \mid f(y_1, \ldots, y_n) = 0\}$, the zero set of S. If $f \ne 0$, then there is no n-box B inside S.

Actually, we will demonstrate the contrapositive of (1.3.5): if S contains an n-box, then $f = 0$. Suppose the n-box is $\{(x_1, \ldots, x_n) \mid a_i \le x_i \le b_i$ $(i = 1, 2, \ldots, n)\}$. Write f as a polynomial in X_n whose coefficients are polynomials in $X_1, \ldots, X_{n-1}$: $f(X_1, \ldots, X_n) = a_k(X_1, \ldots, X_{n-1}) X_n^k + \cdots + a_0(X_1, \ldots, X_{n-1})$. For any $(y_1, \ldots, y_{n-1})$ in the $(n-1)$-box $B' = \{(x_1, \ldots, x_{n-1}) \mid a_i \le x_i \le b_i$ $(i = 1, 2, \ldots, n - 1)\}$, the polynomial $a_k(y_1, \ldots, y_{n-1}) X_n^k + \cdots + a_0(y_1, \ldots, y_{n-1})$ is zero for every value of X_n

between a_n and b_n. A polynomial in one variable, however, has only finitely many roots, unless it is the zero polynomial. So for each $(y_1, \ldots, y_{n-1})$ we indeed have the zero polynomial, which means that the box B' is contained in the zero sets of the polynomials $a_i(X_1, \ldots, X_{n-1})$ for $i = 0, \ldots, k$. Now we have polynomials in one less variable whose zero sets contain boxes. We can repeat the reduction process with each of these to eliminate another variable, and so on, until ultimately we discover that $f = 0$.

The application of (1.3.5) to matrices comes as follows: n by n matrices are just n^2-tuples of numbers. Let f be any nonzero polynomial function of n^2 variables. Then we can evaluate f on a matrix by evaluating it on the corresponding n^2-tuple. The probability of choosing a point in the unit cube at random and having it lie in the zero set of S is zero by (1.3.5). Since we can translate the unit cube around to cover up the n^2-tuples, we can assert:

(1.3.6) If an n by n matrix is chosen at random, the probability that it is a zero of a given (non-zero) polynomial function is zero. It is a consequence of determinant formulas [property 6 of (1.2.3)] that the determinant is a polynomial function of matrix entries. The probability of zero determinant is the probability of noninvertibility, by (1.2.4), and this is zero probability by (1.3.6). Phrased positively this says:

(1.3.7) The probability that a randomly chosen n by n matrix is invertible is one. Other applications of (1.3.6), to eigenvalues, are given in Chapter 5.

1.4 READING FORTRAN

FORTRAN, like most computer languages, has provisions for labeling storage spaces, carrying out operations on stored information, iterating groups of operations, creating and calling procedures, and inputting data and outputting results. In this section we will discuss the FORTRAN conventions for all these provisions. It is not complete enough to serve as a guide for *writing* FORTRAN programs, but it is complete enough to serve as a guide for *reading* them. In particular, all the features used in the FORTRAN programs in this book are explained in this section.

(1.4.1) Storage Labels. Individual storage locations in FORTRAN are designated by symbols of a maximum length of six characters beginning with a letter; examples are A, RCOND, J, IPROB. If the first letter is I, J, K, L, M, N then the location contents are treated as an integer; otherwise, the contents are regarded as a floating-point real number of seven significant digits. Some special locations need declarations: those intended to hold double-precision numbers (14 significant digits) or complex numbers, as well as groups (or arrays) of storage locations. All other types are created at their first mention.

(1.4.2) Basic Operations. The contents of storage locations can be manipulated in various ways. The assignment symbol in FORTRAN is $=$. A statement such as $A = B$ assigns the contents of location B to location A. The arithmetic operations addition, subtraction, multiplication, and division are given by $A + B$, $A - B$, $A * B$, and A/B, respectively. Exponentials are given by A**B (this means raise A to the B power). Logical operations are carried out using IF (logical expression); for example, a FORTRAN statement such as IF (A.EQ.B) GO TO 90 will cause the program to skip to line 90 if the contents of A and B are the same; otherwise, the program will go on to the next statement. The connectives used are equals—.EQ.; not equal—.NE.; greater than—.GT.; less than—.LT.; greater than or equal—.GE.; and less than or equal—.LE.

(1.4.3) Iteration. To cause FORTRAN to repeat a block of statements M times, we add a numbered statement at the end of the block giving the command CONTINUE and precede the block with a statement of the form DO number $I = 1, M$. Here is a symbolic example:

```
        DO 10  I = 1, M
100   CONTINUE
```

The counter I is available for use within the block of statements also. The symbol chosen for the counter can be anything that represents an integer, unless the DO loop occurs inside another. In such a case (nested DO loops) each loop needs a distinct counter symbol.

(1.4.4) Subroutines. A program which is to be used by another program is defined in FORTRAN by giving the program a name, which includes a list of parameters (this means a list of symbols for storage locations which will be either input or output for the subroutine) prefixed by the designation SUBROUTINE, and ending the program with RETURN. For example, a program designed to add the contents of locations A and B and store the result in location X would be given by

```
SUBROUTINE SUM(A, B, X)
X = A + B
RETURN
```

To use a subroutine in another program the name of the subroutine, with defined storage locations for all the input parameters in its parameter list, is preceded by the command CALL. For example, using the above subroutine we can compute 1.1 + 2.2 and store the result in Y by

$$Z = 1.1$$
$$W = 1.2$$
$$\text{CALL SUM}(Z, W, Y)$$

The "CALL" command is similarly used to access library subroutines already stored on line in the machine, such as the LINPACK procedures.

(1.4.5) Arrays. FORTRAN vectors (one-dimensional arrays) and matrices (two-dimensional arrays) are created by declaration statements. To create, for example, a 2×3 matrix A, a 3×3 matrix B, a 5-vector C, and a 10-vector D, a single declaration suffices:

$$\text{REAL A}(2, 3), B(3, 3), C(5), D(10)$$

If we need integer matrices or vectors, these are obtained by declarations such as

$$\text{INTEGER I}(2, 3), J(3, 3), K(5), L(10)$$

The FORTRAN array created by the declaration

$$\text{REAL A}(M, N)$$

and that created by

$$\text{REAL A}(MN)$$

are essentially the same: the two-dimensional array of size $M \times N$ is treated like a one-dimensional array with MN entries, counting down the columns in order; entry $A(I, J)$ of the two-dimensional array is $I + (J - 1)M$ of the one-dimensional array. Symbolically, we identify the matrix

$$A = \begin{bmatrix} a_{11} & \cdots & a_{1n} \\ \vdots & & \vdots \\ a_{m1} & \cdots & a_{mn} \end{bmatrix}$$

with the vector

$$\begin{bmatrix} a_{11} \\ \vdots \\ a_{m1} \\ a_{12} \\ \vdots \\ a_{m2} \\ \vdots \\ a_{mn} \end{bmatrix}$$

As we will see, this feature is very handy for picking out columns from a matrix and regarding them as vectors.

(1.4.6) Input/Output. Whenever possible we read data in and write it out without specifying a format. For input this takes the form

$$\text{READ(5, *) } \underline{\text{list}}$$

where 5 is the number of the input device (card reader) and $\underline{\text{list}}$ is a list of storage location names (separated by commas) whose values are to be read. For output it takes the form

$$\text{WRITE (6, *) } \underline{\text{list}}$$

where 6 is the number of the printer and $\underline{\text{list}}$ is a list of storage location means (separated by commas) whose values are to be printed.

When a specific format for the input or output is required, numbered FORMAT statements are used and the number of the statement replaces the asterisk in the READ or WRITE statement. *We do not use formatted input in this book.* In a write FORMAT statement, the first specification is the spacing control:

'+' (plus) means stay on same line.
' ' (blank) means single space to next line.
'0' (zero) means double space to next line.
'1' (one) means go to the top of a new page.

Other specifications are:

nX—n blanks.
Iw—integer w digits wide.

Fw.d—floating-point real number w spaces wide including the sign and decimal point with d digits after the decimal point (e.g., 12.45 is F6.2).
Ew.d—exponential real number w spaces wide including the sign, a leading zero, an E, a sign for the exponent, and a two-digit exponent, with d digits after the decimal point (e.g., 0.1234E + 06 is E12.5).

Moreover, characters enclosed in apostrophes are copied exactly as they appear. Here is a comprehensive example:

```
100    FORMAT ('0 THE LENGTH OF THE '12,'-VECTOR X IS ', E10.3)
       N = 2
       XLEN = 1.414214
       WRITE (6,100) N,XLEN
```

causes the following to be printed:

THE LENGTH OF THE 2-VECTOR X IS 0.141E + 01

(1.4.7)   Other FORTRAN Key Words.   To halt a FORTRAN program we use the command STOP. The last statement in a FORTRAN program is the word END; this is not part of the program but is used by the compiler. Values that are unlikely to change in a program can be assigned using the DATA statement: DATA LDA/50/ assigns the value 50 to the storage location LDA on compilation.

(1.4.8)   Line Format and Program Organization in FORTRAN.   A FORTRAN statement with a C in column 1 is a comment statement; whatever occurs in that line is just printed with the program. All other FORTRAN statements have an (optional) number in columns 1 to 5, a blank in column 6, and begin in column 7 or later. All declarations come before any executions in a FORTRAN program. FORMAT statements can be put anywhere, but we always put them at the beginning. The last line in a program must be the END statement.

(1.4.9)   Accuracy in FORTRAN.   FORTRAN has seven-digit accuracy. This means that $10^{-7} = 0$, as far as FORTRAN computations are concerned. It is often necessary, therefore, to round off answers when the unformatted WRITE is used: a matrix entry of the form 0.0000000375 is really a zero. Formatting output will do the round-off automatically, but because of the resultant program complexity we have not done this in the sample programs.

The programs used in this book are intended to be simple and direct. No real subtleties are used in them, and program elements are kept the same from program to program, as far as possible. Experienced FORTRAN programmers will want to "customize" the programs to improve the looks of the output or simplify intermediate steps; occasionally exercises are given with such goals in mind.

PART 1

STATIC AND STEADY-STATE MODELS

══ 2 ══

SYSTEMS WITH A UNIQUE SOLUTION

2.1 LINEAR EQUATIONS AND THE *L-U* DECOMPOSITION

Consider a general system of n linear equations in n unknowns:

$$(2.1.1) \qquad \begin{cases} a_{11}x_1 + \cdots + a_{1n}x_n = b_1 \\ \qquad\qquad \vdots \\ a_{n1}x_1 + \cdots + a_{nn}x_n = b_n \end{cases}$$

We want to discover all the solutions of (2.1.1) of which there may be one, infinitely many, or none. We can conceive of situations in which discovering these solutions is so simple that it is automatic (three such situations will be considered shortly). The main idea behind any systematic approach to solving systems of linear equations is to figure out a method to alter the equations until they assume one of these simple forms—without altering the set of solutions. This idea, which is so basic we rarely articulate it, is of sufficient importance to deserve a name:

(2.1.2) The Principle of Elimination. To solve a system of linear equations, change the equations, without changing the solution set, into a simple system that can easily be solved.

There are three basic forms of simple systems we have in mind:

A DIAGONAL SYSTEM

$$(2.1.3) \qquad \begin{cases} d_1 x_1 = c_1 \\ \quad \vdots \\ d_n x_n = c_n \end{cases} \qquad (d_i \neq 0, \quad i = 1, \ldots, n)$$

A (STRICTLY) UPPER TRIANGULAR SYSTEM

$$(2.1.4) \qquad \begin{cases} x_1 + u_{12} x_2 + \cdots \qquad\qquad + u_{1n} x_n = d_1 \\ \qquad x_2 + u_{21} x_3 + \cdots + u_{2n} x_n = d_2 \\ \qquad\qquad\qquad\qquad\qquad \vdots \\ \qquad\qquad\qquad\quad x_{n-1} + u_{n-1,n} x_n = d_{n-1} \\ \qquad\qquad\qquad\qquad\qquad\qquad x_n = d_n \end{cases}$$

A (STRICTLY) LOWER TRIANGULAR SYSTEM

$$(2.1.5) \qquad \begin{cases} x_1 \qquad\qquad\qquad\qquad\qquad\qquad = e_1 \\ l_{21} x_1 + x_2 \qquad\qquad\qquad\qquad\quad = e_2 \\ \quad \vdots \\ l_{n1} x_1 + l_{n2} x_2 + \cdots + l_{n,n-1} x_{n-1} + x_n \quad = e_n \end{cases}$$

It is easy to see how these simple systems are solved. For the diagonal system (2.1.3) we immediately have the solution

$$(2.1.6) \qquad\qquad x_1 = d_1^{-1} c_1, \ldots, x_n = d_n^{-1} c_n$$

For the strictly upper triangular system (2.1.4), we see immediately from the last equation what x_n must be. Then, knowing x_n, we can determine x_{n-1} from the next to last equation. By continuing the process we determine all the values of the x_i:

$$(2.1.7) \qquad \begin{cases} x_n = d_n \\ x_{n-1} = d_{n-1} - u_{n-1,n} x_n \\ \quad \vdots \\ x_1 = d_1 - u_{12} x_2 - \cdots - u_{1n} x_n \end{cases}$$

(This process is known as *back substitution*.)

For the strictly lower triangular system (2.1.5) we again solve by back substitution, this time starting with the first equation and working down:

(2.1.8)
$$\begin{cases} x_1 = e_1 \\ x_2 = e_2 - l_{21}x_1 \\ \vdots \\ x_n = e_n - l_{n1}x_1 - l_{n2}x_2 - \cdots - l_{n,n-1}x_{n-1} \end{cases}$$

Thus it is clear that one of the simple systems (2.1.3), (2.1.4), or (2.1.5) really can be solved automatically. In order to have a good theory of solving the general system (2.1.1) based on the principle of elimination, we must see how to pass from the general system to one of the simple systems.

To see how this works, we rewrite (2.1.1) in matrix form:

(2.1.9) $\quad Ax = b \qquad A = \begin{bmatrix} a_{11} & \cdots & a_{1n} \\ \vdots & & \vdots \\ a_{n1} & \cdots & a_{nn} \end{bmatrix} \qquad x = \begin{bmatrix} x_1 \\ \vdots \\ x_n \end{bmatrix} \qquad b = \begin{bmatrix} b_1 \\ \vdots \\ b_n \end{bmatrix}$

The traditional way to pass from the original system to a simple system is to operate in two ways on the system:

1. It is permitted to multiply an equation by a constant and subtract the result from another equation.
2. It is permitted to interchange the order of two equations.

[In terms of the matrix form of the system (2.1.9) these operations change A by (1) subtracting a multiple of a row from another or (2) switching two rows.]

Neither of these operations affect the set of solutions, and so the principle of elimination (2.1.2) is valid for changes by these types of operations. Moreover, it is not too difficult to devise a scheme for systematically applying the operations to guarantee that a system solvable by back substitution, plus division, results. (Such schemes are taught in the beginning of first courses in linear algebra, and we assume our readers are familiar with this process.)

Our approach here will take another tack: we are going to approach the simplification problem as one of *factoring* matrices, rather than *operating* on them. This is much more complicated, at least to start, and for a good reason: We are delving into the multiplicative structure of the set of invertible matrices, which is a deep subject in advanced mathematics known as the theory of the general linear group. On the other hand, this approach will allow us to replace the conceptually difficult problem of discussing the process of operating on a matrix with a much easier to discuss equation of matrix factorization.

In fact, the two approaches are logically equivalent, as will be obvious in the exercises. Moreover, it will be necessary, in Chapter 3, to return to the "operation" viewpoint in order to discuss row reduction.

For now, we return to our system of equations (2.1.1) written in the matrix form $Ax = b$ (2.1.9). We begin by supposing that our matrix A can be factored into a product of a very special kind:

$$A = LDU \qquad L = \begin{bmatrix} 1 & & & & \\ l_{21} & 1 & & & \\ \vdots & & \ddots & & \\ l_{n1} & l_{n2} & \cdots & l_{nn-1} & 1 \end{bmatrix}$$

(2.1.10)

$$D = \begin{bmatrix} d_1 & & \\ & \ddots & \\ & & d_n \end{bmatrix} \qquad U = \begin{bmatrix} 1 & u_{12} & \cdots & & u_{1n} \\ & 1 & u_{23} & \cdots & u_{2n} \\ & & \ddots & & \vdots \\ & & & & 1 \end{bmatrix}$$

(The assumption that A has such a factorization is not as farfetched as it may seem right now. Indeed, in the terms of Section 1.3, it has such a factorization with probability one, as we will see below. For the moment, we just suppose that we are lucky enough to have such a factorable A.)

The problem (2.1.9), $Ax = b$, can then be written $LDUx = b$ using (2.1.10). We can regard this as a sequence of three problems:

$$Lz = b$$

(2.1.11) $$Dy = z$$

$$Ux = y$$

to be solved in the order indicated. If x is the solution of the third problem, then $Ax = LDUx = LDy = Lz = b$ so x is the solution of (2.1.9). And the three problems (2.1.11) are all of the simple type previously considered: $Lz = b$ is a strictly lower triangular system solvable by back substitution, as is the strictly upper triangular system $Ux = y$; the diagonal system $Dy = z$ is also immediately solvable, provided $d_1 \cdots d_n$ are nonzero.

We've already claimed that a factorization like (2.1.10) happens for almost any A we pick. It's time to see how to find it. For the purposes of this calculation, we will combine D and U together into a single matrix (it will be easy enough to recover D and U from this matrix: D is the diagonal and U is found by dividing each row by its diagonal entry). We label the product matrix DU as U also, following tradition, and thus the factorization we seek is:

(2.1.12)   The *L-U* Decomposition

$$\begin{bmatrix} a_{11} & \cdots & a_{1n} \\ \vdots & & \vdots \\ a_{n1} & \cdots & a_{nn} \end{bmatrix} = \begin{bmatrix} 1 & & & \\ l_{21} & 1 & & \\ \vdots & \vdots & \ddots & \\ l_{n1} & l_{n2} & \cdots & 1 \end{bmatrix} \begin{bmatrix} d_1 & u_{12} & \cdots & u_{1n} \\ & d_2 & & u_{2n} \\ & & \ddots & \vdots \\ & & & d_n \end{bmatrix}$$

$$\qquad\quad A \qquad\qquad\qquad\qquad L \qquad\qquad\qquad\qquad U$$

In (2.1.12), the ith row of L is $L^i = [l_{i1} \ l_{i2} \ \cdots \ l_{i,i-1} \ 1 \ 0 \ \cdots \ 0]$ and the ith row of U is $U^i = [0 \ \cdots \ 0 \ d_i \ u_{i,i+1} \ \cdots \ u_{i,n}]$. From the product $A = LU$, we can write down the rows of A as linear combinations of the rows of U, obtaining the n equations

(2.1.13)
$$\begin{cases} A^1 = U^1 \\ A^2 = l_{2,1}U^1 + U^2 \\ A^3 = l_{3,1}U^1 + l_{3,2}U^2 + U^3 \\ \quad\vdots \\ A^n = l_{n,1}U^1 + \cdots + l_{n,n-1}U^{n-1} + U^n \end{cases}$$

And (2.1.13) can be solved for the rows of U:

(2.1.14)
$$\begin{cases} U^1 = A^1 \\ U^2 = A^2 - l_{2,1}U^1 \\ U^3 = A^3 - l_{3,1}U^1 - l_{3,2}U^2 \\ \quad\vdots \\ U^n = A^n - l_{n,1}U^1 - \cdots - l_{n,n-1}U^{n-1} \end{cases}$$

Back in (2.1.12), A was given and we were to find L and U. The equations (2.1.14) show how to do that: initially we know A, so from the first equation of (2.1.14) we determine U^1. Now, in the second equation of (2.1.14), A^2 and U^1 are known. If we look just at first entries, the equation becomes

$(U^2)_1 = (A^2)_1 - l_{2,1}(U^1)_1$, or $0 = a_{21} - l_{21}d_1$. From this, l_{21} is determined, and then U^2 is known. Proceeding to the third equation of (2.1.14), it is possible to determine $l_{3,1}$ by considering first entries, so the equation becomes $0 = a_{31} - l_{31}d_1$, and then to determine $l_{3,2}$ by considering second entries, so the equation becomes $0 = a_{32} - l_{31}u_{12} - l_{32}d_2$. Once l_{31} and l_{32} are determined, of course, U^3 is known.

This sort of "bootstrap" solution method can clearly be continued to produce L and U from A. Our chosen solution scheme will be somewhat different, because we want to connect L-U decomposition and the traditional methods to solving systems of equations. But the bootstrap method will certainly work. Here is a concrete example for the case $n = 3$.

Example (2.1.15)

$$A = \begin{bmatrix} 3 & -1 & 0 \\ 6 & 0 & 1 \\ 9 & 5 & 5 \end{bmatrix}$$

Find the L-U (2.1.12) decomposition of A. Equations (2.1.14) become:

$$U^1 = A^1$$

$$U^2 = A^2 - l_{21}U^1$$

$$U^3 = A^3 - l_{31}U^1 - l_{32}U^2$$

or

(1) $[d_1 \quad u_{12} \quad u_{13}] = [3 \quad -1 \quad 0]$

(2) $[0 \quad d_2 \quad u_{23}] = [6 \quad 0 \quad 1] - l_{21}[d_1 \quad u_{12} \quad u_{13}]$

(3) $\quad [0 \quad 0 \quad d_3] = [9 \quad 5 \quad 5] - l_{31}[d_1 \quad u_{12} \quad u_{13}] - l_{32}[0 \quad d_2 \quad u_{23}]$

Equation (1) shows that $d_1 = 3$, $u_{12} = -1$, $u_{13} = 0$. Equation (2) says that: (a) $0 = 6 - l_{21}d_1$; (b) $d_2 = 0 - l_{21}u_{12}$; and (c) $u_{23} = 1 - l_{21}u_{13}$. Since $d_1 = 3$ by (1), $l_{21} = 2$ by (a). Since $u_{12} = -1$ by (1), $d_2 = 2$ by (b). Since $u_{13} = 0$ by (1), $u_{23} = 1$ by (c).

Equation (3) says that: (a) $0 = 9 - l_{31}d_1$; (b) $0 = 5 - l_{31}u_{12} - l_{32}d_2$; and (c) $d_3 = 5 - l_{31}u_{13} - l_{32}u_{23}$. Since $d_1 = 3$ by (1), $l_{31} = 3$ by (a). Since

$u_{12} = -1$ by (1) and $d_2 = 2$ by (2) (b), $l_{32} = 4$ by (b). Since $u_{13} = 0$ by (1) and $u_{23} = 1$ by (2) (c), $d_3 = 1$ by (c). Thus

$$\begin{bmatrix} 3 & -1 & 0 \\ 6 & 0 & 1 \\ 9 & 5 & 5 \end{bmatrix} = \begin{bmatrix} 1 & 0 & 0 \\ 2 & 1 & 0 \\ 3 & 4 & 1 \end{bmatrix} \begin{bmatrix} 3 & -1 & 0 \\ 0 & 2 & 1 \\ 0 & 0 & 1 \end{bmatrix}.$$

$$\quad\quad A \quad\quad\quad\quad\quad L \quad\quad\quad\quad\quad U$$

The method we are now going to describe for obtaining the L-U decomposition of A from Eqs. (2.1.4) looks more complicated (although this is mostly due to notation), but in fact will ultimately be seen to be more natural. What we are going to do is solve (2.1.14) in n stages. After stage 1 we will know U^1, U^2, and $l_{21}, l_{31}, \ldots, l_{n1}$. After stage 2, we will know, in addition, U^3 and $l_{32}, l_{42}, \ldots, l_{n2}$, and so forth. That is, at each stage we learn a new row of U and a new column of L. The idea is to consider (2.1.4) as n systems of equations: a system of equations for first entries, then for second entries, and so forth. To keep track of these systems, we introduce some auxiliary notation: For $p = 1, 2, \ldots, n$, define the matrix $A^{(p)}$ so that row i of $A^{(p)}$ is given by

$$(2.1.16) \quad (A^{(p)})^i = \begin{cases} U^i & \text{if } i \le p \\ A^i - l_{i,1}U^1 - \cdots - l_{i,p-1}U^{p-1} & \text{if } i \ge p \end{cases}$$

[Of course, this means $A^{(1)} = A$ and $(A^{(p)})^1 = U^1$ for all p.]
For the matrix A of (2.1.15) we list the matrices $A^{(p)}$:

Example (2.1.15) (Continued)

$$A^{(1)} = \begin{bmatrix} 3 & -1 & 0 \\ 6 & 0 & 1 \\ 9 & 5 & 5 \end{bmatrix} \quad A^{(2)} = \begin{bmatrix} 3 & -1 & 0 \\ 0 & 2 & 1 \\ 0 & 8 & 5 \end{bmatrix} \quad A^{(3)} = \begin{bmatrix} 3 & -1 & 0 \\ 0 & 2 & 1 \\ 0 & 0 & 1 \end{bmatrix}$$

We can see here that $A^{(1)} = A$ and $A^{(3)} = U$ [and in fact from (2.1.16) we will always have $A^{(1)} = A$ and $A^{(n)} = U$ for any A], but we can also see how the intermediate matrix $A^{(2)}$ fits in: $A^{(2)}$ agrees with U in rows 1 and 2, and it agrees with U in column 1. In fact, the matrices $A^{(1)}, A^{(2)}, \ldots, A^{(n)}$ go from A to U in just this fashion: $A^{(p)}$ agrees with U in rows 1 to p and columns 1 to $p - 1$, as we now show:

$$(2.1.17) \quad\quad\quad (A^{(p)})_j = U_j \quad \text{for} \quad j = 1, \ldots, p - 1$$

$$\text{and} \quad (A^{(p)})^i = U^i \quad \text{for} \quad i = 1, \ldots, p$$

We can prove (2.1.17) by writing out the rows of $A^{(p)}$, taking the Eqs. (2.1.14) into account:

$$A^{(p)} = \begin{bmatrix} A^1 \\ A^2 - l_{2,1}U^1 \\ \vdots \\ A^p - l_{p,1}U^1 - \cdots - l_{p,p-1}U^{p-1} \\ A^{p+1} - l_{p+1,1}U^1 - \cdots - l_{p+1,p-1}U^{p-1} \\ \vdots \\ A^n - l_{n,l}U^1 - \cdots - l_{n,p-1}U^{p-1} \end{bmatrix}$$

$$= \begin{bmatrix} U^1 \\ U^2 \\ \vdots \\ U^p \\ U^{p+1} + l_{p+1,p}U^p \\ \vdots \\ U^n + l_{n,p}U^p + \cdots + l_{n,n-1}U^{n-1} \end{bmatrix}$$

This shows that $(A^{(p)})^i = U^i$ for $i = 1, \ldots, p$ [which also is part of (2.1.16) too]. Now since for $j < k$ we have $(U^k)_j = 0$, when we take jth entries on both sides of the above matrix equation, for $j = 1, 2, \ldots, p - 1$, on the right-hand side we have

$$\begin{bmatrix} (U^1)_j \\ (U^2)_j \\ \vdots \\ (U^p)_j \\ (U^{p+1})_j + l_{p+1,p}(0) \\ \vdots \\ (U^n)_j + l_{n,p}(0) + \cdots + l_{n,n-1}(0) \end{bmatrix} = \begin{bmatrix} (U^1)_j \\ \cdot \\ \cdot \\ \cdot \\ \cdot \\ \cdot \\ (U^n)_j \end{bmatrix} = U_j$$

while on the left-hand side we simply have $(A^{(p)})_j$. This proves the rest of (2.1.17).

In the definition of $A^{(p)}$, (2.1.16), we see that we form it by starting with $A^{(1)} = A$, then form $A^{(2)}$ by subtracting multiples of U^1 from the rows 2 to n, then form $A^{(3)}$ from $A^{(2)}$ by subtracting multiples of U^2 from rows 3 to n, and so forth. This process is written in matrix form as

$$(2.1.18) \quad A^{(p+1)} = A^{(p)} - \begin{bmatrix} 0 \\ \vdots \\ 0 \\ l_{p+1,p} \\ \vdots \\ l_{n,p} \end{bmatrix} U^p \quad \text{(for } p = 1, 2, \ldots, n-1)$$

From (2.1.17) we have that $A^{(p+1)}$ and U match up in columns 1 to p, so when we rewrite (2.1.18) as a column equation for pth columns, we get

$$(2.1.19) \quad U_p = (A^{(p+1)})_p = (A^{(p)})_p - \begin{bmatrix} 0 \\ \vdots \\ 0 \\ l_{p+1,p} \\ \vdots \\ l_{n,p} \end{bmatrix} (U^p)_p$$

We want to use Eqs. (2.1.19) and (2.1.18) to pass from $A^{(p)}$ to $A^{(p+1)}$. If $A^{(p)}$ is already computed, then by (2.1.17) we know rows 1 through p of U. That means we have, in particular, computed the pth entries in each of those rows, namely, $(U_p^1) = U_{1,p}, \ldots, (U^p)_p = d_p$. These are the first p entries in the pth column of p, U_p. But we also know the remaining $n - p$ entries: these are all zero! So once $A^{(p)}$ is computed, we can use (2.1.19) to solve for $l_{p+1,p}, \ldots, l_{n,p}$. In terms of individual entries, (2.1.19) becomes (only entries $p + 1$ to n are written):

$$(2.1.20) \quad \begin{cases} 0 = (A^{(p)})_{p+1,p} - l_{p+1,p} d_p \\ 0 = (A^{(p)})_{p+2,p} - l_{p+1,p} d_p \\ \vdots \\ 0 = (A^{(p)})_{n,p} - l_{n,p} d_p \end{cases}$$

This of course determines $l_{p+1,p}, \ldots, l_{n,p}$. Then (2.1.18) gives $A^{(p+1)}$.

We have, finally, arrived at our algorithm for obtaining the *L-U* decomposition of the matrix A. Knowing now that it works, we can dispense with some of the notational complexities and restate our method in simpler language:

(2.1.21) Method of Gaussian Elimination. Starting with the n by n matrix A, construct a sequence of matrices $A^{(1)}, A^{(2)}, \ldots, A^{(n)}$ as follows:

1. $A^{(1)} = A$.
2. To compute $A^{(p+1)}$ from $A^{(p)}$, each row of $A^{(p)}$ from row $p + 1$ to row n is to have a multiple of row p of $A^{(p)}$ subtracted from it. The multipliers, denoted $l_{p+1,p}, \ldots, l_{n,p}$, are selected so that after the subtraction the entry in column p of the row is zero.

After the process is complete, we have

$$A = LU$$

where

$$A^{(n)} = U \quad \text{and} \quad L = \begin{bmatrix} 1 & & & \\ l_{2,1} & 1 & & \\ \vdots & & \ddots & \\ l_{n,1} & \cdots & l_{n,n-1} & 1 \end{bmatrix}$$

We review our Example (2.1.15) using (2.1.21):

Example (2.1.15) (Concluded)

$$A^{(1)} = A = \begin{bmatrix} 3 & -1 & 0 \\ 6 & 0 & 1 \\ 9 & 5 & 5 \end{bmatrix}$$

To pass to $A^{(2)}$, we need to get zeros in the $2,1$ and $3,1$ positions. So we multiply row 1 of $A^{(1)}$ by $l_{2,1} = 2$ and subtract from row 2, and multiply row 1 of $A^{(1)}$ by $l_{3,1} = 3$ and subtract from row 3:

$$A^{(2)} = \begin{bmatrix} 3 & -1 & 0 \\ 0 & 2 & 1 \\ 0 & 8 & 5 \end{bmatrix}$$

To pass to $A^{(3)}$, we need to get a zero in the $3,2$ position. So we multiply row 2 of $A^{(2)}$ by $l_{3,2} = 4$ and subtract from row 3:

$$A^{(3)} = \begin{bmatrix} 3 & -1 & 0 \\ 0 & 2 & 1 \\ 0 & 0 & 1 \end{bmatrix}.$$

Thus

$$U = \begin{bmatrix} 3 & -1 & 0 \\ 0 & 2 & 1 \\ 0 & 0 & 1 \end{bmatrix} \quad \text{and} \quad L = \begin{bmatrix} 1 & 0 & 0 \\ 2 & 1 & 0 \\ 3 & 4 & 1 \end{bmatrix}$$

We have obtained the $A = LU$ decomposition of A of (2.1.12). If we want the decomposition $A = LDU$ of (2.1.10), we just factor the diagonal out of U:

$$(+)A = \begin{bmatrix} 1 & 0 & 0 \\ 2 & 1 & 0 \\ 3 & -1 & 1 \end{bmatrix} \begin{bmatrix} 3 & 0 & 0 \\ 0 & 2 & 0 \\ 0 & 0 & 1 \end{bmatrix} \begin{bmatrix} 1 & -\frac{1}{3} & 0 \\ 0 & 1 & \frac{1}{2} \\ 0 & 0 & 1 \end{bmatrix}$$
$$\qquad\qquad L \qquad\qquad\quad D \qquad\qquad\quad U$$

Now suppose we have a system of linear equations with A as matrix of coefficients, for example;

$$(*) \quad \begin{cases} 3x_1 - x_2 & = 4 \\ 6x_1 \qquad + x_3 = 8 \\ 9x_1 + 5x_2 + 5x_3 = 14 \end{cases} \quad \text{or} \quad Ax = b$$

$$\text{where } x = \begin{bmatrix} x_1 \\ x_2 \\ x_3 \end{bmatrix} \quad \text{and} \quad b = \begin{bmatrix} 4 \\ 8 \\ 14 \end{bmatrix}$$

Using $(+)$ we can rewrite $(*)$ as in (2.1.11) as

$$(a) \quad \begin{cases} z_1 & = 4 \\ 2z_1 + z_2 & = 8 \\ 3z_1 + 4z_2 + z_3 = 14 \end{cases} \quad \text{or} \quad Lz = b \quad \text{where } z = \begin{bmatrix} z_1 \\ z_2 \\ z_3 \end{bmatrix}$$

$$(b) \quad \begin{cases} 3y_1 = z_1 \\ 2y_2 = z_2 \\ y_3 = z_3 \end{cases} \quad \text{or} \quad Dy = z \quad \text{where } y = \begin{bmatrix} y_1 \\ y_2 \\ y_3 \end{bmatrix}$$

$$(c) \quad \begin{cases} x_1 - \frac{1}{3}x_2 & = y_1 \\ x_2 + \frac{1}{2}x_3 = y_2 \\ x_3 = y_3 \end{cases} \quad \text{or} \quad Ux = y$$

Solving system (a), we obtain

$$z_1 = 4$$

$$z_2 = 8 - 2z_1 = 0$$

$$z_3 = 14 - 3z_1 - 4z_2 = 2$$

Using this, we solve (b):

$$y_1 = \tfrac{1}{3}z_1 = \tfrac{4}{3}$$

$$y_2 = \tfrac{1}{2}z_2 = 0$$

$$y_3 = z_3 = 2$$

And finally we solve (c) (from the bottom up):

$$x_3 = y_3 = 2$$
$$x_2 = y_2 - \tfrac{1}{2}x_3 = -1 \quad \text{or} \quad x = \begin{bmatrix} 1 \\ -1 \\ 2 \end{bmatrix}$$
$$x_1 = y_1 + \tfrac{1}{3}x_2 = 1$$

The middle step in solving ($*$), that is, solving system (b), is, in practice, usually combined with step (c): instead of using $A = LDU$ to solve first $Lz = b$, then $Dy = z$, and finally $Ux = y$, it is more common to use $A = LU$ and solve $Ly = b$, $Ux = y$. This means rewriting ($*$) as

(d) $\qquad \begin{cases} y_1 & = 4 \\ 2z_1 + z_2 & = 8 \\ 3z_1 + 4z_2 + z_3 = 14 \end{cases}$ or $Ly = b$ where $y = \begin{bmatrix} y_1 \\ y_2 \\ y_3 \end{bmatrix}$

(e) $\qquad \begin{cases} 3x_1 - x_2 & = y_1 \\ 2x_2 + x_3 = y_2 \\ x_3 = y_3 \end{cases}$ or $Ux = y$

And, of course, solving (d) from the top down and then (e) from the bottom up is a simple matter leading to the solution $x_1 = 1$, $x_2 = -1$, $x_3 = 2$ as before.

It is this latter approach (using the L-U decomposition) to solving equations which is coded in LINPACK and is the one we will follow, although in deeper studies of the theory of invertible matrices, which is known as the theory of algebraic groups, it is the L-D-U decomposition which is most important.

To summarize the work of this section, we outline the procedures developed to solve systems of linear equations.

(2.1.22) Matrix-Factorization-Backsolving Method. To solve a system of n linear equations in n unknowns:

Step 0. write the system of equations as a single matrix equation $AX = b$.

Step 1. use the method of Gaussian elimination to factor $A = LU$.

Step 2. replace $Ax = b$ by $Ly = b$ and $Ux = y$ and solve for y then x by back substitution.

EXERCISES 2.1

1. Use the method of Gaussian elimination (2.1.21) to find the L-U decomposition of the following matrices:

   (a) $\begin{bmatrix} 1 & 2 \\ 4 & 11 \end{bmatrix}$ (b) $\begin{bmatrix} -1 & -3 \\ -3 & -7 \end{bmatrix}$

   (c) $\begin{bmatrix} 1 & 1 & 1 \\ 1 & 2 & 2 \\ 1 & 2 & 3 \end{bmatrix}$ (d) $\begin{bmatrix} -1 & 1 & 0 \\ -2 & 4 & 1 \\ -3 & 3 & 2 \end{bmatrix}$

   (e) $\begin{bmatrix} 1 & 1 & 1 & 1 \\ 1 & 2 & 2 & 2 \\ 1 & 2 & 3 & 3 \\ 1 & 2 & 3 & 4 \end{bmatrix}$

2. Use the matrix-factorization-backsolving method (2.1.22) to solve the following systems of linear equations:

   (a) $x_1 + 2x_2 = 1$
   $4x_1 + 4x_2 = -1$

   (b) $-x_1 + x_2 = 5$
   $-2x_1 + 4x_2 + x_3 = 0$
   $-3x_1 + 3x_2 + 2x_3 = 1$

   (c) $x_1 + x_2 + x_3 + x_4 = 4$
   $x_1 + 2x_2 + 2x_3 + 2x_4 = 3$
   $x_1 + 2x_2 + 3x_3 + 3x_4 = 2$
   $x_1 + 2x_2 + 3x_3 + 4x_4 = 1$
   [*Hint*: Use your answers to 1(a), 1(d), and 1(e).]

3. Let $A = \begin{bmatrix} a & b \\ c & d \end{bmatrix}$ have $a \neq 0$ and $\det(A) \neq 0$. Find a formula for the L-U decomposition of A.

4. Prove that if the $n \times n$ matrix A has an L-U decomposition, then the factors $A = LU$ are unique.

5. Suppose the $n \times n$ matrix A has an L-D-U decomposition, and suppose further that A is symmetric (i.e., $A = A^T$). Prove that in the decomposition $A = LDU$ we have $U = L^T$.

6. Give an example of two 2×2 matrices A and B such that each one has an L-U decomposition but their product AB does not have an L-U decomposition.

7. A matrix A is said to have a "U-L" decomposition if there is an upper triangular matrix U' with one on the diagonal and a lower triangular matrix L' such that $A = U'L'$.

   (a) Prove that if a 2×2 matrix has an L-U decomposition it has a U-L decomposition.

   (b) (Difficult) Reformulate (2.1.21) using column operations and show that in the reformulation the U-L decomposition is obtained.

   (c) (Difficult) Prove that a matrix has a U-L decomposition if and only if it has an L-U decomposition. [This will be easier to do after (2.2.6)].

8. (Elementary matrices) The $n \times n$ matrix with 1 in position (i, j) and 0 elsewhere is denoted E_{ij}.

   (a) Show that $E_{ij}E_{kl} = 0$ if $j \neq k$ and $E_{ij}E_{jl} = E_{il}$.

   (b) When does $E_{ij}E_{kl} = E_{kl}E_{ij}$?

   (c) Let A be an $n \times m$ matrix. Show that $(I + tE_{ij})A$ is obtained from A by adding t times row j to row i.

   (d) Let B be an $m \times n$ matrix. Show that $B(I + tE_{ij})$ is obtained from B by adding t times column i to column j.

   (e) Show that $I - tE_{ij}$ is the inverse of $I + tE_{ij}$, $i \neq j$.

   (f) Using your answer to part (c), show that the method of Gaussian elimination (2.1.21) gives

   $U = EA$ where E is the product

   $$E = (I - l_{n,n-1}E_{n,n-1})(I - l_{n,n-2}E_{n,n-1})$$
   $$\times (I - l_{n-1,n-2}E_{n,n-2}) \cdots (I - l_{3,1}E_{3,1})(I - l_{3,2}E_{3,2}).$$

   (g) Use your answers to parts (e) and (b) to show that in part (f) the matrix E is the matrix L^{-1} of (2.1.21).

2.2   GAUSSIAN ELIMINATION WITH ROW INTERCHANGES

There is a problem with the method for solving linear equations obtained in Section 2.1—it doesn't always work. There are some simple matrices for which the method of Gaussian elimination (2.1.21) just can't be carried out, because stages are reached at which it becomes impossible to select multi-pliers. Here is an example:

Example (2.2.1)

$$A^{(1)} = A = \begin{bmatrix} 3 & -1 & 0 \\ 6 & -2 & 1 \\ -3 & 3 & 1 \end{bmatrix}$$

To pass to $A^{(2)}$, use multipliers $l_{2,1} = 2$ and $l_{3,1} = -1$:

$$A^{(2)} = \begin{bmatrix} 3 & -1 & 0 \\ 0 & 0 & 1 \\ 0 & 2 & 1 \end{bmatrix}$$

According to (2.1.21), we need to choose $l_{3,2}$ so that row 3 minus $l_{3,2}$ times row 2 has a zero in the $(3, 2)$ position, but there is no such $l_{3,2}$.

The appropriate "fixup" to take here is to observe that if the second and third rows of A are switched, this problem would never have arisen. We would instead have the following matrix at stage 2:

$$\begin{bmatrix} 3 & -1 & 0 \\ 0 & 2 & 1 \\ 0 & 0 & 1 \end{bmatrix}$$

having used multipliers $l_{2,1} = -1$ and $l_{3,1} = 2$, and then we would finish with $l_{3,2} = 0$. We could then go on and solve systems of equations with the resulting factorization, as long as we remember the switch we made at the start so as to be able to unswitch the answer at the finish.

To systematically analyze the difficulty exemplified by (2.2.1) we need to address two points:

1. How can we predict if there is going to be trouble with applying the method of Gaussian elimination to a matrix?
2. If we have predicted trouble, how can we correct for it in advance?

So suppose we are using the method of Gaussian elimination on the matrix A, and we have successfully reached the matrix $A^{(p)}$. In the next step, to pass from $A^{(p)}$ to $A^{(p+1)}$, we need to solve Eqs. (2.1.20), of which the typical one is

$$0 = \left(A^{(p)} \right)_{i,p} - l_{i,p} d_p \qquad (p + 1 \le i \le n)$$

To solve this for $l_{i,p}$, we will need $d_p \ne 0$. So where Gaussian elimination can run into trouble is when $(A^{(p)})_{p,p} = 0$ for some p. [This happens in Example (2.2.1) for $p = 2$.]

So we see what it means for Gaussian elimination to fail. But this isn't yet a complete answer to point number 1 above: we want to be able to *predict* trouble. And to do that, we must look at what $(A^{(p)})_{p,p} = 0$ means in a rather indirect fashion. First, we write out $A^{(p)}$ in some detail:

$$(2.2.2) \qquad A^{(p)} = \begin{bmatrix} d_1 & u_{1,2} & & \cdots & & u_{1,n} \\ & d_2 & & \cdots & & u_{2,n} \\ & & \ddots & & & \vdots \\ & & & d_p & \cdots & u_{p,n} \\ & & & * & \cdots & * \\ & & & \vdots & & \vdots \\ & & & * & \cdots & * \end{bmatrix}$$

(The entries in columns p through n of rows $p + 1$ through n are symbolized by a "$*$".) Here we have $d_1 = (A^{(1)})_{1,1}$, $d_2 = (A^{(2)})_{2,2}, \ldots, d_p = (A^{(p)})_{p,p}$. Notice that

$$(2.2.3) \qquad \det([d_1]) = d_1, \quad \det\left(\begin{bmatrix} d_1 & u_{12} \\ 0 & d_2 \end{bmatrix}\right) = d_1 d_2,$$

$$\det\left(\begin{bmatrix} d_1 & u_{1,2} & u_{13} \\ & d_2 & u_{23} \\ & & d_3 \end{bmatrix}\right) = d_1 d_2 d_3, \qquad \ldots,$$

$$\det\begin{bmatrix} d_1 & \cdots & u_{1,p} \\ & d_2 \cdots & u_{2,p} \\ & & \ddots \\ & & d_p \end{bmatrix} = d_1 d_2 \cdots d_p$$

Since we got to $A^{(p)}$, we have $d_1 \neq 0, \ldots, d_{p-1} \neq 0$, so the first $p - 1$ of these determinants are nonzero, and the last one is zero only if $d_p = 0$. It will turn out that all these determinants are computable directly from the matrix A, and this will be the basis of our predictive analysis. Here is the standard terminology for these determinants:

(2.2.4) Let B be an n by n matrix. For $1 \leq i \leq n$, the ith *leading minor determinant of B* is the determinant of the i by i matrix made up of the first i entries of the first i rows of B. We denote this minor determinant as $\det_i(B)$.

Example (2.2.1) (Continued). The leading minor determinants of

$$A = \begin{bmatrix} 3 & -1 & 0 \\ 6 & -1 & 1 \\ -3 & 3 & 1 \end{bmatrix}$$

are $\det_1(A) = 3$, $\det_2(A) = 0$, and $\det_3(A) = -6$, and the leading minor determinants of

$$A^{(2)} = \begin{bmatrix} 3 & -1 & 0 \\ 0 & 0 & 1 \\ 0 & 2 & 1 \end{bmatrix}$$

are $\det_1(A^{(2)}) = 3$, $\det_2(A^{(2)}) = 0$, and $\det_3(A^{(3)}) = -6$. Notice that $\det_1(A^{(2)}) \neq 0$ and $\det_2(A^{(2)}) = 0$ is a signal that $d_2 = 0$ and Gaussian elimination is in trouble, and that $\det_i(A) = \det_i(A^{(2)})$ for $i = 1, 2, 3$.

We use the minor determinants at stage p to detect the problem with $A^{(p)}$. It also turns out, as in our example, that the minor determinants stay the same from stage to stage:

(2.2.5) $\det_i(A^{(p)}) = \det_i(A)$ for $i = 1, \ldots, n$ and $p = 1, \ldots, n$

To prove (2.2.5), we reason as follows: for $p = 1$, this is certainly true, since $A^{(1)} = A$. Now suppose we have proved (2.2.5) for some p, and we want to pass to $p + 1$. We write out $A^{(p+1)}$:

$$A^{(p+1)} = \begin{bmatrix} d_1 & & & & & \cdots & u_{1,n} \\ & d_2 & & & & \cdots & u_{2,n} \\ & & \ddots & & & & \vdots \\ & & & d_p & & \cdots & u_{p,n} \\ & & & & d_{p+1} & \cdots & u_{p+1,n} \\ & & & & * & \cdots & * \\ & & & & \vdots & & \vdots \\ & & & & * & \cdots & * \end{bmatrix}$$

The leading minor determinants of $A^{(p+1)}$ from the first to the pth are the same as those of $A^{(p)}$, since $A^{(p+1)}$ and $A^{(p)}$ agree in rows 1 to p [see (2.2.2)]. For the rest, if we are computing the $(p + k)$th minor determinant, we notice the matrix made of the first $p + k$ entries of rows 1 to $p + k$ of $A^{(p+1)}$ comes from the matrix made of the first $p + k$ entries of rows 1 to $p + k$ of $A^{(p)}$ by multiplying row p of the latter by $l_{j,p}$ and subtracting from row j, for $j = p + 1, \ldots, p + k$, and this sort of row operation doesn't change determinants. So the two $(p + k)$th minor determinants agree. Thus $\det_i(A^{(p)}) = \det_i(A^{(p+1)})$ for $i = 1, \ldots, n$, and since we already knew that $\det_i(A^{(p)}) = \det_i(A)$ for $i = 1, \ldots, n$ we get $\det_i(A^{(p+1)}) = \det_i(A)$ for $i = 1, \ldots, n$. So (2.2.5) is true for $p = 1$, and if it's true for some p we showed it's true for $p + 1$, and this then means it's true for $p = 1, 2, \ldots, n$.

We can now summarize our analysis:

(2.2.6) Predicting Gaussian Elimination

1. Gaussian elimination applied to the n by n matrix A works up to step p and fails there if $\det_1(A) \neq 0, \det_2(A) \neq 0, \ldots, \det_{p-1}(A) \neq 0$ and $\det_p(A) = 0$.

2. Gaussian elimination applied to A succeeds if the product $\det_1(A)\det_2(A) \cdots \det_n(A)$ is nonzero.

The product in (2.2.6) number 2 is a certain polynomial in the entries of the matrix A. For example, if $n = 3$ and

$$A = \begin{bmatrix} a_{11} & a_{12} & a_{13} \\ a_{21} & a_{22} & a_{23} \\ a_{31} & a_{32} & a_{33} \end{bmatrix}$$

then $\det_1(A) \det_2(A) \det_3(A) = (a_{11})(a_{11}a_{22} - a_{21}a_{12})[(a_{11}a_{22}a_{33}) + (a_{12}a_{21}a_{32}) + (a_{13}a_{23}a_{31}) - (a_{13}a_{22}a_{31}) - (a_{12}a_{21}a_{33}) - (a_{11}a_{23}a_{32})]$. We can apply the principle of the irrelevance of polynomial inequalities (1.3.6) here to conclude:

(2.2.7) Gaussian elimination can be successfully applied to an n by n matrix chosen at random, with probability one.

Of course probable success is not certain success, as our original example (2.2.1) showed. As we will now see, we can always get out of trouble with row switches. This will answer the second point we needed to address, namely, that of correcting predicted problems in advance. Since we now have a good method for spotting problems from (2.2.6), it is easy to be systematic about corrections. We are going to explain this on two levels: first, we will do the correction by row interchanges, and, second, we will do the row interchanges by matrix multiplication.

(2.2.8) (Row-Interchange Preprocessing for Gaussian Elimination). Let A be an n by n matrix with $\det(A) \neq 0$. Then it is possible, by interchanging the rows of A, to obtain a matrix $\overline{A}$ for which $\det_1(\overline{A})$, $\det_2(\overline{A}), \ldots, \det_n(\overline{A})$ are all nonzero.

Before we prove (2.2.8), we observe that whenever we interchange rows of a matrix, we change only the sign of the determinant. Also, for definiteness, whenever a row interchange is necessary we are going to do the first one possible. But this is not a requirement, and in later work we will make other choices. Now to start: if $\det_1(A) = 0$, then $A_{11} = 0$. The first column of A must contain a nonzero entry since $\det(A) \neq 0$, so we choose the first row after row 1 which begins with a nonzero entry and exchange that row with row 1. This gives us a matrix $B_{(2)}$ with $\det_1(B_{(2)}) \neq 0$, and $\det(B_{(2)}) = \pm \det(A)$. (If no switch was required, we let $B_{(2)} = A$.) Now suppose we have obtained a matrix $B_{(p)}$ from A by row interchanges with $\det_1(B_{(p)}), \ldots, \det_{p-1}(B_{(p)})$ all nonzero, and $\det(B_{(p)}) \neq 0$. So we can apply Gaussian elimination to $B_{(p)}$ up to stage p and obtain a matrix

$$C = \begin{bmatrix} d_1 & u_{1,2} & \cdots & u_{1,n} \\ & \ddots & & \vdots \\ & & d_p & \cdots & u_{p,n} \\ & & * & \cdots & * \\ & & \vdots & & \vdots \\ & & * & \cdots & * \end{bmatrix} \quad \text{with}$$

$$\det(C) = d_1 \cdots d_{p-1} \det \begin{bmatrix} d_p & \cdots & u_{p,n} \\ \vdots & & \vdots \\ * & \cdots & * \\ \vdots & & \vdots \\ * & \cdots & * \end{bmatrix}$$

By (2.2.5), $\det_i(C) = \det_i(B_{(p)})$ for $i = 1, \ldots, n$. If $\det_p(B_{(p)}) = 0$, then $d_p = 0$. At least one of the remaining $p - 1$ entries in the pth column of C below d_p is nonzero, since $\det(C) = \det_n(C) = \det_n(B_{(p)})$ is nonzero. We take the first such entry and interchange its row, call it k, with row p of $B_{(p)}$, to get a new matrix $B_{(p+1)}$. Since the first $p - 1$ rows of $B_{(p)}$ are not touched, $\det_i(B_{(p+1)}) = \det_i(B_{(p)})$ for $i = 1, \ldots, p - 1$. So we can carry out Gaussian elimination on $B_{(p+1)}$ up to stage p, and obtain a matrix C', which differs from C only in having row p interchanged with row k. By (2.2.5), $\det_p(C') = \det_p(B_{(p+1)})$, and by construction $\det_p(C') \neq 0$. So $\det_i(B_{(p+1)}) \neq 0$ for $i = 1, 2, \ldots, p$, and $\det(B_{(p+1)}) = \pm \det(A)$. [If $\det_p(B_{(p)}) \neq 0$, we let $B_{(p+1)} = B_{(p)}$.] By the time we reach $B_{(n)}$, we have obtained a matrix $\overline{A}$ which meets the criteria of (2.2.8).

Example (2.2.9) Let

$$A = \begin{bmatrix} 0 & 1 & 2 \\ 0 & 0 & 3 \\ 1 & -1 & 0 \end{bmatrix}$$

Then $\det(A) = 3$, but $\det_1(A) = 0$. Switch rows 1 and 3. We obtain

$$B_{(2)} = \begin{bmatrix} 1 & -1 & 0 \\ 0 & 0 & 3 \\ 0 & 1 & 2 \end{bmatrix}$$

Then $\det_1(B_{(2)}) = 1$ but $\det_2(B_{(2)}) = 0$. Switch rows 2 and 3. We obtain

$$B_{(3)} = \begin{bmatrix} 1 & -1 & 0 \\ 0 & 1 & 2 \\ 0 & 0 & 3 \end{bmatrix}$$

Then $\det_1(B_{(3)}) = 1$, $\det_2(B_{(3)}) = 1$, and $\det_3(B_{(3)}) = 3$.

Take $A = B_{(3)}$.

Warning: Example (2.2.9) was carefully chosen so that no elimination steps needed to be calculated. In general, in trying to follow the procedure of (2.2.8), Gaussian elimination needs to be conducted simultaneously. What you do in that case is keep a record of all row interchanges as they are done.

Finally, we need to discuss how to do row interchanges by matrix multiplication. Suppose we want to rearrange the rows of the n by n matrix A so that rows $1, 2, \ldots, n$ become rows $\sigma(1), \sigma(2), \ldots, \sigma(n)$, where $\sigma(i)$, $i = 1, \ldots, n$, is a *permutation* (or rearrangement) of $1, \ldots, n$. In other words, we want a matrix $\overline{A}$ with $(\overline{A})^{\sigma(i)} = A^i$. Suppose we want to write A as $P\overline{A}$ for some n by n matrix P, with entries $p_{i,j}$. Then $(\overline{A})^{\sigma(i)} = A^i = (P\overline{A})^i = p_{i,1}\overline{A}^1 + \cdots + p_{i,n}\overline{A}^n$. So we define P by

$$p_{i,j} = \begin{cases} 0 & j \neq \sigma(i) \\ 1 & j = \sigma(i) \end{cases} \qquad \text{for } i = 1, 2, \ldots, n$$

Then $P\overline{A} = A$.

Note: The ith row of P is the same as the $\sigma(i)$th row of I_n (the n by n identity). This is useful to remember in constructing P: we permute the rows of I_n the reverse way the rows of A were permuted to form $\overline{A}$. For this reason P is usually termed a *permutation matrix*.

Example (2.2.9) (Continued).   The matrix $\overline{A}$ is obtained from A by having row 1 become row $\sigma(1) = 2$, row 2 become row $\sigma(2) = 3$, and row 3 become row $\sigma(3) = 1$. Thus to form P from I_3 we want to let row $\sigma(1) = 2$ be row

1, row $\sigma(2) = 3$ be row 2, and row $\sigma(3) = 1$ be row 3. Then we can check

$$\begin{bmatrix} 0 & 1 & 0 \\ 0 & 0 & 1 \\ 1 & 0 & 0 \end{bmatrix} \begin{bmatrix} 1 & -1 & 0 \\ 0 & 1 & 2 \\ 0 & 0 & 3 \end{bmatrix} = \begin{bmatrix} 0 & 1 & 2 \\ 0 & 0 & 3 \\ 1 & -1 & 0 \end{bmatrix}$$

$$\quad\quad P \quad\quad\quad\quad \overline{A} \quad\quad\quad\quad\quad A$$

Now we can complete our discussion of matrix factorization, at least in theory:

(2.2.10) Gaussian Elimination with Row Interchanges. Let A be an invertible n by n matrix. Then there is a permutation matrix P, a lower triangular matrix L with unit diagonal, and an upper triangular matrix U with $A = PLU$. These matrices are found as follows:

1. By row-interchange preprocessing for Gaussian elimination, we can interchange rows of A to obtain a matrix $\overline{A}$ for which $\det{}_i(\overline{A}) \neq 0$, $i = 1, \ldots, n$. We can write $A = P\overline{A}$ for a permutation matrix P.
2. By the method of Gaussian elimination, we can construct the L-U decomposition of $\overline{A}$ and write $\overline{A} = LU$.
3. Finally, $A = P\overline{A} = PLU$.

To illustrate (2.2.10) we'll apply it to Example (2.2.1).

Example (2.2.1) (Continued). We recall that

$$A = \begin{bmatrix} 3 & -1 & 0 \\ 6 & -2 & 1 \\ -3 & 3 & 1 \end{bmatrix}$$

that it was necessary to switch rows 2 and 3, and that the multipliers were $l_{2,1} = -1$, $l_{3,1} = 2$, and $l_{3,2} = 0$. So we have

$$\begin{bmatrix} 3 & -1 & 0 \\ 6 & -2 & 1 \\ -3 & 3 & 1 \end{bmatrix} = \begin{bmatrix} 1 & 0 & 0 \\ 0 & 0 & 1 \\ 0 & 1 & 0 \end{bmatrix} \begin{bmatrix} 1 & & \\ -1 & 1 & \\ 2 & 0 & 1 \end{bmatrix} \begin{bmatrix} 3 & -1 & 0 \\ & 2 & 1 \\ & & 1 \end{bmatrix}$$

$$\quad\quad A \quad\quad\quad\quad\quad P \quad\quad\quad\quad L \quad\quad\quad\quad U$$

We could use this $A = PLU$ factorization to solve a system of linear equations with A as matrix of coefficients, for example,

(∗)
$$\begin{cases} 3x_1 - x_2 = 11 \\ 6x_1 - 2x_2 + x_3 = 24 \\ -3x_1 + 3x_2 + x_3 = -7 \\ \text{or} \end{cases}$$

$$Ax = b \quad \text{where } x = \begin{bmatrix} x_1 \\ x_2 \\ x_3 \end{bmatrix} \text{ and } b = \begin{bmatrix} 11 \\ 24 \\ -7 \end{bmatrix}$$

Since $Ax = b$ and $PLUx = b$ are equivalent, we can solve (∗) by solving $Pz = b$, $Ly = z$, and $Ux = y$ successively, or

(a)
$$\begin{cases} z_1 = 11 \\ z_3 = 24 \\ z_2 = -7 \end{cases} \quad \text{or} \quad Pz = b \quad \text{where } z = \begin{bmatrix} z_1 \\ z_2 \\ z_3 \end{bmatrix}$$

(b)
$$\begin{cases} y_1 = z_1 \\ -y_1 + y_2 = z_2 \\ 2y_1 + y_3 = z_3 \end{cases} \quad \text{or} \quad Ly = z \quad \text{where } y = \begin{bmatrix} y_1 \\ y_2 \\ y_3 \end{bmatrix}$$

(c)
$$\begin{cases} 3x_1 - x_2 = y_1 \\ 2x_2 + x_3 = y_2 \\ x_3 = y_3 \end{cases} \quad \text{or} \quad Ux = y$$

Putting (a) into (b) we obtain

$$y_1 = z_1 = 11$$
$$y_2 = x_1 + y_1 = 4$$
$$y_3 = z_3 - 2y_1 = 2$$

and then putting these results into (c) we get (from the bottom up)

$$\begin{aligned} x_3 &= y_3 = 2 \\ x_2 &= \tfrac{1}{2}(y_2 - x_3) = 1 \quad \text{or} \quad x = \begin{bmatrix} 4 \\ 1 \\ 2 \end{bmatrix} \\ x_1 &= \tfrac{1}{3}(y_1 + x_2) = 4 \end{aligned}$$

It is important to emphasize that solving the system of equations (∗) of Example (2.2.1) using the $A = PLU$ factorization is *not* typical practice.

Finding the matrix P is, in general, far more complicated than this simple example implies. In actual solution of systems of equations, the switches are made in the course of carrying out the Gaussian elimination steps. We will return to this point in Chapter 3 when we will construct a program to do elimination. Here, it is enough to realize that if the factorization of the matrix of coefficients of a system of linear equations has been obtained somehow, then the solution of the system breaks into a sequence of easily managable steps.

EXERCISE 2.2

1. Find the factorization $A = PLU$ of (2.2.10) for each of the following matrices A:

   (a) $\begin{bmatrix} 0 & 1 \\ -1 & 0 \end{bmatrix}$ (b) $\begin{bmatrix} 0 & 2 \\ 3 & -2 \end{bmatrix}$

   (c) $\begin{bmatrix} 1 & 1 & 1 \\ 1 & -1 & 3 \\ 1 & -1 & 0 \end{bmatrix}$ (d) $\begin{bmatrix} 0 & 1 & 4 \\ -2 & -3 & -4 \\ 3 & 3 & 3 \end{bmatrix}$

2. Let $A = \begin{bmatrix} 0 & x \\ y & z \end{bmatrix}$, where $z \neq 0$. Find the factorization $A = PLU$.

3. Find an example of a matrix A, permutation matrices P, P', lower triangular matrices L, L' with ones on their diagonals, and upper triangular matrices U, U' such that $A = PLU$ and $A = P'L'U'$, but at least one of the pairs P, P'; L, L'; U, U' are distinct. [This shows that the factorization (2.2.10) is not unique.]

4. A permutation of $1, 2, \ldots, n$ can be regarded as a function σ sending i to $\sigma(i)$. Prove that if σ corresponds to the matrix P and τ corresponds to the matrix Q, then PQ corresponds to the composite function $\sigma\tau$.

5. Let E_{ij} be the $n \times n$ matrix with 1 in the (i, j) position and zero elsewhere. Let σ be a permutation of $1, \ldots, n$, and let P be the corresponding matrix.

   (a) Prove that $PE_{ij}P^{-1} = E_{kl}$, where $k = \sigma(i)$ and $\sigma(l) = j$.

   (b) Let $A = I + aE_{ij}$ and $B = I + bE_{kl}$. Prove that $PA = BP$.

   (c) A matrix of the form $I + aE_{ij}$ is called elementary. Suppose $E_1, \ldots, E_m$ are elementary matrices and $P_1, \ldots, P_{m+1}$ are permutation matrices. Prove that there are elementary matrices $E_1', \ldots, E_m'$ and a permutation matrix P such that

   $$P_1 E_1 P_2 E_2 P_3 \cdots E_m P_{m+1} = PE_1' \cdots E_m'.$$

2.3   SOME EXAMPLES OF NONSINGULAR SYSTEMS

There are a great number of practical situations which are modeled by a nonsingular system of linear equations. The three categories of such models presented in this section are typical examples of these situations: we have an underlying theory, which emphasizes some points of the actual circumstances and ignores others, from which some balancing equations are constructed. The actual assembling of the specific numerical values for the equations can itself involve some real labor, as our examples will reveal, and even in the relatively modest scale of the problems we deal with here, the solution of systems requires sufficient calculation to justify using a computer. (Techniques to do this are covered in the next section.)

 A.   Voltages and Currents in Resistor–Battery Networks.   Figure (2.3.1) represents an electrical network made up of resistors (the zig-zag symbols labeled by capital R's) and batteries (the alternating long and short lines labeled by lower case e), wired together at nodes (the small circles with numbers in them). A typical network element is illustrated in Figure (2.3.2): this is called branch i of the circuit. Note that it contains a resistor of *resistance* R_k and a battery of *voltage* e_k. In our example, (2.3.1), $e_k = 0$ if $k \neq 6$ so the batteries are omitted in branches 1 through 5. Once all the connections are made in the network, there will be a definite *current* I_k

Figure (2.3.1).

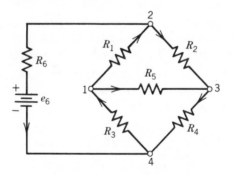

Figure (2.3.2).

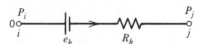

flowing in the branch k, and a definite *voltage drop* E_k between the nodes of branch k. Our problem is to solve for these branch currents and voltages, given the values of the resistors and batteries.

This problem, and others like it, must have a unique answer: once the circuit is wired up, nothing changes, and if it is taken apart and reassembled we expect exactly the same currents and voltages. As we will see later, the answer depends on a system of linear equations constructed from the given resistances and battery voltages. So this is a linear system with a unique solution.

To begin our analysis of the circuit, we need to recall some elementary direct current circuit theory:

Ohm's law. The voltage drop across a resistor is equal to the product of the current and resistance, when these are in units of volts, amperes, and ohms, respectively.

Kirchhoff's first law. The sum of the currents flowing into each node equals the sum of the currents flowing out of that node.

Kirchhoff's second law. The algebraic sum of the voltage drops around any closed loop in the circuit is zero.

To convert these into formulas, we need to introduce some additional quantities which are to represent voltages at the nodes. Of course, voltage has to be measured relative to something, so this voltage will be thought of as relative to some ground potential external to the circuit. We call these new quantities *potentials*; the potential at node i is denoted P_i. (*Note*: P_i is measured relative to some arbitrary external ground.) Now for the formulas:

(2.3.3) In Figure (2.3.2), assume that the potential at node i is P_i, the potential at node j is P_j, and that the current flows in the direction indicated by the arrow. Then the branch current I_k and branch voltage are given by:

(a) $E_k = P_i - P_j$.
(b) $I_k = R_k^{-1}(E_k + e_k)$.

Formula (a) is just the definition of voltage as potential difference, while formula (b) is Ohm's law: voltage equals resistance times current (the voltage here being $E_k + e_k$, the current I_k, and the resistance R_k) solved for current.

From formulas (a) and (b), we can seen that the potentials really control everything: from them and (a) we get voltages and from (a) and (b) we get the currents.

Formula (a) also encompasses Kirchhoff's second law: around any closed loop in the circuit the potentials will be added on and subtracted off to give zero; for example, in Figure (2.3.1) with currents as indicated by the arrows, the loop from node 1 to 2 to 3 to 4 to 1 has voltage sum $E_1 + E_2 + E_4 + E_3$ $= (P_1 - P_2) + (P_2 - P_3) + (P_3 - P_4) + (P_4 - P_1) = 0$, and the loop from node 1 to 2 to 3 to 1 has voltage sum (note the arrow in branch 5) $E_1 + E_2 - E_5 = (P_1 - P_2) + (P_2 - P_3) - (P_1 - P_3) = 0$. (This also indicates that the assigning of arrows in a circuit is completely arbitrary: we just think of E and I with signs switched if we want the current to flow in the other direction.)

From (2.3.3), then we will have two sets of six linear equations, one for each branch of forms (a) and (b), recording the information from Ohm's law and Kirchhoff's second law. In addition, we will have four equations, one for each node, from Kirchhoff's first law. These appear below:

(2.3.4)   Equations for Figure (2.3.1)

OHM'S LAW

$$I_1 = R_1^{-1}E_1 \qquad I_3 = R_3^{-1}E_3 \qquad I_5 = R_5^{-1}E_5$$

$$I_2 = R_2^{-1}E_2 \qquad I = R_4^{-1}E_4 \qquad I_6 = R_6^{-1}(E_6 + e_6)$$

KIRCHHOFF'S FIRST LAW

$$I_1 - I_3 + I_5 = 0 \quad \text{(node 1)} \qquad -I_2 + I_4 - I_5 = 0 \quad \text{(node 3)}$$

$$-I_1 + I_2 + I_6 = 0 \quad \text{(node 2)} \qquad I_3 + I_4 + I_6 = 0 \quad \text{(node 4)}$$

KIRCHHOFF'S SECOND LAW

$$E_1 = P_1 - P_2 \qquad E_3 = P_4 - P_1 \qquad E_5 = P_1 - P_3$$

$$E_2 = P_2 - P_3 \qquad E_4 = P_3 - P_4 \qquad E_6 = P_2 - P_1$$

Our problem is to solve the systems (2.3.4) for E_k, I_k, $k = 1, \ldots, 6$, given R_k, $k = 1, \ldots, 6$, and e_6. Of course, we want to write these in matrix forms. For this, we introduce the *incidence matrix* A of the circuit: this will be a matrix whose rows correspond to nodes and columns to branches, where for each node we put a $+1$ for the branches flowing into it, a -1 for the branches flowing out of it, and a zero for the branches unconnected to it, in the corresponding row of A.

(2.3.5)   Incidence Matrix for Figure (2.3.1)

Nodes		Branches 1	2	3	4	5	6
1		1	0	-1	0	1	0
2	$A =$	-1	1	0	0	0	1
3		0	-1	0	1	-1	0
4		0	0	1	-1	0	-1

To write (2.3.4) efficiently in matrix form, we also need to introduce the diagonal matrix of reciprocal resistance, which figures in the Ohm's law part of the equations. Since reciprocal resistances are called conductances in circuit theory, we call the resulting matrix the *conductance* matrix:

(2.3.6)   Conductance Matrix for Figure (2.3.1).

$$R^{-1} = \begin{bmatrix} R_1^{-1} & & & & & \\ & R_2^{-1} & & & & \\ & & R_3^{-1} & & & \\ & & & R_4^{-1} & & \\ & & & & R_5^{-1} & \\ & & & & & R_6^{-1} \end{bmatrix}$$

Finally, we need vectors for the unknowns and remaining constants:

(2.3.7)   Vectors of Voltage, Current, and Potentials for Figure (2.3.1).

$$E = \begin{bmatrix} E_1 \\ E_2 \\ E_3 \\ E_4 \\ E_5 \\ E_6 \end{bmatrix} \quad I = \begin{bmatrix} I_1 \\ I_2 \\ I_3 \\ I_4 \\ I_5 \\ I_6 \end{bmatrix} \quad P = \begin{bmatrix} P_1 \\ P_2 \\ P_3 \\ P_4 \end{bmatrix} \quad e = \begin{bmatrix} e_1 \\ e_2 \\ e_3 \\ e_4 \\ e_5 \\ e_6 \end{bmatrix} = \begin{bmatrix} 0 \\ 0 \\ 0 \\ 0 \\ 0 \\ e_6 \end{bmatrix}$$

And now, we restate Eqs. (2.3.4) in matrix form:

(2.3.8)   Equations for Figure (2.3.1), Using (2.3.5) – (2.3.7).

OHM'S LAW

$$R^{-1}(E + e) = I$$

KIRCHHOFF'S FIRST LAW

$$AI = 0$$

KIRCHHOFF'S SECOND LAW

$$A^T P = E$$

These three equations can be combined into one: putting Ohm's law into Kirchhoff's first law gives $A(R^{-1}(E + e)) = 0$ or $AR^{-1}E = -AR^{-1}e$, and putting Kirchhoff's second law into this equation gives

$$(2.3.9) \qquad (AR^{-1}A^T)P = -AR^{-1}e$$

To write down the matrix of coefficients of (2.3.6), $AR^{-1}A^T$, and the vector of constants, $-AR^{-1}e$, we use a procedure applicable to all circuits, although with this example a simple direct multiplication is almost as quick. We have

(2.3.10)

$$(AR^{-1}A^T)_{ij} = A_{i1}R_1^{-1}A_{j1} + A_{i2}R_2^{-1}A_{j2} + \cdots$$

$$= \begin{cases} 0 & \text{if } i \neq j \text{ and no branch connects nodes } i \text{ and } j \\ -R_k^{-1} & \text{if } i \neq j \text{ and branch } k \text{ connects nodes } i \text{ and } j \\ \text{the sum of the } R_l^{-1} \text{ such that branch } l \text{ ends or starts at } i \\ \text{if } i = j \end{cases}$$

$$(2.3.11) \qquad (-AR^{-1}e)_i = -\left(A_{i1}R_1^{-1}e_1 + A_{i2}R_2^{-1}e_2 + \cdots\right)$$

Using (2.3.10) and (2.3.11) with Figure (2.3.1) we find

$AR^{-1}A^T$

$$= \begin{bmatrix} R_1^{-1} + R_3^{-1} + R_5^{-1} & -R_1^{-1} & -R_5^{-1} & -R_3^{-1} \\ -R_1^{-1} & R_1^{-1} + R_2^{-1} + R_6^{-1} & -R_2^{-1} & -R_6^{-1} \\ -R_5^{-1} & -R_2^{-1} & R_2^{-1} + R_4^{-1} + R_5^{-1} & -R_4^{-1} \\ -R_3^{-1} & -R_6^{-1} & -R_4^{-1} & R_3^{-1} + R_4^{-1} + R_6^{-1} \end{bmatrix}$$

$-AR^{-1}e$

$$= \begin{bmatrix} 0 \\ -R_6^{-1}e_6 \\ 0 \\ R_6^{-1}e^d 6 \end{bmatrix}$$

Unfortunately, the matrix $AR^{-1}A^T$ is singular: for example, all row sums are zero, so the vector all of whose entries are one is a nonzero vector which $AR^{-1}A^T$ multiplies to zero. Thus there can be no unique solution P to (2.3.9).

We could have predicted this in advance: the potentials P_i were measured relative to some arbitrary external ground potential. If we change the external ground to a different value, that changes the values of all the P_i by some constant, although it doesn't affect their differences, so the voltages E_k in the branches remain the same.

Actually, this phenomenon is an asset, not a liability: since we can set ground potential at anything, we *choose* it to be the potential at one of the nodes, for definiteness, say the last one in numerical order. That is, we set $P_4 = 0$. Now everything else should be determined.

Setting $P_4 = 0$ means that in Kirchhoff's second law, the third equation of (2.3.8), we can ignore the last column of A^T and the last entry of P in forming E. Ignoring the last column of A^T is similar to deleting the last row of A, a matrix we will now form and name:

(2.3.12) The *reduced incidence matrix* B, formed by deleting the last row from the incidence matrix A, for Figure (2.3.1), is

$$B = \begin{bmatrix} 1 & 0 & -1 & 0 & 1 & 0 \\ -1 & 1 & 0 & 0 & 0 & 1 \\ 0 & -1 & 0 & 1 & -1 & 0 \end{bmatrix}$$

If we let Q be the vector obtained by deleting the last entry of P, then we can rewrite the Kirchhoff laws in (2.3.8) as $BI = 0$ and $B^T Q = E$. Then, as before, from these two laws and Ohm's law we obtain

$$(2.3.13) \qquad (BR^{-1}B^T)Q = -BR^{-1}e$$

To write this down explicitly for Figure (2.3.1), we note that formulas (2.3.10) and (2.3.11) apply as before, except that the i and j indices stay at or below 3. (In other words, we drop the last row and column of $AR^{-1}A^T$ and the last entry of $-AR^{-1}e$.) This leaves the system

$$
\begin{bmatrix}
R_1^{-1} + R_3^{-1} + R_5^{-1} & -R_1^{-1} & -R_5^{-1} \\
-R_1^{-1} & R_1^{-1} + R_2^{-1} + R_6^{-1} & -R_2^{-1} \\
-R_3^{-1} & -R_2^{-1} & R_1^{-1} + R_4^{-1} + R_5^{-1}
\end{bmatrix}
\begin{bmatrix}
P_1 \\ P_2 \\ P_3
\end{bmatrix}
$$

$$
= \begin{bmatrix}
0 \\ -R_6^{-1}e_6 \\ 0
\end{bmatrix}
$$

as the explicit form of (2.3.13). This is solved for P_1, P_2, P_3. Then E is obtained as $B^T P$ and I as $R^{-1}(E + e)$.

Given any resistor–battery network, with, say, m nodes and n branches, we can solve for the n vectors E and I of branch currents and voltages just as we did here: the potentials $P_1, \ldots, P_{m-1}$ form a vector Q of unknowns, to be solved for in Eqs. (2.3.13), while the given data (the branch resistances R_k and battery voltages e_k, and the circuit connections) are used to form the matrix of coefficients and the vector of constants in (2.3.13) using the techniques of (2.3.10) and (2.3.11). Once Q is found, $E = B^T P$ and $I = R^{-1}(E + e)$ are obtained as before. An example of a problem of this type is presented in Exercise 1.

The circuit (2.3.1) we've used here as an example is known as a *Wheatstone Bridge*: R_6 is actually the internal resistance of the battery in branch 6 and R_5 is the internal resistance of a voltmeter in branch 5. R_1 and R_2 (along with R_5 and R_6) are known resistances, R_4 is unknown, and R_3 is a variable resistor, or potentiometer. By varying R_3 until the voltmeter reads 0, the value of R_4 can be determined. [For details, see, e.g., the *Radio Amateur's Handbook* published by the American Radio Relay League (annual editions); the author, who operates an amateur radio station WD5BDK, based Figure (2.3.1) on the circuit in the 1976 edition.]

B. Leontieff Production Models for Firms and Communities. We want to study now economic entities, such as a company or a community, which has both buying and selling transactions with an external economy and also conducts internal transactions among its constituent parts. For example, a medium-size company with several product lines will need to make some external purchases of materials and will make external sales of finished goods; but at the same time its various divisions will be exchanging products and materials among themselves. Or a community with several types of economic sectors (called industries) will have both imports and exports, while the various industries will be exchanging parts of their outputs among themselves also.

The question to be studied is At what production level do the various parts of the entity have to run in order to meet given outside demands? The answer, of course, must take into account the various internal demands among these various parts that the outside demands generate. We will assume that this internal coupling is linear, and be led to a system of linear equations.

The method we use is called *input–output analysis*, invented by Wassily Leontieff, and it merited the 1973 Nobel Prize in Economics. Leontieff's method is to organize the various transactions in the entity into a table, called an input–output table, from which a system of linear equations will be developed.

Figure (2.3.14) represents such a table, describing the annual transactions of a fictional electronics company called Oklahoma Instruments. The company has six divisions: (1) industrial products, which manufactures devices such as automatic testing equipment; (2) consumer products, which manufactures items such as calculators; (3) circuit boards, which manufactures items such as single-board computers which other manufacturers purchase to incorporate in their own products; (4) semiconductor products, which manufactures integrated circuits; (5) software products, which develops programs and operating systems; and (6) research and development, which invents new products and improves current ones.

The table is arranged so that the rows represent sales and the columns represent purchases. The inside transactions are all listed in the 6 by 6 table contained inside the double lines. For example, division 4 (semiconductor products) had sales of $0.125 to division 1, $0.1 to division 2, $0.1 to division 3, $0.2 to division 5, and no sales to divisions 4 and 6 for a total internal sales of $0.525 (in $1 million units). Division 3 (circuit boards) had internal purchases of $0.15 from division 1, $0.1 from division 4, $0.1 from division 5 and none from divisions 2, 3, and 6, for total internal purchases of $0.35 (in $1 million units). The column labeled "outside demand," the seventh column in the table, lists the external sales of each division, and the column labeled "total output," the eighth column of the table, lists the total sales—internal and external—of each division. For example, division 4 had

Figure (2.3.14).

Purchases

				Internal				Outside demand	Total output
		①	②	③	④	⑤	⑥		
Sales Internal	①	0.375	0.4	0.15	0.13	0.6	0.26	0.705	2.5
	②	0.025	0	0	0	0.1	0	1.875	2.0
	③	0.25	0.1	0	0	0.2	0.065	0.415	1.0
	④	0.125	0.1	0.1	0	0.2	0	0.775	1.3
	⑤	0.25	0.3	0.1	0.39	0.2	0.65	0.41	2.0
	⑥	0.375	0.3	0	0.26	0.1	0.26	0.005	1.3
External cost		1.1	0.8	0.65	0.52	0.6	0.065		3.735
Total input		2.5	2.0	1	1.3	2.0	1.3	4.185	13.835

Oklahoma Instruments
198*
($1 million units)

external sales of $0.775, which when added to the internal sales of $0.525, gives a total output of $1.3 (in $1 million units). The row labeled "external cost," the seventh row of the table, lists the purchases each division made from outside, and the row labeled "total input," the eighth row of the table, lists the total purchases—internal and external—of each division. For example, division 3 had external purchases of $0.65, which added to the internal purchases of $0.35 gives a total input of $1.0 (in $1 million units). The total external sales is the last entry in column 7 ($4.185 million), the total external purchases is the last entry in row 7 ($3.735 million), and the last entry in row 8 and column 8 is the sum of total outputs and external sales ($13.835 million).

Figure (2.3.14) represents the actual activity of the company in some year. From it, we want to make a forecast of the following type: suppose we have projected outside demands each of the divisions needs to meet in a given year, and we want to determine what the total output levels of each division must be in that year in order to meet the projected outside demands. To make this projection, we will need to extract from the table the information regarding the mutual demands the divisions make on each other.

To begin this process, we rewrite Figure (2.3.14) symbolically for an economic unit of n divisions:

(2.3.15) Input – Output Table for n-Sector Economics.

PURCHASES

		Division 1	Division 2	$\cdots$	Division n	Outside Demand	Total Output
S	Division 1	a_{11}	a_{12}	$\cdots$	a_{1n}	b_1	x_1
A	Division 2	a_{21}	a_{22}	$\cdots$	a_{2n}	b_2	x_2
L	$\vdots$	$\vdots$	$\vdots$		$\vdots$	$\vdots$	$\vdots$
E							
S	Division n	a_{n1}	a_{n2}	$\cdots$	a_{nn}	b_n	x_n
	External Cost	d_1	d_2	$\cdots$	d_n		Σd_i
	Total Input	X_1	X_2	$\cdots$	X_n	b_i	$\Sigma X_i + b_i$

Here a_{ij} = the sales of division i to division j
or a_{ij} = the purchases of division j from division i
   x_i = the total production of division i
   b_i = the production of division i available for outside demand
   d_i = the purchases of division i from outside
(all in dollars).

The table is constructed so that there are n output equations

$$(*) \qquad x_i = a_{i1} + a_{i2} + \cdots + a_{in} + b_i \qquad i = 1, 2, \ldots, n$$

and n input equations

$$(**) \qquad X_j = a_{1j} + a_{2j} + \cdots + a_{nj} + d_j \qquad j = 1, 2, \ldots, n$$

The Leontieff analysis is based on the assumption that for each division j *the ratio of the amount of purchases from division i to the total output x_j is a constant for each i*. Another way of saying this is to assert that the dollar amount of the purchases from division i necessary to increase the output of division j by \$1.00 is the same, regardless of the output level. Of course, this is not realistic over all possible output ranges: obviously, the capital costs to go from \$0.0 to \$1.0 are large, and when plant capacity is at its upper limit the same problem occurs. The assumption really makes sense only over a certain middle range of output levels.

In formulas, the assumption says, in terms of (2.3.15), that the ratios (2.3.16) $c_{ij} = b_{ij}/x_j$, $1 \le i$, $j \le n$, are constant independent of the year used to produce the table. With these numbers, which are called *input* or *consumption coefficients*, since c_{ij} is the amount division j purchases (inputs) from division i to produce \$1.00's worth of output j, we can rewrite (2.3.15) in matrix form. We have

(2.3.17)

CONSUMPTION MATRIX

$$C = \begin{bmatrix} c_{11} & \cdots & c_{1n} \\ \vdots & & \vdots \\ c_{n1} & \cdots & c_{nn} \end{bmatrix} \quad \left(\text{where } a_{ij}/X_j = c_{ij} \right)$$

PRODUCTION MATRIX

$$x = \begin{bmatrix} X_1 \\ \vdots \\ X_n \end{bmatrix}$$

EXTERNAL DEMAND VECTOR

$$b = \begin{bmatrix} b_1 \\ \vdots \\ b_n \end{bmatrix}$$

In this notation, equations (∗) become $x_i = c_{i1}x_1 + \cdots + c_{in}x_n + b_i$, $i = 1, \ldots, n$, or

(2.3.18) $x = Cx + b$ or $(I - C)x = b$ (I is the n by n identity).

In (2.3.18), remember, we are trying to predict production levels, that is, solve for x. b is given, since it is the forecasted external demand, and C is calculated from an input–output table for some year, by dividing the internal purchase amounts by total inputs. For example, for the Oklahoma Industries example (2.3.14) we find a consumption matrix

(2.3.19)

0.15	0.02	0.15	0.1	0.3	0.2
0.01	0	0	0	0.005	0
0.1	0.05	0	0	0.1	0.5
0.05	0.05	0.1	0	0.1	0.
0.1	0.15	0.1	0.3	0.1	0.5
0.15	0.15	0	0.2	0.05	0.2

[To produce, for example, \$1.00's worth of semiconductor products (division 4), requires \$0.10 worth of industrial products (division 1), \$0.30 worth of software products (division 5), and \$0.20 worth of research and development (division 6).]

In (2.3.18) we are given C and b and are to find x, that is, solve $Ax = b$ for x, where $A = I - C$, which will be done by the methods of Sections 2.1 and 2.2. But there is an extra ingredient here, if our solution vector x is to be meaningful: we must know that all the entries of x are nonnegative. This will indeed be the case, under certain assumptions on C, which will be verified in our example. The theory we are going to develop now to deal with this problem will also be used again in a number of different contexts in later chapters.

We define a matrix A to be nonnegative (or positive) and write $A \geq 0$ (or $A > 0$) if every entry of A is nonnegative (or positive), and we use similar notions for vectors. The basic result we will need is

(2.3.20)   Productive Matrix Theorem.   Let C be a nonnegative n by n matrix. Then if there is a nonnegative vector x_0 such that every entry of x_0 is larger than the corresponding entry of Cx_0, then for every nonnegative vector b the equation $(I - C)x = b$ has a nonnegative solution x.

Before proving (2.3.20), we want to restate it in a couple of ways. First, the hypothesis says that, regarding C as a consumption matrix, there is some production levels at which every division produces a surplus available for outside demand, and then the conclusion says that any possible outside demand level can be met from some production level. Second, if we write the result in matrix form the hypothesis says that $x_0 - Cx_0 > 0$ for some x_0, while the conclusion asserts that if $b \geq 0$ there exists $x \geq 0$ with $(I - C)x = b$. By choosing $b = e_1, e_2, \ldots, e_n$, where e_i is the vector with 1 in position i and zero elsewhere, we find nonnegative vectors x_i, $i = 1, \ldots, n$, with $(I - C)x_i = e_i$. If A is the matrix whose columns are $x_1, \ldots, x_n$ then $(I - C)A = I$, so $A = (I - C)^{-1}$ and the columns of A are nonnegative, so $A \geq 0$. That is, (2.3.20) asserts that $I - C$ is invertible with a nonnegative inverse.

This second reformulation makes it easy to see that the converse of (2.3.20) is also true, giving an "if and only if" version of (2.3.20):

(2.3.21) Let C be an n by n matrix and nonnegative. There is a vector $x_0 \geq 0$ with $x_0 - Cx_0 > 0$ if and only if $I - C$ is invertible and $(I - C)^{-1} \geq 0$. For a proof of (2.3.21), we use (2.3.20) for the "only if" part. If $I - C$ is invertible with $(I - C)^{-1} \geq 0$, let b_0 be the vector all of whose entries are one. Then entry i of $x_0 = (I - c)^{-1}b_0$ is the sum of the entries in row i of $(I - C)^{-1}$, so $x_0 \geq 0$, and $x_0 - Cx_0 = (I - C)x_0 = (I - C)(I - C)^{-1}b_0 = b_0 > 0$.

We still have to prove (2.3.20). We will derive it by a simple consequence of the following fact:

(2.3.22) If $C \geq 0$ and there is an $x \geq 0$ with $x - Cx > 0$, then for all vectors y, if $y - Cy \geq 0$ then $y \geq 0$.

To prove (2.3.22), we observe that if x has entries $x_1, \ldots, x_n$ then $x - Cx > 0$ implies $x_i > (c_{i1}x_1 + \cdots + c_{in}x_n)$ and $c_{i1}x_1 + \cdots + c_{in}x_n \geq 0$ since $C \geq 0$ and $x \geq 0$, so $x_i > 0$. Now suppose that $y - Cy \geq 0$ and y has entries $y_1, \ldots, y_n$. Let $a = \max\{-y_i/x_i | i = 1, \ldots, n\}$, say $a = -y_k/x_k$. If y is not non-negative, then at least one y_i is negative, and then $-y_i/x_i$ is positive, so certainly a is positive. If $z = y + ax$, then its ith coordinate z_i is $y_i + ax_i$ and $y_i + ax_i \geq b_i + (-y_i/x_i)x_i = 0$, so $z \geq 0$, and $z_k = y_k + ax_k = y_k + (-y_k/x_k)x_k = 0$. We are assuming $y \geq Cy$ and $x > Cx$. If y is not non-negative, then $a > 0$ so $ax > aCx = Cax$, and then $z \geq 0$ so $Cz \geq 0$, and then $0 < Cz = Cy + Caz < y + ax = z$. Thus $z > 0$, but we had $z_k = 0$, so this is impossible. Our assumption on y must be wrong, so $y \geq 0$ as desired.

From (2.3.22) we conclude that if $y - Cy = 0$ then $y = 0$: for (2.3.22) implies that $y \geq 0$, and since we also have $0 = -[y - (y)] = (-y) - C(-y)$ then (2.3.22) shows that $-y \geq 0$, and so $y = 0$. Thus $(I - C)y = 0$

implies that $y = 0$, so $I - C$ is invertible. If x is a solution of $(I - C)x = b$ and $b \geq 0$, then $x - Cx \geq 0$ so by (2.3.22) we have $x \geq 0$. Now we have established all of (2.3.20).

The criterion of (2.3.20) is not easy to apply to a given matrix C. How can we know, for example, that there is a vector $x \geq 0$ with $x - Cx > 0$ for the matrix C of (2.3.19)? One way is to look again at the criteria of (2.3.21), and note that since $C \geq 0$ exactly when $C^T \geq 0$ and $I - C$ is invertible with positive inverse exactly when $(I - C)^T = I - C^T$ is, then there is an $x_0 \geq 0$ with $x_0 - Cx_0 > 0$ if and only if there is a $z_0 > 0$ with $z_0 - C^T z_0 > 0$.

Now in a consumption matrix C, as in (2.3.17), the jth-column sum $c_{1j} + c_{2j} + \cdots + c_{kj}$ represents the total amount division j needs from all other divisions to produce \$1.00 of output. If we assume division j is profitable, then this sum must be less than 1. This sum is also the jth entry of the product $C^T z_0$, where z_0 is the vector all of whose entries are one. If all divisions are profitable, then $z_0 > C^T z_0$, so there must be an $x_0 \geq 0$ with $x_0 - Cx_0 > 0$. In other words:

(2.3.23) If the column sums of a consumption matrix are less than one, then there is an $x_0 > 0$ with $x_0 - Cx_0 > 0$. If all divisions are profitable, then any outside demand can be met [by (2.3.20)].

We have used the example of the company throughout this section. In the theory of community economics, we only change the labels in the Table (2.3.15): the divisions are called industries, the outside demand is called export, and the external cost is called import. Some examples are given in Exercises 2 and 3.

C. Electrostatics and Heat. Suppose we have a solid object, like the block in Figure (2.3.24a), which has been heated or given an electrostatic charge, and whose faces are insulators, so that there is no flow of charge or

Figure (2.3.24a).

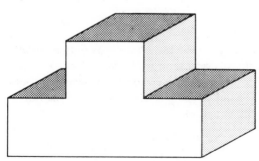

heat across them. We can easily measure the charge or temperature at any point in the faces. How can we use this information to determine the distribution of charge or heat throughout the solid?

We can't experimentally probe the interior of the block without disrupting the steady state. But we can still speak of the charge or temperature at an interior point. At the point (a, b, c) in the coordinate system of x, y, z axes of Figure (2.3.24b), we assume that the charge or temperature is $u(a, b, c)$. So the problem is: given the values of u on the face of the block (i.e., given the boundary values of u), determine u at the interior point.

Figure (2.3.24b).

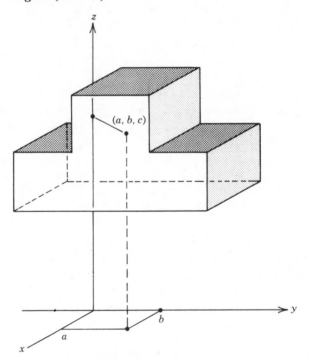

Common sense, and basic physics, tell us that u is determined inside by its boundary values: every time we bring the block to a steady state with given values of u on the faces we expect the same distribution of values of u inside. In addition, advanced physics tells us that the function u satisfies the partial differential equation

$$\frac{\partial^2 u}{\partial x^2} + \frac{\partial^2 u}{\partial y^2} + \frac{\partial^2 u}{\partial z^2} = 0 \quad \text{(Laplace's equation)}$$

If we slice the block in the plane $x = a$, that is, if we restrict u to the plane $x = a$, then u satisfies the partial differential equation

$$\frac{\partial^2 u}{\partial y^2} + \frac{\partial^2 u}{\partial z^2} = 0 \quad \text{(Laplace's equation in two dimensions)}$$

This implies that u is a harmonic function. Such functions have the property that their values at any point, such as (a, b, c), are the average value around any circle centered at that point [Fig. (2.3.24c)],

$$(2.3.25) \qquad u(a, b, c) = \frac{1}{2\pi r} \int_C u(a, y, z)\, ds$$

This formula seems to only say that if we know the function u, we can compute u, but actually it does give us some information: in words, it implies that the value of u at a point is the average of the values at

Figure (2.3.24c).

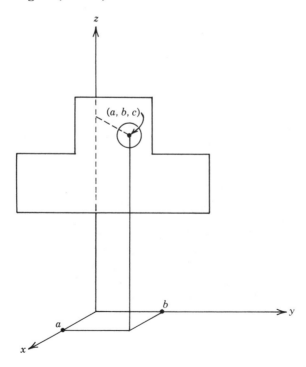

equidistant neighboring points. Since u is known at some points, namely, the edges of the slice, we can hope to work from them inward.

Actually, we are not going to compute u at every point in the slice. We are going to pick out a family of equally spaced points in the slice, called *lattice points*—the points labeled p_1 to p_{10} in Figure (2.3.24d)—and compute the value u_i of u at p_i for $i = 1, \ldots, 10$. Now all our chosen points are equidistant, so we can interpret (2.3.25) as saying that the value of u at an interior lattice point is the average of the values of u at its neighbors. This will lend itself to a system of linear equations to solve for the unknown values of u.

Figure (2.3.24d).

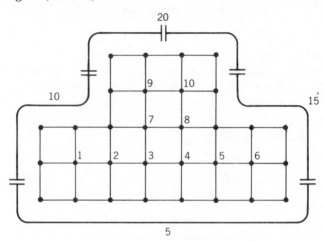

Before we start this process, several comments are in order: first, we chose the spacing of lattice points. Smaller spacing gives more points, so a bigger linear problem, but also more accuracy. Next, we must remember that we don't really take a slice physically. So to study the original block, we actually need to consider slices at various choices of $x = a$. If we take, say, 100 such slices, and have 100 unknown lattice points in each slice, then we would have 100 linear problems with 100 by 100 matrices of coefficients. And if we depart from steady state, but consider that at various "slices of time" we have a three-dimensional steady-state problem which we can solve by these methods, we can easily end up with an enormous number of large linear problems. Such situations—very large-scale linear algebra problems arising from partial differential equations—have been one of the major spurs to the development of fast and efficient linear algebra computer packages.

To spare ourselves the huge size of the problems arising in three dimensions, we will just work out the solutions in the two-dimensional slices. And if the boundary values of u are the same for each slice, which sometimes happens, then the interior values will also be the same for all slices, and we will have a three-dimensional solution.

Now we return to Figure (2.3.24d). The boundary values of u are given in that figure, and we write down the equations for u_1 through u_{10}. The point p_1 has four neighbors: the point above it, where $u = 10$, the point p_2 to its left where $u = u_2$, the point below it where $u = 5$, and the point to its right where $u = 10$. Taking the average gives the equation $u_1 = \frac{1}{4}(10 + u_2 + 5 + 10)$. Proceeding in the same fashion around the point p_2 up to p_{10} gives the system:

(2.3.26)

$$\begin{cases} u_1 = \frac{1}{4}u_2 + \frac{25}{4} \\ u_2 = \frac{1}{4}u_1 + \frac{1}{4}u_3 + \frac{15}{4} \\ u_3 = \frac{1}{4}u_2 + \frac{1}{4}u_4 + \frac{1}{4}u_7 + \frac{5}{4} \\ u_4 = \frac{1}{4}u_3 + \frac{1}{4}u_5 + \frac{1}{4}u_8 + \frac{5}{4} \\ u_5 = \frac{1}{4}u_4 + \frac{1}{4}u_6 + 5 \\ u_6 = \frac{1}{4}u_5 + \frac{35}{4} \\ u_7 = \frac{1}{4}u_3 + \frac{1}{4}u_8 + \frac{1}{4}u_9 + \frac{10}{4} \\ u_8 = \frac{1}{4}u_4 + \frac{1}{4}u_7 + \frac{1}{4}u_{10} + \frac{15}{4} \\ u_9 = \frac{1}{4}u_7 + \frac{1}{4}u_{10} + \frac{15}{2} \\ u_{10} = \frac{1}{4}u_8 + \frac{1}{4}u_9 + \frac{35}{4} \end{cases}$$

To write (2.3.26) in matrix form we introduce the following:

(2.3.27)

$$u = \begin{bmatrix} u_1 \\ u_2 \\ u_3 \\ u_4 \\ u_5 \\ u_6 \\ u_7 \\ u_8 \\ u_9 \\ u_{10} \end{bmatrix} \quad b = \frac{1}{4}\begin{bmatrix} 25 \\ 15 \\ 5 \\ 5 \\ 20 \\ 35 \\ 10 \\ 15 \\ 30 \\ 35 \end{bmatrix} \quad C = \begin{bmatrix} 0 & \frac{1}{4} & 0 & 0 & 0 & 0 & 0 & 0 & 0 & 0 \\ \frac{1}{4} & 0 & \frac{1}{4} & 0 & 0 & 0 & 0 & 0 & 0 & 0 \\ 0 & \frac{1}{4} & 0 & \frac{1}{4} & 0 & 0 & \frac{1}{4} & 0 & 0 & 0 \\ 0 & 0 & \frac{1}{4} & 0 & \frac{1}{4} & 0 & 0 & \frac{1}{4} & 0 & 0 \\ 0 & 0 & 0 & \frac{1}{4} & 0 & \frac{1}{4} & 0 & 0 & 0 & 0 \\ 0 & 0 & 0 & 0 & \frac{1}{4} & 0 & 0 & 0 & 0 & 0 \\ 0 & 0 & \frac{1}{4} & 0 & 0 & 0 & 0 & \frac{1}{4} & \frac{1}{4} & 0 \\ 0 & 0 & 0 & \frac{1}{4} & 0 & 0 & \frac{1}{4} & 0 & 0 & \frac{1}{4} \\ 0 & 0 & 0 & 0 & 0 & 0 & \frac{1}{4} & 0 & 0 & \frac{1}{4} \\ 0 & 0 & 0 & 0 & 0 & 0 & 0 & \frac{1}{4} & \frac{1}{4} & 0 \end{bmatrix}$$

Now, using (2.3.27), (2.3.26) becomes

$$(2.3.28) \qquad u = Cu + b \quad \text{or} \quad (I - C)u = b$$

The matrix $I - C$ in (2.3.28) is 10 by 10, although of course many of its 100 entries are zero. The number of interior lattice points in Figure (2.3.24d) is probably unrealistically small, however. Cutting the lattice spacing in half, as in Figure (2.3.24e), would give a better approximation. But now there are 59 lattice points, so we are talking about a system of 59 equations in 59 unknowns, with a matrix of coefficients with 3481 entries! And we are still dealing with a fairly coarse estimate.

Figure (2.3.24e).

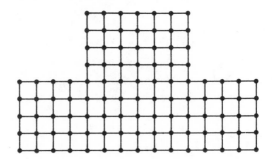

In the dimension of Figure (2.3.24), we have been vague about whether u was temperature or charge. It can be either, or in fact any harmonic function with the given boundary values.

EXERCISES 2.3

1. Find the system of Eqs. (2.3.13) for the potentials for the resistor–battery network of Figure (2.3.29).

2. The classic "peasant," or rural subsistence, village economy consists of small groups of extended families engaged in three "industries": agriculture, animal husbandry, and handicraft. Figure (2.3.30) records the annual economic activity (converted to dollar values) of such a village. The agriculture sector, for example, produced $10,500, of which $7500 went back into agriculture, $500 into animal husbandry, $2000 into handicraft, (most of these costs are of course food costs for the workers involved) and $500 into export trade with other villages (these figures are row 1 of the table.) From column 1, we see that agriculture took

Figure (2.3.29).

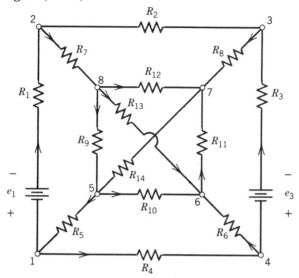

$e_1 = e_3 = 6$ V K ohm $= 10^3$ ohm
$R_1 = R_2 = R_3 = R_4 = 5$ K ohms
$R_5 = R_6 = R_7 = R_8 = 10$ K ohms
$R_9 = R_{10} = R_{11} = R_{12} = 15$ K ohms
$R_{13} = R_{14} = 20$ K ohms

Figure (2.3.30).

	Input ①	Input ②	Input ③	Export	Total output
Output ①	75	5	20	5	105
Output ②	10	75	10	10	105
Output ③	10	15	40	7	82
Import	10	10	12		32
Total input	105	105	82	22	314

Industry ① = agriculture.
Industry ② = animal husbandry.
Industry ③ = handicraft.

(Annual values in hundreds of dollars.)

$7500 of its own output, $1000 from both animal husbandry and trade, and $1000 worth of imports, Use Figure (2.3.30) to construct an equation similar to (2.3.18) for production levels necessary to meet specified export demands.

3. Figure (2.3.31) represents the annual economic activity of a closely linked economic/geographic region consisting of several small industrial centers along with their associated agricultural and raw-material-producing hinterlands. [This table is constructed according to the principles of Figure (2.3.30)]. Find the production level/export demand equation (2.3.18) for this example.

Figure (2.3.31).

	①	②	③	④	⑤	⑥	Export	Total output
①	3.0	1.0	1.0	0.0	0.0	1.0	2.1	8.1
②	0.0	3.0	0.5	0.5	1.0	2.0	2.7	9.7
③	0.1	0.5	1.0	0.5	2.0	1.0	2.5	7.6
④	1.0	0.5	2.0	1.0	4.0	1.0	0.1	9.6
⑤	3.0	3.0	2.0	5.0	1.0	0.5	4.5	19.0
⑥	1.0	1.0	1.0	2.0	1.0	3.0	0.1	9.1
Import	0.0	0.7	0.1	0.6	10.0	0.6		12.1
Input	8.1	9.7	7.6	9.6	19.0	9.1	12.0	63.1

① = Agriculture.   ④ = Mining.
② = Light industry.   ⑤ = Energy production.
③ = Heavy industry.   ⑥ = Services.

($1 trillion units)

Figure (2.3.32).

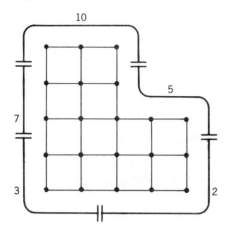

4. Figure (2.3.32) represents a thin sheet of plastic on which an electrical charge has been placed. Assume that the boundaries of the sheet are perfect insulators and that the values of the charge on the boundary are as indicated. Using the 21 lattice points indicated in Figure (2.3.32), write Eq. (2.3.28) for the charge distribution. (It will be a system of five equations in five unknowns.)

5. Repeat problem 4 with the 65 lattice points of Figure 2.3.33, obtaining a system of 33 equations.

Figure (2.3.33).

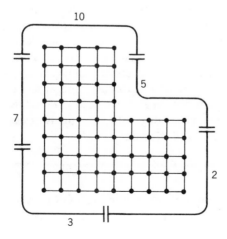

2.4   SOLVING NONSINGULAR SYSTEMS WITH LINPACK

In this section we take up the problem of actually solving a system of linear equations in practice, using the computer. Our methods will be based on the LINPACK package of linear algebra procedures.

We are trying to solve a system of n linear equations in n unknowns written in matrix form:

(2.4.1) $Ax = b$ where A is an n by n matrix and x, b are n-vectors.

Our method, from Sections 2.1 and 2.2, is to first *factor A*,

$$(2.4.2)   A = LU$$

and then *solve* the triangular systems

$$(2.4.3)   Ly = b$$

$$Ux = y$$

So, in outline form, a computer program to solve (2.4.1) would look like:

1.   Input A.
2.   Factor $A = LU$.
3.   Input b.
4.   Solve $Ly = b$ and $Ux = y$.
5.   Write x.

We know, from Section 2.2., that not every matrix A has an L-U decomposition. In the factor step 2, we may be interchanging rows to avoid zeros on the diagonal of U (in fact, for reasons of numerical stability, row interchanges are built into the algorithm to avoid small diagonal entries also), so the equation "$A = LU$" should be thought of symbolically, not literally. More seriously, it is possible that A is singular, or appears singular to the computer because its determinant is small. In this case, it will not be possible to proceed beyond the factor step, and in fact the factor step itself will have an incomplete outcome. So we need to quit. On the other hand, we won't know about this possibility until we actually attempt factorization, so step 2 needs to be enlarged to read:

2.   Factor $A = LU$ and check if A is singular. If it is, stop.

Now we want to convert this outline to a FORTRAN program. To begin, even before we input the matrix A we need to reserve a place for it to go.

We do this by declaring a FORTRAN two-dimensional array of sufficient size to hold any of the coefficient matrices we are likely to be considering. For the problems and examples in this book, 50 by 50 is sufficient. We are going to use the name "A" for this 50 by 50 array, but we need to remember that the coefficient matrix A that we input in step 1 will only occupy the n by n upper left-hand corner of the array A. We suppose that the coefficient matrix is on cards, with each new row beginning on a new card, and that the size n of A is on the first card, by itself. Step 1 translates to the following FORTRAN statements:

```
      REAL A(50,50)
      READ (5,*)N
      DO 10  I = 1,N
      READ (5,*)(A(I,J),J = 1,N)
   10 CONTINUE
```

The DO loop (DO 10 ... 10 CONTINUE) reads the rows of A in order from row 1 to row n. The parenthetical expression in the read statement is called an "implied DO": it means that for each value of the I counter the numbers $A(I,1), A(I,2), \ldots, A(I,N)$ will be read in. Every time the I counter advances a new card is read, so the rows of A must begin on new cards, but a row doesn't have to be on just one card—rows can occupy as many cards as needed, as long as they begin on new cards.

To do step 2, we will need to use the LINPACK procedure which factors a matrix into its L-U decomposition. There are several of these: the one we use here is called SGECO: "S" stands for single precision, "GE" for general matrix, and "CO" for condition number, which is a number we will use in the second part of step 2, when we check to see if A is singular. The factor step is then accomplished by the FORTRAN statement

```
      CALL SGECO (A,LDA,N,IPVT,RCOND,Z)
```

where A and N have their previously assigned meanings; LDA (the leading dimension of A) is the size of the first dimension of the array A (in our use LDA = 50); IPVT is a one-dimensional integer array and Z is a one-dimensional real array, both of dimension at least N; and RCOND will be the reciprocal condition number. We need to have previously declared the arrays IPVT and Z and assigned a value to LDA.

LINPACK is very careful about conserving space. It puts the L-U decomposition in the same place that the matrix A was originally stored: in the upper left-hand corner of the array A. U occupies the upper triangle of the corner, and the numbers necessary to obtain L are stored in the lower triangle. The record of row interchanges is kept in the array IPVT, and Z is used for work space. After SGECO is called, the original matrix A is lost. If we want A for any reason, or if we want to print it, we must do so before SGECO is called. In our final version of the program, we will print A as it is read in, for this reason.

The number RCOND, which SGECO computes, gives an estimate of how far A is from being a singular matrix. If RCOND = 0, then, the matrix appears singular. So we will accomplish the second part of step 2 by checking to see if RCOND = 0. For various reasons of machine accuracy, we actually check to see if RCOND + 1 = 1. So we complete step 2 with the following FORTRAN statements:

$$T = RCOND + 1.0$$
$$IF\ (T.EQ.1.0)\ GO\ TO\ 90$$

For step 3, we need to read b into a (previously declared) one-dimensional array B, of at least dimension n. We assume that each entry of B is on a separate card. This input is then accomplished by the following DO loop:

$$DO\ 20\ I = 1,N$$
$$READ\ (5,*)\ B(I)$$
$$20\quad CONTINUE$$

Step 4 will use the LINPACK procedure SGESL which takes the information about the $L\text{-}U$ decomposition of the matrix A, in the form that it is stored in the arrays A and IPVT after the call to SGECO, and uses it to solve $Ly = b$ and $Ux = y$. "SGE" in SGESL has the same meaning as before (Single-precision GEneral matrix), and "SL" stands for solve. The FORTRAN statement for step 4 is thus:

$$CALL\ SGESL\ (A,LDA,N,IPVT,B,0)$$

Here A, LDA, N, and IPVT all are as they were after the call to SGECO and B contains b from step 3. The final parameter, 0, means we are solving $Ax = b$. If it were some other number than 0, SGESL would solve $A^T x = b$ instead. The procedure SGESL leaves A, LDA, N, and IPVT alone, but it writes the solution vector x in the array B, wiping out the values of b stored there. So if we want to see b, we need to print it before we call SGESL.

Step 5, writing the answer x, then is done by the following DO loop:

$$DO\ 30\ I = 1,N$$
$$WRITE\ (6,*)B(I)$$
$$30\quad CONTINUE$$

All that remains to have a complete FORTRAN program is to associate the various translations of our outline program steps, making sure that all necessary declarations are made in advance. Such a program is listed in Figure (2.4.4a). A sample output is shown in Figure (2.4.4b), based on the input data shown in Figure (2.4.4c). These data are the 3 by 3 matrix (2.1.15), and we note that the computed answer agrees with our original.

Figure (2.4.4a).

```
C   SOLVES A SYSTEM OF N EQUATIONS IN N UNKNOWNS
C   USES LINPAK SGECO AND SGESL
C       FIRST CARD  N
C       NEXT CARDS MATRIX OF COEFFICIENTS BY ROWS
C          (EACH NEW ROW STARTS ON NEW CARD)
C       NEXT CARDS VECTOR OF CONSTANTS
C          (EACH ENTRY ON A NEW CARD)
    999 FORMAT('0 THE MATRIX IS SINGULAR')
    100 FORMAT('0')
    120 FORMAT('0  MATRIX A OF SIZE  ',I2,2X,'BY  ',I2)
    130 FORMAT('0  RCOND=  ',E10.3)
    140 FORMAT('0  THE VECTOR B OF CONSTANTS')
    150 FORMAT('0  THE SOLUTION VECTOR X')
        REAL A(50,50),B(50),Z(50)
        INTEGER  IPVT(50)
        DATA LDA/50/
        READ(5,*) N
        WRITE(6,120)  N,N
        WRITE(6,100)
        DO 10 I=1,N
        READ(5,*)    (A(I,J),J=1,N)
        WRITE(6,*)   (A(I,J),J=1,N)
     10 CONTINUE
        CALL SGECO(A,LDA,N,IPVT,RCOND,Z)
        WRITE(6,130) RCOND
        T=1.0+RCOND
        IF(T.EQ.1.0)   GO TO 90
        WRITE(6,140)
        WRITE(6,100)
        DO 20 I=1,N
        READ(5,*)  B(I)
        WRITE(6,*)  B(I)
     20 CONTINUE
        CALL SGESL(A,LDA,N,IPVT,B,0)
        WRITE(6,150)
        WRITE(6,100)
        DO 30 I=1,N
        WRITE(6,*)  B(I)
     30 CONTINUE
        STOP
     90 WRITE(6,999)
        STOP
        END
```

Figure (2.4.4b).

```
MATRIX A OF SIZE    3  BY   3

3.00000000        -1.00000000         .0
6.00000000          .0               1.00000000
9.00000000         5.00000000        5.00000000

RCOND=   0.706E-02

THE VECTOR B OF CONSTANTS

4.00000000
8.00000000
14.0000000

THE SOLUTION VECTOR X

1.00000095
-.999996245
1.99999428
```

Figure (2.4.4c).

```
3


3.0   -1.0   0.0

6.0    0.0   1.0

9.0    5.0   5.0
```

EXERCISES 2.4

In problems 1 to 9, use the program of Figure (2.2.4a) to solve the indicated systems of linear equations:

1. The systems of problem 2 of Exercises 2.1.
2. The system of Eqs. (2.3.13) for Figure (2.3.1), where R_i is given the value 10 for $i = 1, \ldots, 6$ and $e_6 = 6$. Also determine the branch voltages and currents for each branch.
3. The same as problem 2, except for the system of equations of problem 1 of Exercises 2.3.
4. The system of Eqs. (2.3.18) for the consumption matrix (2.3.19), where the external demand vector is

$$b = \begin{bmatrix} 0.30 \\ 0.97 \\ 0.20 \\ 0.51 \\ 0.17 \\ 0.001 \end{bmatrix} \quad \text{(\$1 million units)}$$

5. The same as problem 4, except for the system of equations of problem 2 of Exercises 2.3, where the external demand vector is

$$b = \begin{bmatrix} 3 \\ 8 \\ 10 \end{bmatrix} \quad (\$100 \text{ units})$$

6. The same as problem 4, except for the system of equations of problem 3 of Exercises 2.3, where the external demand vector is

$$b = \begin{bmatrix} 1.9 \\ 1.1 \\ 1.3 \\ 0.2 \\ 2.1 \\ 0.2 \end{bmatrix} \quad (\$10 \text{ million units})$$

7. The system of Eqs. (2.3.28).

8. The same as problem 7, except for the system of equations of problem 4 of Exercises 2.3.

9. Let A be the 2×2 matrix

$$A = \begin{bmatrix} 1 & 1 + x \\ 1 - x & 1 \end{bmatrix}$$

   (a) Prove: if $x \neq 0$, A is invertible and the system of equations $Au = b$ has a unique solution for any b.

   (b) By hand calculation find the vector u with

$$Au = \begin{bmatrix} 1 \\ 0 \end{bmatrix} \quad \text{for} \quad x = 10^{-7}$$

   (c) Try to solve part (b) using the program of Figure (2.2.4a). Why does FORTRAN regard A as having a zero determinant?

10. (Programming problem) Write a program incorporating the program of Figure (2.4.4a) which accepts as inputs 4-tuples (i, j, R_k, e_k) describing the branches in a resistor–battery network and returns as outputs the branch currents and voltages.

11. (Programming problem) Write a program which obtains the $L\text{-}U$ decomposition of a matrix A using the method of Gaussian elimination (2.1.21). Test the program on the matrices of problem 1 Exercise 2.1.

2.5 SYSTEMS SOLVABLE BY ITERATION

The first form of the Leontieff model equation (2.3.18) $x = Cx + b$ or the steady-state distribution equation (2.3.28) $u = Cu + b$ have the look of a FORTRAN assignment statement: you take a value for the unknown, and update it by replacing it by multiplying by C and adding b. In some fortuitous cases, this actually can be used as a solution method:

(2.5.1) Iterative Scheme for $x = Cx + b$. Start with a given vector $x^{(0)}$. Define

$$x^{(1)} = Cx^{(0)} + b$$
$$x^{(2)} = Cx^{(1)} + b$$
$$\vdots$$
$$x^{(k+1)} = Cx^{(k)} + b$$

The process (2.5.1) produces a sequence of vectors $x^{(0)}, x^{(1)}, x^{(2)}, \ldots$. We hope that as k gets large the vectors $x^{(k)}$ approach the solution vector x. To check whether that happens, we can examine the error vectors $e^{(k)} = x - x^{(k)}$; if we examine successive error vectors we discover that

$$(2.5.2)\quad e^{(k+1)} = x - x^{(k+1)} = (Cx + b) - (Cx^{(k)} + b) = C(x - x^{(k)})$$

$$e^{(k+1)} = Ce^{(k)}$$

Tracking (2.5.2) back gives

$$(2.5.3)\qquad e^{(k+1)} = Ce^{(k)} = C^2 e^{(k-1)} = \cdots = C^{k+1} e^{(0)}$$

This means:

(2.5.4) If C^k goes to zero as k goes to infinity, then so does $e^{(k)}$, and hence $x^{(k)}$ is approximately equal to x for large enough k, *regardless of the choice of a start vector $x^{(0)}$.*

For a given matrix C it may be very hard to tell in advance whether the criterion of (2.5.4) ($C^k \to 0$) is really satisfied, although we will see later that in some cases we can verify it easily. From a practical point of view, it is probably best to just plunge ahead with the scheme (2.5.1). If the successive $x^{(k)}$'s are within a certain prespecified tolerance of each other at a certain point, we stop and say we have an approximate solution. And if we've carried out the scheme for a certain number of prespecified steps and the $x^{(k)}$'s are still differing by more than the tolerance, we can quit and try something else.

More formally, we are watching the differences $x^{(k+1)} - x^{(k)} = \Delta x^{(k)}$. The equation $x^{(k+1)} = Cx^{(k)} + b$ then becomes $Cx^{(k)} + b = x^{(k)} + \Delta x^{(k)}$. If the absolute values of the entries of $\Delta x^{(k)}$ are sufficiently small (for instance, less than 10^{-7} in single-precision FORTRAN) this equation is numerically indistinguishable from $Cx^{(k)} + b = x^{(k)}$ in the computer.

We have left the choice of $x^{(0)}$ open. Actually, the best one is probably $x^{(0)} = 0$. Here's why: if we trace the first few steps of the iteration scheme back to the start we obtain the general pattern

$$x^{(1)} = Cx^{(0)} + b$$

$$x^{(2)} = C^2x^{(0)} + Cb + b$$

$$\vdots$$

$$x^{(k+1)} = C^{k+1}x^{(0)} + C^kb + C^{k-1}b + \cdots + Cb + b$$

Now if $C^k \to 0$, the term $C^{k+1}x^{(0)}$ becomes increasingly irrelevant. If it doesn't, we can always choose a start vector so that $e^{(0)}$ is any vector we want. Then (2.5.3) shows that $e^{(k)}$ doesn't go to zero for a suitable choice of $x^{(0)}$. So if the scheme (2.5.1) is workable, we might as well work it with $x^{(0)} = 0$ as our start vector.

We can now describe, in outline, a procedure for working the iteration scheme (2.5.1):

1. Input a tolerance level.
2. Input n, C, and b.
3. Set $x^{(0)} = 0$.
4. Form $x^{(1)} = Cx^{(0)} + b$.
5. Check the absolute values of the entries in $x^{(1)} - x^{(0)}$:
    (a) If they are less than the tolerance level, print $x^{(1)}$ (the approximate solution).
    (b) If some exceed the tolerance level, replace $x^{(0)}$ by $x^{(1)}$ and repeat from step 4, except don't repeat more than a prespecified number of times.

Step 1 is trivial and step 2 is similar to steps 1 and 3 in Section 2.4. It is not difficult to write, directly, FORTRAN statements that realize the remaining steps. For example, for step 3, assuming we have previously declared a one-dimensional array X to hold $x^{(0)}$, we could write:

```
        DO 10 I = 1,N
        X(I) = 0.0
    10  CONTINUE
```

It turns out, however, that it will be more convenient to construct the FORTRAN statements using the Basic Linear Algebra Subroutines, or BLAS, that the LINPACK procedures rely on. These are a collection of vector operations in the form of FORTRAN functions and procedures.

The sort of vector operations we will need are the following:

Scalar multiplication: replace the vector x by $a \cdot x$ (scalar a).

Add a multiple of a vector to another: replace the vector y by $ax + y$ (scalar a, vector x).

Assignment: replace the vector x by the vector y.

Maximal entry: find the index of the entry of largest absolute value in the vector x.

There are BLAS procedures and functions to do all of these. For reasons which will become clear shortly, they are set up to deal with vectors stored as regularly spaced elements of an array. For example, we might have an array X dimensioned as REAL X(20) in which the 5-vector v is stored in positions $x(2)$, $x(5)$, $x(8)$, $x(11)$, and $x(14)$. Here the first entry of v is in location $x(2)$, and the remaining are found by *incrementing* the storage index by 3. We could say: v is a vector of length 5 and increment 3 with first entry in $x(2)$.

Such storage schemes occur often in dealing with matrices. For example, suppose we have a 3 by 3 matrix stored in a 3 by 3 two-dimensional array A. As we discussed in Section (1.4.5), the storage reserved for A is the same as if A were a one-dimensional array of length 9. In (2.5.5) we picture how the second row and column of the matrix are located in this storage arrangement of A:

(2.5.5).

$$
\begin{array}{l}
A(1,1) \\
A(2,1) \\
A(3,1) \\
A(1,2) \\
\text{row 2} \rightarrow A(2,2) \\
A(3,2) \\
A(1,3) \\
A(2,3) \\
A(3,3)
\end{array}
$$

[column 2: starts with $A(1,2)$ and has increment 1]

column 2   [row 2: starts with $A(2,1)$ and has increment 3]

Now we can describe the BLAS to be used to construct the iteration program (details are in *LINPACK User's Guide*, Appendix *D*).

(2.5.6) Let v and w be N-vectors stored in the FORTRAN arrays X and Y, with first entries in positions X(initial) and Y(initial) and increments IX and IY, respectively, and let T be a real scalar. Then:

The BLAS procedure SSCAL(N,T,X(initial),IX) replaces v by $T \cdot v$.

The BLAS procedure SAXPY(N,T,X(initial),IX,Y(initial),IY) replaces w by $T \cdot v + w$.

The BLAS procedure SCOPY(N,X(initial),IX,Y(Initial),IY) replaces w by y.

The BLAS function ISAMAX(N,X(initial),IX) gives the least integer i such that the absolute value of the ith entry of v is less than or equal to the absolute values of the other entries.

[If the first entries of v or w are in the first entries of X or Y, then the FORTRAN default reading of X as X(first subscript), and similarly for Y, can be used.]

Now we return to our problem of translating the outline for the iteration scheme into FORTRAN. Step 3 can now be handled with a single call to SSCAL:

CALL SSCAL (N,0.0,X,1)

For step 4, we will actually construct a procedure which takes an input vector (in our case $x^{(0)}$), multiplies it by a matrix (C), and adds a constant vector (b). Because we need to compare the size of the entries of $x^{(1)} - x^{(0)}$, we will construct the procedure to keep both the input vector and the new vector. If the input vector is called x, the matrix A, and the constant vector b, then we want to form $Ax + b$. In terms of the column structure of A, this looks like the following (see Section (1.2.2)):

$$A = [A_1 \cdots A_n] \qquad x = \begin{bmatrix} x_1 \\ \vdots \\ x_n \end{bmatrix}$$

$$Ax + b = b + x_1 A_1 + \cdots + x_n A_n$$

So to construct $Ax + b$, we can do the following:

Move x into a work space, which we call y.

Move b into x.

As i goes from 1 to n, multiply the ith entry of y (which is x_i) times the vector A_i and add the result to x.

Using the BLAS SCOPY to do the "moving" and SAXPY to do the "multiply and add," we can accomplish this by the subroutine in Figure (2.5.7). (Note that column i of A is treated as the vector of length N starting at $A(1, I)$ of increment 1.)

Figure (2.5.7).

```
          SUBROUTINE AXPB(N,A,X,B,Y)
  C   ON ENTRY A IS N BY N, X,B,Y ARE N VECTORS
  C   ON RETURN X CONTAINS AX+B AND Y CONTAINS X
          REAL A(50,50),B(50),X(50),Y(50)
          INTEGER N
          CALL SCOPY(N,X,1,Y,1)
          CALL SCOPY(N,B,1,X,1)
          DO 10 I=1,N
          T=Y(I)
          CALL SAXPY(N,T,A(1,I),1,X,1)
   10   CONTINUE
          RETURN
          END
```

The next step of our outline, step 5, requires comparing the absolute values of the entries of $x^{(1)} - x^{(0)}$. If $x^{(1)}$ is contained in an array X and $x^{(0)}$ in an array Y then we can do this as follows in FORTRAN:

CALL SAXPY (N, − 1.0,X,1,Y,1) (forms $-x^{(1)} + x^{(0)}$ and puts it in Y)

I = ISAMAX(N,Y,1) (find *index* of largest absolute value entry of $y = x^{(0)} - x^{(1)}$)

YMAX = ABS (Y(I)) (finds *absolute value* of entry of largest absolute value in y)

Now we compare this with our previously determined tolerance. It it's less, we stop, if more, we continue, except we want an upper limit to the number of iterations done.

In the program listed here, we go up to 300 steps in the iteration scheme (so up to $x^{(300)}$) in blocks of 10 at a time. Figure (2.5.8) shows a complete program incorporating the subroutine AXPB.

Finally, we return to the question of deciding in advance whether iteration is going to work; that is, whether in the scheme (2.5.1) we really

Figure (2.5.8).

```
C   SOLVES X=AX+B BY ITERATION
C   A IS N BY N
C   HALTS AT TOL OR 300 ITERATES
C FIRST CARD TOL AS 1.0E-K, K.LE.10
C   NEXT CARD N
C   NEXT CARDS A BY ROWS
C   NEXT CARDS B BY ENTRIES

 1000 FORMAT('0 ')
  120 FORMAT('0 MATRIX A OF SIZE  ',I2,2X,'BY  ',I2)
  130 FORMAT('0 RCOND=  ',E10.3)
  140 FORMAT('0 THE VECTOR B OF CONSTANTS')
  150 FORMAT('0 THE SOLUTION VECTOR X')
  160 FORMAT('0 TOLERANCE  ',E9.2,2X,'AFTER  ',I4,2X,'ITERATIONS')
  170 FORMAT('0 ITERATION STOPPED AT 300')
  180 FORMAT('0 CURRENT MAX DIFFERENCE  ',E9.2)
      REAL A(50,50),B(50),X(50),Y(50)
      READ(5,*)  TOL
      READ(5,*) N
      WRITE(6,120)  N,N
      WRITE(6,1000)
      DO 10 I=1,N
      READ(5,*)    (A(I,J),J=1,N)
      WRITE(6,*)   (A(I,J),J=1,N)
   10 CONTINUE
      WRITE(6,140)
      WRITE(6,1000)
      DO 20 I=1,N
      READ(5,*)  B(I)
      WRITE(6,*)  B(I)
   20 CONTINUE
      CALL SSCAL(N,0.0,X,1)
      ITER=0
    1 DO 30 I=1,10
      CALL AXPB(N,A,X,B,Y)
   30 CONTINUE
      ITER=ITER+10
      IF(ITER.GE.300)  GO TO 99
      CALL SAXPY(N,-1.0,X,1,Y,1)
      I=ISAMAX(N,Y,1)
      YMAX=ABS(Y(I))
      IF(YMAX.GT.TOL)  GO TO 1
      WRITE(6,160)  TOL,ITER
      GO TO 5
   99 WRITE(6,170)
      WRITE(6,180)  YMAX
    5 WRITE(6,150)
      WRITE(6,1000)
      DO 40 I=1,N
      WRITE(6,*)  X(I)
   40 CONTINUE
      STOP
      END
```

have C^k going to zero as k goes to infinity. It turns out if C happens to satisfy the Productive Matrix Theorem (2.3.20) then iteration is sure to work, as the following argument taken from *The Theory of Linear Economic Models* shows:

(2.5.9) Let C be a nonnegative n by n matrix. Suppose there is a nonnegative vector x such that $x - Cx > 0$. Then C^k goes to 0 as k goes to infinity. In (2.3.22) we saw that $x > 0$. Let $y = Cx$ and let $l = \max\{y_i/x_i | i = 1, \ldots, n\}$. Then since $x_i > y_i$ for all i we have $0 \le l < 1$ so $lx_i \ge y_i$ for all i. Choose λ, $0 < \lambda < 1$ and $l < \lambda$. Then $\lambda x_i > y_i$ for all i, so we have $\lambda x > Cx$. Thus $\lambda^k x > C^k x$ for all k, so $C^k x$ goes to zero as k goes to infinity. If e_i is the vector with ith entry one and the rest zero, then $x = x_1 e_1 + \cdots + x_n e_n$ and $C^k x = x_1 C^k e_1 + \cdots + x_n C^k e_n$. Since $x_i > 0$, and $C^k e_i \ge 0$, this expression can go to zero only if $C^k e_i$ goes to zero for each i. But $C^k e_i$ is just column i of C^k, so C^k also goes to zero.

Since we saw in (2.3.23) that if C represents the consumption matrix of a company with all its divisions profitable, then there is an $x \ge 0$ with $x - Cx > 0$, so (2.5.9) applies and solution by iteration is guaranteed to work.

EXERCISES 2.5

In problems 1 to 6, use the program of Figure (2.5.8) to solve the indicated systems of linear equations by iteration:

1. Problem 4 of Exercises (2.4).
2. Problem 5 of Exercises (2.4).
3. Problem 6 of Exercises (2.4).
4. Problem 7 of Exercises (2.4).
5. Problem 8 of Exercises (2.4).
6. The system of problem 5 of Exercises (2.4). (The declaration statement for A, B, X, Y needs to be increased from 50 to 65 in the program.)
7. Let $A = \begin{bmatrix} 1 & y \\ 0 & 1 \end{bmatrix}$

    (a) Show that $A^n = \begin{bmatrix} 1 & ny \\ 0 & 1 \end{bmatrix}$ for $n = 1, 2, 3, \ldots$.

    (b) Try to use the program of Figure (2.5.8) to solve $x = Ax + b$ by iteration, for $y = 1$ and $x = \begin{bmatrix} 1 \\ 0 \end{bmatrix}$ and $b = \begin{bmatrix} 0 \\ 1 \end{bmatrix}$. Explain your output using part (a).

3

SYSTEMS WITH MANY SOLUTIONS

3.1 LINEAR EQUATIONS, RANK, AND ROW REDUCTION

Consider a general system of m linear equations in n unknowns

$$(3.1.1) \qquad \begin{cases} a_{11}x_1 + \cdots + a_{1n}x_n = b_1 \\ \qquad \vdots \\ a_{m1}x_1 + \cdots + a_{mn}x_n = b_m \end{cases}$$

We want to discover all the solutions of (3.1.1), of which there may be one, infinitely many, or none. In Chapter 2 the first case was studied. We now want to consider the other possibilities. We still keep the same general philosophy as enunciated in *The Principle of Elimination* (2.1.2): "To solve a system of linear equations, change the equations, without changing the solution set, into a simple system that can easily be solved." In keeping with this principle, there are two points to consider: (1) what qualifies as a "simple system that can easily be solved"?; and (2) how can (3.1.1) be *systematically* changed into such a system, keeping the same set of solutions?

The type of simple system (3.1.1) that we have in mind is one with a large number of zero coefficients starting off each equation. Formally, we define:

(3.1.2) The system (3.1.1) is *reduced* if there is a number r, less than or equal to the minimum of m and n, and numbers $1 = j_1 < j_2 < \cdots < j_r$ such that:

1. The first nonzero coefficient in equation i is the j_ith for $i \leq r$.
2. All the coefficients in the rest of the equations (if any) are zero.

Here is an example of a reduced system:

$$(3.1.3) \quad \begin{cases} x_1 - x_2 + 2x_3 + x_4 + x_5 \quad\quad\quad = c_1 \\ \quad\quad\quad\quad\quad 3x_4 + 5x_5 + 2x_6 = c_2 \\ \quad\quad\quad\quad\quad\quad\quad\quad\quad\quad 4x_6 = c_3 \\ \quad\quad\quad\quad\quad\quad\quad\quad\quad\quad\quad 0 = c_4 \end{cases}$$

In (3.1.3), $m = 4$, $n = 6$, $r = 3$, $j_1 = 1$, $j_2 = 4$, and $j_3 = 6$. [The fourth equation here ($0 = c_4$) looks silly. We should remember that this is an example of a simple system to which a system is to be changed, and it is quite possible (as we will see below) that in the starting system the fourth equation is initially nontrivial.]

The general pattern for a reduced system will be as follows:

$$(3.1.4) \quad \begin{cases} u_{11}x_1 + \quad\quad \cdots \quad\quad + u_{1n}x_n = c_1 \\ \quad u_{2,j_2}x_{j_2} + \quad \cdots \quad + u_{2n}x_n = c_2 \\ \quad\quad\quad u_{r,j_r}x_{j_r} + \cdots + u_{rn}x_n = c_r \quad\quad \left(u_{i,j_i} \neq 0,\ i = 1, \ldots, r\right) \\ \quad\quad\quad\quad\quad\quad\quad\quad 0 = c_{r+1} \\ \quad\quad\quad\quad\quad\quad\quad\quad\quad \vdots \\ \quad\quad\quad\quad\quad\quad\quad\quad 0 = c_m \end{cases}$$

Reduced systems are intended to be simple in the sense of being easy to solve. So we solve (3.1.4). First, we look at the last $m - r$ equations: these can be "solved" if $c_{r+1}, c_{r+2}, \ldots, c_m$ are all zero; otherwise there is no solution. The first interesting equation is the rth: it says that $xj_r = u_{r,j_r}^{-1}(c_r - u_{r,j_r+1}x_{j_r+2} - \cdots - u_{rn}x_n)$. In other words, equation r puts constraints on x_{j_r}, in terms of the variables from x_{j_r+1} up to x_n. But note that, so far, there are no conditions on these variables. Similarly, equation $r - 1$ allows us to solve for $x_{j_{r-1}}$ in terms of variables with larger subscripts, but there are no conditions on this group of variables, except for the conditions already noted for x_{j_r} imposed by equation r. Continuing up through the system of equations we find that equations one through r allow us to solve for the variables $x_{j_1}, x_{j_2}, \ldots, x_{j_r}$ in terms of the rest; and that there are no conditions on the rest. We can describe this formally as follows:

(3.1.5) Solving A Reduced System. In (3.1.4), the variables $x_{j_1}, \ldots, x_{j_r}$ are called *dependent* variables, and the rest are called *free* variables:

1. (3.1.4) has no solutions if and only if at least one of $c_{r+1}, c_{r+2}, \ldots, c_m$ is nonzero. In this case, (3.1.4) is said to be *inconsistent*.

2. If (3.1.4) is consistent, all its solutions are obtained by assigning arbitrary values to the free variables and then solving, from equation r back to equation one, for the dependent variables.

Here's how the solution process (3.1.5) works for the system in (3.1.3): The dependent variables in (3.1.3) are x_1, x_4, and x_6, and the free variables are x_2, x_3, and x_5. For (3.1.3) to be consistent, we need $c_4 = 0$. Suppose this is the case. Assign arbitrary values u, v, and w to the free variables x_2, x_3, and x_5. Then we solve back from the third equation to the first equation:

$$x_6 = \tfrac{1}{4}c_3$$

$$x_4 = \tfrac{1}{3}\left(c_2 - 5w - \tfrac{1}{4}c_3\right)$$

$$x_1 = c_1 + u - 2v - \tfrac{1}{3}\left(c_2 - 5w - \tfrac{1}{4}c_2\right) - w$$

This can be written more presentably as:

$$\begin{cases} x_1 = \left(c_1 - \tfrac{1}{3}c_2 + \tfrac{1}{12}c_3\right) + u - 2v + \tfrac{5}{3}w \\ x_2 = u \\ x_3 = v \\ x_4 = \left(\tfrac{1}{3}c_2 - \tfrac{1}{12}c_3\right) - \tfrac{5}{3}w \\ x_5 = w \\ x_6 = \tfrac{1}{4}c_3 \end{cases}$$

Finally, we can express the solution in vector form. Let

$$
x = \begin{bmatrix} x_1 \\ x_2 \\ x_3 \\ x_4 \\ x_5 \\ x_6 \end{bmatrix} \qquad
d = \begin{bmatrix} c_1 - \frac{1}{3}c_2 + \frac{1}{12}c_3 \\ 0 \\ 0 \\ \frac{1}{3}c_2 - \frac{1}{12}c_3 \\ 0 \\ \frac{1}{4}c_3 \end{bmatrix} \qquad
y_1 = \begin{bmatrix} 1 \\ 1 \\ 0 \\ 0 \\ 0 \\ 0 \end{bmatrix}
$$

$$
y_2 = \begin{bmatrix} -2 \\ 0 \\ 1 \\ 0 \\ 0 \\ 0 \end{bmatrix} \qquad
y_3 = \begin{bmatrix} \frac{5}{3} \\ 0 \\ 0 \\ -\frac{5}{3} \\ 1 \\ 0 \end{bmatrix}
$$

then $x = d + u y_1 + v y_2 + w y_3$.

We want to write the outcome of the solution process (3.1.5) applied to system (3.1.4) in vector form, also. The notation for the intermediate steps is pretty unwieldy, but the final outcome is easy to predict on the basis of the preceding example (further practice can be found in Exercise 2.):

(3.1.6) Vector Form of the Solution of (3.1.4). Assume (3.1.4) to be consistent. All solutions of (3.1.4) are then obtained as follows: there are n-vectors $d, y_1, \ldots, y_{n-r}$ such that for every assignment of values $t_1, \ldots, t_{n-r}$ to the free variables of (3.1.4), in order of increasing subscripts,

$$
x = \begin{bmatrix} x_1 \\ \vdots \\ x_n \end{bmatrix} = d + t_1 y_1 + \cdots + t_{n-r} y_{n-r}
$$

is a solution.

The two parts of the solution process (3.1.5), namely, examining the system for consistency and then solving the first r equations, are really separate and independent operations: we could just as well solve the system obtained from the first r equations of (3.1.4) first (it's automatically consistent) in the form (3.1.6) and then look at the last $m - r$ equations for consistency. Practically speaking, this could be inefficient—we don't want to waste time solving an inconsistent system—but it has some theoretical value for us, as we will see when we study the question of which right-hand sides for (3.1.1) reduce to consistent systems.

To continue the analysis of (3.1.4), it will be convenient to rewrite it in matrix form:

$$(3.1.7) \quad Ux = c \quad U = \begin{bmatrix} u_{11} & & \cdots & & u_{1n} \\ & u_{2,j2} & & \cdots & u_{2n} \\ & & u_{r,j_r} & \cdots & u_{rn} \\ & & & & 0 \\ & & & & \vdots \\ & & & & 0 \end{bmatrix}$$

$$x = \begin{bmatrix} x_1 \\ \vdots \\ x_n \end{bmatrix} \quad c = \begin{bmatrix} c_1 \\ \vdots \\ c_m \end{bmatrix}$$

We call the matrix U *row-reduced of rank* r.

We continue to assume consistency, that is, that $c_{r+1} = \cdots = c_m = 0$. Then (3.1.6) says that $Ux = c$ if and only if $x = d + t_1 y_1 + \cdots + t_{n-r} y_{n-r}$ for some numbers $t_1, \ldots, t_{n-r}$. If we let $t_1 = \cdots = t_{n-r} = 0$, we then obtain that $Ud = c$, so that $0 = Ux - Ud = U(t_1 y_1 + \cdots + t_{n-r} y_{n-r})$. Conversely, if $U(t_1 y_1 + \cdots + t_{n-r} y_{n-r}) = 0$, we have $U(d + t_1 y_1 + \cdots + t_{n-r} y_{n-r}) = Ud + 0 = c$. So we conclude:

(3.1.8) $Uy = 0$ if and only if $y = t_1 y_1 + \cdots + t_{n-r} y_{n-r}$ for some numbers $t_1, \ldots, t_{n-r}$. Moreover, $Ux = c$ if and only if $x = d + y$ where $Ud = c$ and $Uy = 0$.

We now have the necessary theoretical tools to describe the full theory of the solutions of (3.1.4), which will also turn out to be the theory of the solutions of (3.1.1), also.

(3.1.9) The Solutions of A Reduced System of Equations. Let $Ux = c$ be the matrix from (3.1.7) of a reduced system of m linear equations in n unknowns. Then:

1. $Ux = c$ has at least one solution d if and only if the last $m - r$ entries of c are zero.

2. There are linearly independent vectors $y_1, \ldots, y_{n-r}$ such that $Uy = 0$ if and only if there are numbers $t_1, \ldots, t_{n-r}$, uniquely determined by y, such that $y = t_1 y_1 + \cdots + t_{n-r} y_{n-r}$.

3. If $Ux = c$ has at least one solution, and such a solution d is chosen and fixed, then there are linearly independent vectors $y_1, \ldots, y_{n-r}$ such that $Ux = c$ if and only if there are numbers $t_1, \ldots, t_{n-r}$, uniquely determined by x, such that $x = d + t_1 y_1 + \cdots + t_{n-r} y_{n-r}$.

We have already verified most of (3.1.9): assertion number 1 is the matrix form of part 1 of (3.1.5), and assertions 2 and 3 are a restatement of (3.1.8), with the additional assertion that $y_1, \ldots, y_{n-r}$ are linearly independent (which will make the numbers $t_1, \ldots, t_{n-r}$ be uniquely determined as claimed). We will now prove this claim of independence.

Consider the m-vectors $e_1, \ldots, e_r$ defined by the condition that the only nonzero entry of e_i is the ith, and that's one. All of them have their last $m - r$ entries zeros, so by part 1 of (3.1.9) there are n-vectors $d_1, \ldots, d_r$ with $Ud_i = e_i$. If z is any n-vector, Uz has its last $m - r$ entries zero, so there are numbers $s_1, \ldots, s_r$ so that $Uz = s_1 e_1 + \cdots + s_r e_r$. Then $U(z - s_1 d_1 - \cdots - s_r d_r) = 0$, so by (3.1.8) there are numbers $t_1, \ldots, t_{n-r}$ such that $z - s_1 d_1 - \cdots - s_r d_r = t_1 y_1 + \cdots + t_{n-r} y_{n-r}$. This means that $z = t_1 y_1 + \cdots + t_{n-r} y_{n-r} + s_1 d_1 + \cdots + s_r d_r$. In other words, an arbitrary n-vector z is a linear combination of the vectors $y_1, \ldots, y_{n-r}, d_1, \ldots, d_r$. There are n vectors in this list, and they span the space of n-vectors, so, as we recalled in Chapter 1, (1.2), they are a basis and so also are linearly independent. In particular, the first $n - r$ vectors $y_1, \ldots, y_{n-r}$ are independent. We have now established all of (3.1.9).

We've now seen that the reduced systems of Eqs. (3.1.4) are "simple," in the sense of being easy to solve: the solutions are obtained by the methods of (3.1.5), and, in matrix form, they have a good theoretical description (3.1.9). It's time to see that a general system (3.1.1) can be converted systematically to a reduced system. As we did with the square matrices of Chapter 2, we first consider this conversion to have been accomplished by a matrix factorization, and see how the theory of solutions (3.1.9) carries over.

(3.1.10) The Solution of A Factorizable System of Equations. Let A be an $m \times n$ matrix, and suppose there is an invertible $m \times m$ matrix H and a row-reduced rank r $m \times n$ matrix U with $A = HU$:

1. If b is an m-vector, then $Ax = b$ has at least one solution d if and only if $(H^{-1})^i b = 0$ for $i = m - r, \ldots, m$. [We recall that $(H^{-1})^i$ denotes row i of H^{-1}.]

2. There are linearly independent vectors $y_1, \ldots, y_{n-r}$ such that $Ay = 0$ if and only if $y = t_1 y_1 + \cdots + t_{n-r} y_{n-r}$ for some numbers $t_1, \ldots, t_{n-r}$.

3. If $Ax = b$ has at least one solution, and such a solution d is chosen and fixed, then there are linearly independent vectors $y_1, \ldots, y_{n-r}$ such that $Ax = b$ if and only if $x = d + t_1 y_1 + \cdots + t_{n-r} y_{n-r}$ for some numbers $t_1, \ldots, t_{n-r}$.

To verify (3.1.10), we use the factorization $A = HU$ to convert $Ax = b$ to $Ux = H^{-1}b$ by multiplying through by H^{-1}. Then part 1 of (3.1.10) comes from part 1 of (3.1.9) where we let $c = H^{-1}b$ in the latter: the ith entry of c is then $(H^{-1})^i b$. For part 2 of (3.1.10) we can use part 2 of (3.1.9) directly, since $Ay = 0$ is then the same as $Uy = 0$. For part 3 of (3.1.10), we have $Ud = H^{-1}b$ as our assumption, so part 3 of (3.1.9) then says that $Ax = b$ (or $Ux = H^{-1}b$) means that x has the desired form, so all the claims of (3.1.10) have been proven.

The result (3.1.10) contains, implicitly, the usual facts about row rank, column rank, range, nullity, and so forth, which we will make explicit below in (3.1.21) and in Exercises 3.1.

Actually, all matrices are factorizable, so (3.1.10) is really a complete theory of systems of linear equations. As in the case of the invertible square matrices of Chapter 2, the factorization is a version of a reduction scheme based on the principle of elimination. We will allow ourselves two operations on the systems of equations (3.1.1): (1) multiply an equation by a constant and subtract from another equation; and (2) interchange the order of two equations. These operations do satisfy the principle—they leave the solution set of the system unchanged. We want to verify that they lead, systematically, to a reduced system:

(3.1.11) Reduction of A System of m Equations in n Unknowns. A system of linear equations

$$\begin{cases} a_{11}x_1 + \cdots + a_{1n}x_n = b_1 \\ \qquad \vdots \\ a_{m1}x_1 + \cdots + a_{mn}x_n = b_n \end{cases} \quad \text{(where some coefficient of } x_1 \text{ is nonzero)}$$

can be converted to a reduced system

$$\begin{cases} u_{11}x_1 + \quad \cdots \quad + u_{1n}x_n = c_1 \\ \\ u_{r,j_r}x_{jr} + \cdots + u_{rn}x_n = c_r \quad \left(1 = j_1 < j_2 < \cdots < j_r \text{ and } u_{i,j_i} \neq 0\right) \\ \\ \qquad \vdots \\ \\ 0 = c_m \end{cases}$$

by interchanges of equations and multiplying equations by constants and subtracting from other equations. This can be done systematically as follows:

Stage 1. Using interchanges, if necessary, an equation with a nonzero x_1 coefficient is placed in the equation one position, then multiples of it are subtracted from the remaining equations to get the rest of the coefficients of x_1 to be zero.

To Pass from Stage k to Stage $k + 1$. Suppose that equations one through k have their first nonzero terms as $u_{11}x_1, \ldots, u_{k,j_k}x_{j_k}$ with $1 = j_1 < j_2 < \cdots < j_k$, and that in equations $k + 1$ through m all the coefficients of $x_1, x_2, \ldots, x_{j_k}$ are zero. Let $x_{j_{k+1}}$ be the first variable with a nonzero coefficient in one of the equations $k + 1$ to m; use an interchange if necessary to place its equation in position $k + 1$; and then subtract multiples of equation $k + 1$ from equations $k + 2$ through m to get the coefficients of x_{j_k} to be zero. The process stops when no variables remain with nonzero coefficients in a usable position.

We left an ambiguity in the reduction process—there may be several possible interchanges meeting the requirements at the various stages. This can be remedied by choosing the first possible, or the first possible of maximal absolute value. [This rule seems complicated now, but will be required for numerical stability when a computer program to carry out (3.1.11) is constructed in Section 3.3 below.]

Here's an example illustrating (3.1.11):

Example (3.1.12)

$$3x_4 + 5x_5 + 2x_6 = b_1$$

$$x_1 - x_2 + 2x_3 + x_4 + x_5 \qquad = b_2$$

$$2x_1 - 2x_2 + 4x_3 + 5x_4 + 7x_5 + 6x_6 = b_3$$

$$3x_1 - 3x_2 + 6x_3 + 6x_4 + 8x_6 + 2x_6 = b_4$$

In stage 1, we interchange the first and second equations, then subtract multiples of the new first equation (the old second equation) from the rest: the multiple to subtract from the third equation is 2 and from the fourth equation is 3. This leaves, in stage 2,

$$x_1 - x_2 + 2x_3 + x_4 + x_5 \qquad = b_2$$

$$3x_4 + 5x_5 + 2x_6 = b_1$$

$$3x_4 + 5x_5 + 6x_6 = b_3 - 2b_2$$

$$3x_4 + 5x_5 + 2x_6 = b_4 = 3b_2$$

We finish by subtracting the second equation from the third and fourth equations (the multiplier is 1 in both cases). This leads to the final stage 3:

$$x_1 - x_2 + 2x_3 + x_4 + x_5 \qquad = b_2$$

$$3x_4 + 5x_5 + 2x_6 = b_1$$

$$4x_6 = b_3 - 2b_2 - b_1$$

$$0 = b_4 - 3b_2 - b_1$$

The process (3.1.11) can be applied to matrices: starting with an $m \times n$ matrix

$$(3.1.13) \qquad A = \begin{bmatrix} a_{11} & \cdots & a_{1n} \\ \vdots & & \vdots \\ a_{m1} & \cdots & a_{mn} \end{bmatrix}$$

and by switching rows or subtracting multipliers of a row from another, A can be converted to a row-reduced matrix

(3.1.14)

$$U = \begin{bmatrix} u_{11} & \cdots & & u_{1n} \\ & u_{rj_n} & \cdots & u_{rn} \\ & & & 0 \\ & & & \vdots \\ & & & 0 \end{bmatrix} \qquad 1 = j_1 < \cdots < j_r, \quad u_{i,j_i} \neq 0$$

As with the case of invertible square matrices, we can express the process (3.1.11) in terms of a matrix factorization. And as with the case of preprocessing square matrices for Gaussian elimination (2.2.8), it will be convenient to use determinants to describe this process theoretically.

(3.1.15) Let A be an $m \times n$ matrix. By an $s \times s$ *minor determinant* of A we mean any determinant formed by choosing any s rows and s columns of A in increasing order and computing the $s \times s$ determinant of the s^2 elements of A from those rows and columns. The *determinantal rank of A is t* if some $t \times t$ minor determinant is nonzero and every $s \times s$ minor is zero for s larger than t.

For example, for the matrix

$$A = \begin{bmatrix} 1 & -1 & 2 & 1 & 1 & 0 \\ 0 & 0 & 0 & 3 & 5 & 2 \\ 0 & 0 & 0 & 0 & 0 & 4 \\ 0 & 0 & 0 & 0 & 0 & 0 \end{bmatrix}$$

the 3×3 minor determinant formed from rows 1, 2, 3 and columns 1, 4, 6 is 12, while any 4×4 minor determinant must use row 4 and hence be 0, so the determinantal rank is 3.

(3.1.16) In fact, we have in general that a row-reduced matrix like (3.1.14) has determinantal rank r. Any matrix (3.1.13) can be brought into the row reduced form (3.1.14) by means of the row interchange and subtracting multiples of rows from other operations. We'll see now that these operations preserve determinantal rank, so that the determinantal rank of the original matrix (3.1.13) is also r.

(3.1.17)   Invariance of Determinantal Rank. Let A be an $m \times n$ matrix. The determinantal rank of A stays the same when either of the following occurs:

1. Two rows of A are interchanged.
2. A multiple of a row of A is added to another row.

It's easy to see why item 1 is true: If A' is the matrix resulting from A by a row interchange, then every minor determinant of A is one of A' and vice versa. Item 2 is not much harder to see: Suppose row i of A is multiplied by l and added to row j, resulting in the matrix B. Suppose every $s \times s$ minor determinant of A is zero. The only minor determinants of B which could differ from those of A are those which involve row j but not row i. Suppose we have made such a row choice in computing a $s \times s$ minor, obtaining the value a from A and b from B. Let a' be the $s \times s$ minor determinant of A obtained by choosing row i instead of j. Then by the properties of determinants we have $b = a \pm la'$ (the sign ambiguity results from having to switch row i into the position of row j in the minor). If every $s \times s$ minor determinant of A is zero, then a and a' are zero, so b is zero. Thus every $s \times s$ minor determinant of B is zero also. Now run the same argument through again the other way, using the fact that A results from B by multiplying row i by $-l$ and adding to row j: We conclude that every $s \times s$ minor determinant of A is zero if and only if the same is true for B. Item 2 now follows easily, completing the proof of (3.1.14).

To cast the reduction process (3.1.11) in terms of factorization of the matrix A of (3.1.13), we want to separate the processes of switching rows and subtracting multiples of rows from others by doing all the former in advance. The conclusions 1 and 2 which follow describe a matrix in appropriate condition for the reduction process to work without having to do any row interchanges.

(3.1.18) Preprocessing $m \times n$ Matrices for Row Reduction. Let A be an $m \times n$ matrix whose first column is not all zeros (with determinantal rank r). There is a matrix $\bar{A}$, obtained from A by row interchanges, with the following properties—there are integers $1 = j_1 < j_2 < \cdots < j_r \le n$ such that:

1. If $j_k \le p < j_{k+1}$ then the $m \times p$ matrix of the first p columns of A has determinantal rank k.
2. The minor determinants formed from rows $1, 2, \ldots, k$ and columns $j_1, j_2, \ldots, j_k$ of $\bar{A}$ are nonzero for $k = 1, 2, \ldots, r$.
3. The matrix $\bar{A}$ can be brought into row-reduced form by subtracting multiples of rows from rows below them.

[In this proof $B|p$ denotes the matrix obtained from the first p columns of the matrix B.] To prove (3.1.18), we begin by observing that conclusion 3 above actually follows from conclusions 1 and 2: the row operations referred to in 3 do not affect any of the minor determinants referred to in 2, and by (3.1.17) neither the row operations nor the row interchanges used to produce $\bar{A}$ affect the determinantal ranks in 1. The matrix $\bar{A}|1$ has its $(1, 1)$ entry nonzero, and type 3 operations put it in a row-reduced form. Suppose we know the matrix $\bar{A}|j_k$ can be put in row-reduced from by operations as in conclusion 3. Let B be the result of applying these row operations to $\bar{A}$. For $j_k \le p < j_{k+1}$, we have $B|p$ of determinantal rank k, which means (since $B|j_k$ is row reduced) that all the entries in both columns j_k to $(j_{k+1}) - 1$ and rows $k + 1$ to m are zero; but since the minor determinant of rows $1, \ldots, k + 1$ and columns $j_1, \ldots, j_{k+1}$ of B is nonzero, there is a nonzero entry in the $(k + 1, j_{k+1})$ position of B. The row operations necessary to row reduce $B|j_{k+1}$ are thus also of the type of 3. So we see how 3 follows from 1 and 2. Now to prove conclusions 1 and 2: suppose for some k we have found a matrix $\bar{A}^{(k)}$, coming from A by row interchanges, such that $\bar{A}^{(k)}|j_k$ satisfies 2. For $j_k \le p < j_{k+1}$ we have [by (3.1.17)] that $\bar{A}^{(k)}|p$ also has determinantal rank k and still enjoys property 2. In particular, for $q = j_{k+1}$ we have that $\bar{A}^{(k)}|q - 1$ has properties 1 and 2 (for $r = k$), so can be brought into row-reduced form by operations of type 3. If B denotes the result of these operations applied to $\bar{A}^{(k)}$, then $B|j_{k+1}$ has the form

$$
\begin{bmatrix}
b_{11} & \cdots & & b_{1q} \\
& b_k & \cdots & b_{kq} \\
& & & * \\
& & & \vdots \\
& & & *
\end{bmatrix}
\qquad (q = j_{k+1})
$$

At least one of the entries labeled ∗ is nonzero, since this matrix has determinantal rank $k + 1$. By a row interchange, we can make this entry be the $(k + 1, j_{k+1})$ entry, so the minor determinant of rows $1, \ldots, k + 1$ and columns $j_1, \ldots, j_{k+1}$ is nonzero. This row interchange only affected rows $k + 1$ through m, so all the other minor determinants using rows 1 through k are unchanged. Because the operations of type 3 leave the minor determinants referred to in 2 unchanged, we conclude that if we apply the same row interchange to $\bar{A}^{(k)}$ we obtain a matrix $\bar{A}^{(k+1)}$ satisfying 2 up to $k + 1$. We proceed in this fashion to a matrix $\bar{A} = \bar{A}^{(r)}$ satisfying 1, 2 (and hence 3) completely.

The "preprocessing" of (3.1.18) is purely theoretical: as the proof reveals, to really determine the necessary row interchanges, the matrix A needs to be converted to row-reduced form via the reduction process (3.1.11), but then A has already been row reduced, so no more "pre" processing is necessary. However, (3.1.18) does accomplish our desired theoretical goal of reformulating the reduction process in terms of a matrix factorization. (We recall that a permutation matrix is a matrix obtained from an identity matrix by row interchanges.):

(3.1.19) Factorization of $m \times n$ Matrices. Let A be an $m \times n$ matrix. Then there is an $m \times m$ permutation matrix P, an $m \times m$ lower triangular matrix L with unit diagonal, and a row-reduced $m \times n$ matrix U such that $A = PLU$.

To prove (3.1.19), we begin by obtaining a matrix $\bar{A}$ as in (3.1.18) by row interchanges from A. If rows $1, 2, \ldots, m$ of A become rows $\sigma(1), \sigma(2), \ldots, \sigma(m)$ of $\bar{A}$, we construct P by taking row i of P to be row $\sigma(i)$ of the $m \times m$ identity I_m. Then $A = P\bar{A}$ (see the argument on page 40). Now all the row operations necessary to pass from $\bar{A}$ to U are, by conclusion 3 of (3.1.8), of the form "multiply row i by a constant and subtract from row j, where $i < j$". If the constant is c, this operation is accomplished by left multiplying by the matrix with ones on the diagonal, $-c$ in position (j, i), and zeros elsewhere [see Exercise 8 of (2.1)]. All these matrices are lower triangular and hence so is any product of them. Thus the result of doing all the row operations in conclusion 3 of (3.1.18) can be accomplished by left multiplying $\bar{A}$ by an $m \times m$ lower triangular matrix M with unit diagonal. In other words, $M\bar{A} = U$, so $\bar{A} = M^{-1}U$. Let $L = M^{-1}$; then $A = P\bar{A} = PLU$, as asserted in (3.1.19).

Among other things, (3.1.19) shows that any $m \times n$ matrix A is the product of an invertible $m \times m$ matrix (namely PL) and a row-reduced $m \times n$ matrix U. Back in (3.1.10) we described the theory of solutions of a system of linear equations whose matrix of coefficients happened to have such a factorization. As we now see, every system is factorizable in this sense. This means, in particular, that we can use part 1 of (3.1.10) to detect when a system of equations has at least one solution (in theory, of course; in practice, we test for solutions by trying to find one). It is also of theoretical importance to be able to discuss the right-hand sides of the equations, with given matrix of coefficients, for which a solution exists, as a totality. The factorization (3.1.19) facilitates this discussion, also.

(3.1.20) The *range space*, range (A), of the $m \times n$ matrix A, is the set of all m-vectors b for which the system $Ax = b$ has a solution. The range space has a number of elementary properties, which are listed here. Their verifications are left as exercises:

1. Range(A) is a vector subspace, that is, if b and c are in it, and α is any number, then $\alpha b + c$ also belongs to the range space.
2. If y is any n-vector, then Ay is in the range space of A.
3. The columns of A are in range(A) and every element of range(A) is a linear combination of those columns.
4. If B is a $p \times m$ matrix then range(BA) = B range(A).

(3.1.21) The dimension of the vector space range(A) is denoted *rank(A)*. The rank of A is, by basic properties of dimension, the number of linearly independent elements in a set of vectors spanning range(A). By part 3 of (3.1.20), the columns of A span range(A). So we have:

1. Rank(A) = number of linearly independent columns of A.

Now suppose the $m \times n$ matrix A has been factored as $A = PLU$, as in (3.1.19). The matrix $B = PL$ is invertible, and also, by part 4 of (3.1.20), range(A) = B range(U). The columns $j_1, j_2, \ldots, j_r$ of U [in the notation from (3.1.7)] are linearly independent and a basis of range(U), and multiplying this basis by the invertible matrix B, leads to a basis of the vector subspace B range(U) = range(A). Of course the product of B and column j_k of U is just column j_k of A, so we have:

2. The columns $j_1, \ldots, j_r$ of A form a basis for Range(A).

The number r in 2 above is the determinantal rank of U [and hence also of A, by (3.1.17)], as we have also seen:

3. Rank(A) = determinantal rank of A.

Finally, the definition of determinantal rank is such that A and A^T have the same determinantal rank. So from part 3 above we obtain:

4. Rank(A) = rank(A^T).

Sometimes, because of part 1 of (3.1.21), what we are calling "rank," is called "column rank." The column rank of A^T is the number of linearly independent rows of A, so this is sometimes called "row rank." In these terms, part 4 of (3.1.21) says that row rank and column rank are equal.

The range–space concept is used to discuss which right-hand sides of systems $Ax = b$ admit at least one solution. In part 3 of (3.1.10), it was seen that from one solution, all the rest can be obtained by adding on solutions to $Ay = 0$. Again, it is convenient to discuss the totality of such y in terms of vector spaces:

(3.1.22) The *null space*, null(A), of the $m \times n$ matrix A, is the set of all n-vectors y for which $Ay = 0$. It is an easy exercise to verify

   1.   Null(A) is a vector subspace.

We can thus speak of its dimension, which will be denoted *nullity*(A). Since $A = (PL)U$ by (3.1.19) and PL is invertible, we can apply (3.1.10) to A. Then from part 2 of (3.1.10) we discover that there are $n - r$ n-vectors forming a basis for null(A), where r is the rank of U, and hence of A. We thus have

   2.   Nullity(A) + rank(A) = number of columns of A.

The equation in 2 above refers to the sum of dimensions of spaces of n-vectors [null(A)] and m-vectors [range(A)]. But from part 4 of (3.1.21), we also have nullity(A) + rank(A^T) = n, and rank(A^T) is the dimension of range(A^T), which is also a space of n-vectors. Suppose $y_1, \ldots, y_{n-r}$ is a basis of null(A) and $z_1, \ldots, z_r$ is a basis of range(A^T). If the set $B = \{y_1, \ldots, y_{n-r}, z_1, \ldots, z_r\}$ is linearly dependent, we have numbers $a_1, \ldots, a_{n-r}, b_1, \ldots, b_r$, not all zero, with $a_1 y_1 + \cdots + a_{n-r} y_{n-r} + b_1 z_1 + \cdots + b_r z_r = 0$. If all the a's are zero, then so are all the b's because $z_1, \ldots, z_r$ are independent, and so there is a nonzero a. Similar reasoning applied to the b's shows that there is at least one nonzero b. Now $0 \neq w = a_1 y_1 + \cdots + a_{n-r} y_{n-r} = (-b_1) z_1 + \cdots + (-b_r) z_r$ is in both null(A) and range(A^T). Since w is in range(A^T), $w = A^T x$ for some m-vector x. Then $0 \neq \Sigma a_i^2 + \Sigma b_i^2 = wTw = (A^T x)^T w = x^T(Aw) = x^T 0 = 0$, which is a contradiction [we have $Aw = 0$ since w is in null(A)]. So in fact B is linearly independent, and since it has n elements it is a basis for the space of n-vectors. Thus we have proven:

   3.   The union of a basis for null(A) and a basis for range(A^T) gives a basis for the space of n-vectors.

4. If x is in null(A) and y is in range(A^T), then $y^T x = 0$. [To see 4, use $y = A^T z$ for some z. Then $y^T x = (A^T z)^T x = z^T (Ax) = 0$.]

As has been noted several times in this section, we have been concentrating on the theoretical and in principle solution of systems of linear equations. In actual practice, we will never indulge in a matrix factorization, but proceed immediately to a row reduction. It is unnatural to treat the two sides of a system of equations differently during this process. It turns out that the convenient way to treat them both the same is to increase the number of columns of the matrix of coefficients by one and put the right-hand side in as a final column, and then reduce this *augmented* matrix. Formally, this proceeds as follows:

(3.1.23) Solution of A Linear System by Row Reduction of the Augmented Matrix. The following system of m linear equations in n unknowns

$$(*) \quad \begin{cases} a_{11}x_1 + \cdots + a_{1n}x_n = b_1 \\ \quad \vdots \\ a_{m1}x_1 + \cdots + a_{mn}x_n = b_m \end{cases}$$

is to be solved for $x_1, \ldots, x_n$. The *augmented matrix of coefficients* of $(*)$ is the $m \times (n + 1)$ matrix

$$A = \begin{bmatrix} a_{11} & \cdots & a_{1n} \ b_1 \\ \vdots & & \vdots \\ a_{m1} & \cdots & a_{mn} \ b_m \end{bmatrix}$$

Suppose A is row reduced, by the procedure (3.1.11), to the $m \times (n + 1)$ matrix

$$U = \begin{bmatrix} u_{11} & \cdots & & u_{1n} & c_1 \\ & u_{r, j_r} & \cdots & u_{rn} & c_r \\ & & & & c_{r+1} \end{bmatrix}$$

[Note, especially, the final column of U; it will have zero entries in rows $r + 2$ through m. This happens because if the matrix of coefficients of $(*)$ (*not* the augmented matrix A) has rank r, then at stage r in the row reduction of A we will have a matrix which looks like U in all respects except possibly the final column. If all the entries of this $(n + 1)$th column from row $r + 1$ to m are zero, then we stop. If not, we get a nonzero entry in the $(r + 1, n + 1)$ position by row interchange, and then use it to get zeros in rows $r + 2$ to m.]

Translating back from U, we have that the solutions of ($*$) are the same as those of the system

$$(**) \quad \begin{cases} u_{11}x_1 + \quad \cdots \quad + u_{1n}x_n = c_1 \\ \\ u_{r,j_r}x_{j_r} + \cdots + u_{rn}x_n = c_r \\ \\ 0 = c_{r+1} \end{cases}$$

If $c_{r+1} \neq 0$, the system ($**$) and hence ($*$), has no solution. If $c_{r+1} = 0$, the solutions of ($**$), and hence of ($*$), are obtained by free choice of the free variables and back substitution for the dependent variables as in (3.1.5).

The one subtlety to notice here is the following: by row reduction of the augmented matrix we determine the solutions, if any, for a particular given right-hand side of ($*$). What we don't discover is criteria for determining which right-hand sides of ($*$) do allow solutions. This latter task can be done by (3.1.10), which means constructing the (3.1.19) factorization of the matrix of coefficients. In small-scale examples this is not too hard, but for larger-scale problems it becomes formidable. In our applications, we will therefore stick to the augmented matrix method.

EXERCISES 3.1

1. Find the row-reduced matrix U obtained from the matrix A by row interchanges and subtractions for $A =$

   (a) $\begin{bmatrix} 1 & -2 & 1 \\ 2 & -4 & 3 \end{bmatrix}$

   (b) $\begin{bmatrix} 1 & 0 & 7 \\ 2 & 4 & -2 \\ 1 & -2 & 15 \end{bmatrix}$

   (c) $\begin{bmatrix} 2 & 2 & -1 & 1 \\ 3 & 6 & 0 & 1 \\ 1 & -2 & -2 & 1 \\ 1 & 4 & 1 & 0 \end{bmatrix}$

   (d) $\begin{bmatrix} 1 & 3 & 5 \\ 6 & -1 & 3 \\ 2 & 4 & 1 \\ 1 & 1 & 0 \end{bmatrix}$

2. Write the following matrices in the form $A = PLU$ as in (3.1.19).

   (a) $\begin{bmatrix} 1 & 2 & 3 \\ 1 & 2 & 5 \\ 2 & 4 & 4 \end{bmatrix}$

   (b) $\begin{bmatrix} 2 & 1 & 0 & 3 \\ 2 & 1 & 3 & 5 \\ 2 & 1 & 3 & 4 \\ 2 & 1 & 6 & 4 \end{bmatrix}$

   (c) $\begin{bmatrix} 1 & 2 & 3 \\ 1 & 3 & 5 \\ 1 & 3 & 6 \\ 3 & 8 & 14 \end{bmatrix}$

   (d) $\begin{bmatrix} 0 & 0 & 1 \\ 2 & 1 & -1 \\ 3 & 2 & 2 \end{bmatrix}$

3. Reduce each of the following systems of linear equations to row-reduced form. Determine if they are consistent. If they are, find all solutions [in the form of part 3 of (3.1.10)]:

(a) $\quad x_1 + 2x_2 + 3x_3 = 2$ (b) $\quad x_1 + 7x_3 = 1$

$\quad x_1 + 2x_2 + 5x_3 = 4$ $2x_1 + 4x_2 - 2x_3 = 2$

$\quad 2x_1 + 4x_2 + 4x_3 = 2$ $x_1 - 2x_2 + 15x_3 = 4$

(c) $\quad x_1 + 2x_2 + 3x_3 = 10$

$\quad x_1 + 3x_2 + 5x_3 = 14$

$\quad x_1 + 3x_2 + 6x_3 = 15$

$\quad 3x_1 + 8x_2 + 14x_3 = 39$

4. Find a basis for the range space and null space of each of the matrices in problem 1.

5. Find a basis for the range space and null space of each of the matrices in problem 2.

6. Prove the assertions 1–4 of (3.1.20).

7. Prove that if B is an $m \times m$ matrix of rank m and B' is obtained from B by discarding any r columns then B' has rank $m - r$.

8. Let A be an $m \times n$ matrix. Prove that there is an $m \times (m - r)$ matrix B' of rank $m - r$ and an $r \times n$ matrix U' of rank r such that $A = B'U'$. [*Hint*: write $A = PLU$ as in (3.1.9), let $B = PL$, let U' be the first r rows of U and let B' be B minus its last r columns.] What are the ranks of B' and U'? What are range(U') and null(C')?

9. Prove that an $n \times n$ matrix A has rank one if and only if there is a nonzero n-vector x with $A = xx^T$.

3.2 SOME EXAMPLES OF UNDERDETERMINED SYSTEMS

There are many situations which, although they are easily modeled by systems of linear equations, do not admit a unique solution. In work with such underdetermined systems, we are concerned with questions like: "For what values of the adjustable parameters is the system consistent?"; and "If the system is consistent, which variables are free and how does a choice of them determine the values of the rest of the variables?". The theory of systems of m linear equations in n unknowns from Section 3.1 provides the method of answering these questions—row reduce the system and answer these questions for the corresponding reduced system—and in Section 3.3

the appropriate computer programs to do row reduction are presented. In this section, we concentrate on several examples of situations modeled by underdetermined systems of equations.

A. Network Flow Models. In Section 2.3A we studied the flow of electricity in a resistor–battery network. There are many other situations where we want to study the transportation of some uniform quantity through a sequence of merging and diverging pathways. For example, we may have people or cars moving along through a network of streets or paths, or water flowing in a network of streams and catchments. In these cases we are likely to know or be able to measure the inputs and outputs from the network, but the actual distribution of the flow along the various channels in the network will not be uniquely determined by these input output rates. By balancing the incoming and outgoing flow at each junction in the network we arrive at a system of linear equations (one for each junction) with the channel flows as unknowns. By row reducing this system we can discover how the channel flows are dependent on each other. Here is a concrete example:

Example (3.2.1) Consider a building, such as a post office, through which people typically pass in one direction. They enter, do their business, and depart. We will assume three entrances and three exits, corresponding to

Figure (3.2.2).

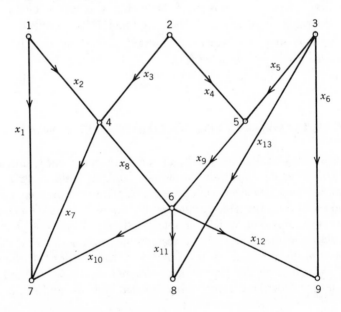

three types of possible services available: entrance and exit one for the post boxes, entrance and exit two for mail pickup, and entrance and exit three for all other business. The various entrances will be located at different levels and sides of the building, however, so that some customers may enter at entrance one for mail pickup, and so on, so that various internal transition points are provided to connect these areas. Schematically, we can describe the pathways in the building by means of a diagram like Figure (3.2.2). In this figure, junctions are the numbered circles, and paths between junctions are the line segments joining them. The arrows on the line segments indicate the permitted direction of flow and the subscripted x's along the paths indicate flow rates. Junctions 1, 2, 3 are entrances one, two, and three, junctions 7, 8, 9 the corresponding exits, and junctions 4, 5, 6 the internal transition points.

Now suppose that we measure the average hourly flow of people in and out of the building, and discover these to be as follows:

Junction	Entering			Exiting		
	1	2	3	7	8	9
	60	70	20	45	55	50

Notice that 150 people enter and 150 leave per hour. We are assuming that no customers remain in the building more than an hour. We make the same assumption about the transition points: the people who enter these areas—which may be stairways or elevators—equal the people leaving them. This is a reasonable assumption to study hourly flow. It might not be if the time unit was much shorter, or if the time necessary to pass through a transition point was much longer.

Since the number of people entering and departing a junction are equal (per hour), we get an equation of the flow rates at each junction. For example, at junction 1 we have, per hour, 60 people entering and $x_1 + x_2$ departing, giving an equation $x_1 + x_2 = 60$ for that junction. At junction 4 we have $x_1 + x_3$ entering and $x_7 + x_8$ departing, giving the equation $x_1 + x_3 = x_7 + x_8$ and for junction 8 we have $x_{11} + x_{13} + x_{14}$ entering and 55 leaving, giving the equation $x_{11} + x_{13} + x_{14} = 55$. Altogether, we can summarize the flows in Figure (3.2.2) in the following equations:

Junction Number	Flow Out		Flow In
1	$x_1 + x_2$	=	60
2	$x_3 + x_4$	=	70
3	$x_5 + x_6 + x_{13}$	=	20
4	$x_7 + x_8$	=	$x_2 + x_3$

Junction Number	Flow Out		Flow In
5	x_9	=	$x_4 + x_5$
6	$x_{10} + x_{11} + x_{12}$	=	$x_8 + x_9$
7	45	=	$x_1 + x_7 + x_{10}$
8	55	=	$x_{11} + x_{13}$
9	50	=	$x_6 + x_{12}$

Rewriting this system of 9 equations in 13 unknowns in standard form gives:

$$
\begin{array}{l}
x_1 + x_2 \qquad\qquad\qquad\qquad\qquad\qquad\qquad\qquad\qquad = 60 \\
\qquad\; x_3 + x_4 \qquad\qquad\qquad\qquad\qquad\qquad\qquad\qquad = 70 \\
\qquad\qquad\quad x_5 + x_6 \qquad\qquad\qquad\qquad\qquad + x_{13} = 20 \\
-x_2 - x_3 \qquad\quad\; + x_7 + x_8 \qquad\qquad\qquad\qquad\; = 0 \\
\qquad\quad -x_4 - x_5 \qquad\qquad x_9 \qquad\qquad\qquad\qquad = 0 \\
\qquad\qquad\qquad\qquad -x_8 - x_9 + x_{10} + x_{11} + x_{12} \quad = 0 \\
x_1 \qquad\qquad\qquad\; + x_7 \qquad\quad + x_{10} \qquad\qquad\qquad = 45 \\
\qquad\qquad\qquad\qquad\qquad\qquad\qquad x_{11} \qquad + x_{13} = 55 \\
\qquad\qquad\qquad x_6 \qquad\qquad\qquad\qquad\qquad + x_{12} \qquad = 50
\end{array}
$$

We proceed to row reduce this system, always using the first available row interchange, when such are necessary. This is relatively easy—very few row subtractions are required—and we obtain the following reduced system:

$$
\begin{array}{l}
x_1 + x_2 \qquad\qquad\qquad\qquad\qquad\qquad\qquad\qquad = \quad 60 \\
-x_2 - x_3 \qquad\qquad\; + x_7 + x_8 \qquad\qquad\qquad\qquad = \quad 0 \\
\qquad\; x_3 + x_4 \qquad\qquad\qquad\qquad\qquad\qquad\qquad = \quad 70 \\
\qquad\quad -x_4 - x_5 \qquad\qquad + x_9 \qquad\qquad\qquad\qquad = \quad 0 \\
\qquad\qquad\quad x_5 + x_6 \qquad\qquad\qquad\qquad + x_{13} = \quad 20 \\
\qquad\qquad\qquad x_6 \qquad\qquad\qquad\qquad + x_{12} \qquad = \quad 50 \\
\qquad\qquad\qquad\; -x_8 - x_9 + x_{10} + x_{11} + x_{12} \qquad = \quad 0 \\
\qquad\qquad\qquad\qquad\qquad -x_9 + x_{10} \qquad\qquad\qquad = -85 \\
\qquad\qquad\qquad\qquad\qquad\qquad\qquad x_{11} \qquad + x_{13} = \quad 55
\end{array}
$$

The free variables here are x_7, x_{10}, x_{12}, and x_{13}. In terms of these free variables, the rest are determined by backsolving the above reduced system. This is tedious, but straightforward, and yields the following equations:

$$x_1 = 45 - x_7 - x_{10} \qquad\qquad x_6 = 50 - x_{12}$$

$$x_2 = 15 + x_7 + x_{10} \qquad\qquad x_8 = -30 + x_{12} - x_{13}$$

$$x_3 = -45 - x_{10} + x_{12} - x_{13} \qquad x_9 = 85 + x_{10}$$

$$x_4 = 115 + x_{10} - x_{12} + x_{13} \qquad x_{11} = 55 - x_{13}$$

$$x_5 = -30 + x_{12} - x_{13}$$

By controlling the values of the free variables x_7, x_{10}, x_{12}, x_{13} we determine the values of the remaining nine. Not all such choices may be useful in studying the model, however: for instance, if we set $x_7 = x_{10} = x_{12} = x_{13} = 0$, we have x_3, x_5, and x_8 negative. Our flow rates are not really set up for negative flows, since we have assumed one-way paths. On the other hand, we can still use our solution to answer various questions about the model. For example, we can ask whether it is possible to reduce the flow x_7 to zero. (Intuitively, this is possible: if you find yourself at junction 4 and wish to go to junction 7, you can travel via junction 6.) Whether this can be done with the same input and output flows is equivalent to finding a solution with $x_7 = 0$ and $x_i \geq 0$ for all i. Since we are closing off the path from junction 4 to junction 7, we will also, to be fair, try to make x_{10} (which is part of the path from 4 to 7 via 6) as large as possible. From the equation for x_6 we see that $x_{12} \leq 50$, so if we set $x_{12} = 50$, and $x_{13} = 0$, the equation for x_3 shows that the maximum for x_{10} is 5. Setting $x_7 = 0$, $x_{10} = 5$, $x_{12} = 50$ and $x_{13} = 0$, we have $x_1 = 40$, $x_2 = 20$, $x_3 = 0$, $x_4 = 70$, $x_5 = 20$, $x_6 = 0$, $x_8 = 20$, $x_9 = 90$ and $x_{11} = 55$. So we could indeed reduce x_7 to zero. ２２７４８Ý

It is important to remember in this type of network analysis that the variables which are designated "free" and those designated "dependent" are strongly determined by which rows come first in the matrix of coefficients. Had we numbered our juncitons in a different order, this would have scrambled the rows, and our row reduction could very well have led to a different set of free variables. General theory tells us that the *number* of free variables (the number of variables minus the rank) is the same for all rearrangements, but the *particular variables* may change. If such things are important to us, we can always renumber and try again to see what some alternative possibilities are.

B.   Resource Allocation.   Suppose we are studying a fixed commodity which is to be allocated among a certain number of uses, over a period of time. It is often the case that, over a period of time, the fraction allocated initially to one use is converted to another. Suppose we know the proportions of these conversions. Is it possible to make the initial allocations so that the fraction of the commodity allocated to each use is constant (despite the conversions)?

To consider a specific example, our commodity will be the campus of a university. Over time, the various grounds and buildings are observed to be converted back and forth among various uses: an older classroom building might be converted to laboratory use, or torn down to make a parking lot, while in another part of the campus a parking lot may be chosen as the site of a new administration building or library addition. After having observed such cyclical conversions of space for some period of time, campus planners have determined with fair accuracy the fraction of the campus in any given use which will be converted to any other given use over a 10-year interval. They would like to use this data to derive a use allocation policy for which the functions remain constant.

We will assume there are eight categories of space use on the campus, and that the 10-year conversion rates are given in the following table:

(3.2.3)   Table of Conversion Factors (10-Year Period)

Terminal Use \ Initial Use	1	2	3	4	5	6	7	8
1	0.82	0.16	0.07	0.02	0.01	0.01	0.02	0.03
2	0.04	0.70	0.06	0.03	0.03	0.01	0.06	0.02
3	0.04	0.05	0.79	0.01	0.22	0.03	0.07	0.02
4	0.02	0.04	0.02	0.61	0.04	0.07	0.02	0.13
5	0.01	0.01	0.01	0.03	0.52	0.02	0.01	0.01
6	0.01	0.01	0.02	0.07	0.15	0.82	0.02	0.06
7	0.05	0.02	0.02	0.03	0.02	0.01	0.78	0.01
8	0.01	0.01	0.01	0.22	0.01	0.03	0.02	0.72

Use categories:

1. Administration building   5. Student residence
2. Classroom building   6. Athletic facility
3. Laboratory building   7. Library building
4. Parking lot   8. Lawns and gardens

To read the table of conversion factors, we note that the entry in row i and column j represents the fraction of space initially allocated to use j which, after 10 years, will be converted to use i. For example, 15% of the student residence space (use 5) will be converted to athletic facilities (use 6), and 2% of the classroom buildings (use 2) will be converted to library buildings (use 7).

The 64 entries in the table of conversion factors form an 8 by 8 matrix P whose i, j entry p_{ij} is the fraction of the commodity initially allocated to use j which is converted to use i. Let the 8-vectors x and y having ith entries x_i and y_i represent the initial fraction allocated to use i (x_i) and the terminal fraction allocated to use i (y_i), respectively. The amount y_i ending up in use i is the sum of the amounts starting in each of the categories, 1 through 8, which are ultimately converted to use i. Thus we have:

$$y_i = p_{i1}x_1 + p_{i2}x_2 + \cdots + p_{i8}x_8 \qquad \text{for } i = 1, \ldots, 8, \text{ or, in matrix form,}$$

$$y = Px$$

To have an allocation policy in which fractions of use remain constant, we need $y = x$, or

$$(3.2.4) \qquad x = Px \quad \text{or} \quad (I - P)x = 0$$

Not every solution of (3.2.4) represents an allocation policy: such a policy vector x must have the property that its entries are all nonnegative and sum to one if it is to really represent fractions of use allocation. We can always arrange for the second condition: if x is a solution of (3.2.4), so is any multiple of it, so we can multiply by the reciprocal of the sum of the entries and get a solution summing to one. The first condition is more delicate and will require a Theorem (3.2.5). Notice also that the column sums of the matrix P are all one, and that each entry of P (being a fraction) is between zero and one.

[In (3.2.4) I is the 8 by 8 identity.] By the theory of systems of linear equations, there are going to be $8 - r$ independent solutions of (3.2.4) [see (3.1.9)], where r is the rank of $I - P$. There is a general theorem regarding the ranks of such matrices.

(3.2.5) Let $P = [p_{ij}]$ be an n by n matrix with all entries positive and between 0 and 1. Assume that the sums of the entries in each column of P is 1. Then $I - P$ has rank $n - 1$. Moreover, there is a nonzero vector x with all entries nonnegative such that $(I - P)x = 0$.

Proof.[†] Let C be the $(n - 1) \times (n - 1)$ matrix made from P by discarding the last row and column. All its entries are nonnegative and the sum of the jth column of C is $1 - P_{nj}$, which is less than 1. Using (2.3.23) and then (2.3.21), we know that $I_{n-1} - C$ is invertible and $(I_{n-1} - C)^{-1} \geq 0$. [Here I_{n-1} is the $(n - 1) \times (n - 1)$ identity.] Let z be the $(n - 1)$-vector made up of the first $(n - 1)$ entries of the nth column of P. Then every entry in $w = (I_{n-1} - C)^{-1}z$ is nonnegative. Let x' be the n-vector whose first $(n - 1)$ entries are those of w and whose nth entry is 1. Now we consider the product Px':

$$Px' = \begin{bmatrix} C & w - Cw \\ p_{n1} \cdots p_{n,n-1} & p_{nn} \end{bmatrix} \begin{bmatrix} w \\ 1 \end{bmatrix}$$

$$= \begin{bmatrix} Cw + (w - Cw) \\ p_{n1}w_1 + \cdots + p_{n,n-1}w_{n-1} + p_{nn} \end{bmatrix} = \begin{bmatrix} w \\ a \end{bmatrix}$$

(Here we have written z in the form $w - Cw$, and use a for the sum $p_{n1}w_1 + \cdots + p_{n,n-1}w_{n-1} + p_{nn}$.) Since $p_{nj} = 1 = \sum_{i=1}^{n-1} p_{ij}$, $p_{nj}w_j = \sum_{i=1}^{n-1}(1 - p_{ij})w_j$ (for $1 \leq j \leq n - 1$). This latter sum is, of course, just the jth entry of the product $(I - C)w$, namely, p_{jn}. So $a = p_{n1} + \cdots + p_{nn}$ is the sum of the entries in the nth column of P, namely, 1. In other words, $Px' = x'$. Since x' is nonzero and a solution of $(I - P)x = 0$, we know that $I - P$ must have rank at most $n - 1$. On the other hand, since $I_{n-1} - C$ is invertible, the $(n - 1) \times (n - 1)$ minor determinant of $I - P$ formed from the first $n - 1$ rows and columns is nonzero, so $I - P$ has rank at least $n - 1$.

Because of the Theorem (3.2.5), we know that in our campus example we can find a use allocation policy $x \neq 0$ satisfying (3.2.4). In practice, we will do this by row reducing $I - P$ and finding a suitable solution to $(I - P)x = 0$ by rank substitution. If we make at least one entry of x positive by appropriate choice of free variables, then all entries will be nonnegative [since all solutions of $(I - P)x = 0$ are multiples of each other and one solution has nonnegative entries], and we can get a policy vector by multiplying this x by the reciprocal of the sum of its entries.

C. Leontieff Exchange Models for Closed Economies.

The economic entities studied in Section 2.3B conducted both external and internal exchanges. We were especially interested in studying, for such entities, the production levels necessary to meet given outside demands. There are a

---

[†]Adapted from B. Noble in *Proceedings Summer Conference for College Teachers on Applied Mathematics*, CUPM, Berkeley, 1971.

number of situations, however, when outside demand is of no particular interest: perhaps there is not outside demand (for instance, we might be considering the entire global economy), or perhaps the production levels are determined by other factors than demand. In such situations, another problem often arises, namely, that of fair pricing. If a particular sector of the economy is overpriced and another underpriced, activity may be skewed in undesirable directions. For instance, low salaries for mathematics teachers and high salaries for data processing professionals may cause many of the former to change their occupations to the latter, ultimately causing serious problems in the training of technicians in the future. As we shall see, the Leontieff input–output analysis of 2.3B can be used to study this pricing problem also.

We assume that our economy is divided up into n sectors, that the input required by each of the sectors comes entirely from the production of itself and the other $n - 1$ sectors, and that the total output of each sector is entirely used up by itself and the other sectors. Each sector will thus input a certain fraction of the total output of the other sectors; it is convenient to record this information in a table:

(3.2.6) Exchange Table for An n-Sector Economy

Input \ Output	Division 1	Division 2	$\cdots$	Division n	Total Output
Division 1	a_{11}	a_{12}	$\cdots$	a_{1n}	b_1
Division 2	a_{21}	a_{22}	$\cdots$	a_{2n}	b_2
$\vdots$	$\vdots$	$\vdots$	$\vdots$	$\vdots$	$\vdots$
Division n	a_{n1}	a_n	$\cdots$	a_{nn}	b_n
Total	b_1	b_2	$\cdots$	b_n	

$a_{ij} = $ (dollar) output of division j purchased by division i

$b_i = a_{1i} + a_{2i} + \cdots + a_{ni} = $ total dollar output of division i

$b_i = a_{i1} + a_{i2} + \cdots + a_{in} = $ total dollar input of division i

[It is important to understand the difference between Table (3.2.6) and Table (2.3.15): in (3.2.6) we tabulate outputs in *columns*, so going down column 1, for example, we see the part of the total output of the first division sent to each of the other divisions, with the column total, b_1, recorded below the double line. Reading across row 1 we see the parts of the outputs of each of the divisions required by division 1, with the row total, b_1, recorded to the right of the double line. The input and output totals of division 1, are the same amounts, b_1, in keeping with assumptions.]

Table (3.2.6) is in dollar units. Remember that our goal is to determine a pricing policy which maintains this table of activity at a constant level. So we need to analyze (3.2.6) for what it says about fundamental relations in the economy, and then use that information to design a pricing policy. Since a_{ij} in (3.2.6) represents the dollar amount division i inputs from division j, and b_j in (3.2.6) represents the dollar amount of the total output of division j, $e_{ij} = a_{ij}/b_j$ represents the fraction of the total output of division j inputted by division i. Thus the total input of division i equation can be represented as $b_i = a_{i1} + \cdots + a_{ij} = e_{i1}b_1 + e_{i2}b_2 + \cdots + e_{in}b_n$, or $b_i = \Sigma e_{ij}b_j$. These "exchange coefficients" e_{ij} represent the fundamental relations of the economy, and we take these as known. The total prices b_i are our unknowns, and in keeping with standard notation conventions we will call these p_i (for "price") instead. So from (3.2.6) we get a linear problem:

(3.2.7)

EXCHANGE MATRIX

$$E = \begin{bmatrix} e_{11} & \cdots & e_{1n} \\ \vdots & & \vdots \\ e_{n1} & \cdots & e_{nn} \end{bmatrix}$$
(where e_{ij} is the fraction of the output of division j inputted by division i)

PRICE VECTOR

$$P = \begin{bmatrix} p_1 \\ \vdots \\ p_n \end{bmatrix}$$
(where p_i is the total price charged by division i for its total output)

EQUILIBRIUM PRICE EQUATIONS

$$p_i = e_{i1}p_1 + \cdots + e_{in}p_n \quad \text{for} \quad i = 1, \ldots, n$$

or $\quad p = Ep$

(the total price charged for the total output of division i equals the total cost of its total inputs)

The equilibrium price equations in (3.2.7) are, of course, identical to the resource allocation equations (3.2.4). Moreover, E, like P in (3.2.4), has column sums all one and all entries between zero and one. So we can solve the price equations exactly as we solved the allocation equations: row reduce $I - E$ to solve the equations in the form $(I - E)p = 0$. With luck, all entries in E will be positive, so we can apply (3.2.5) to guarantee the existence of a solution p with all entries nonnegative, and at least one positive. In this case all prices are nonnegative, as they should be. Any multiple of an equilibrium price vector P is still a solution to $p = Ep$, but there is an additional constraint operating: we recall that p_i represents the value of the total output of division i, so $p_1 + \cdots + p_n$ (the sum of the entries of p) represents the value of the total output of the whole economy. By multiplying p by a suitable positive number we can make this value anything we like; usually we have a value in mind in advance (a "money supply") and so we need to choose our multiplier to hit this value.

How realistic is it to assume that there is no outside demand or surplus production in an economy? Obviously, not very. However, we can with any economy introduce a new division whose input is the outside demand and whose output is the outside supply. (In effect, this is resectoring the global economy so that the divisions of our original economy are global divisions and the rest of the global economy is treated as our one new division.) Then we can study equilibrium pricing for this new economy. Equilibrium prices then tell us what to charge for internal exchanges and also how to price imports and exports.

EXERCISES 3.2

1. The diagram of Figure (3.2.8) is a symbolic representation of a watershed. Rainfall enters the watershed in four main areas (indicated by nodes 1, 2, 3, 4 in the figure), flows along several small creeks into three stream systems (indicated by nodes 5, 6, 7), and then into two river systems (indicated by nodes 8 and 0). The flows are all in the

Figure (3.2.8).

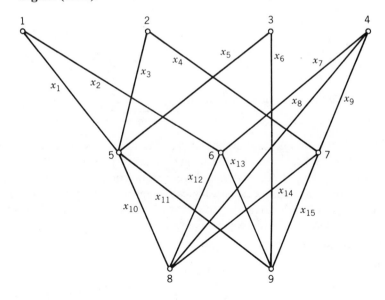

directions indicated by the arrows. The variable x_i represents the flow rates in the segment they label, in units of 10^3 yd^3/hr. Assume a rainstorm yields inputs of 21, 9, 11 and 17 (10^3 yd^3/hr) to nodes 1, 2, 3, and 4, respectively, and that flows from junctions divide equally. Suppose the output at nodes 8 and 9 are both 29 units each. Write the system of linear equations governing the flow.

2. The diagram of Figure (3.2.9) represents an airline terminal. Nodes 1 and 2 represent the international arrival concourses, 6 and 7 the domestic arrivals, 4 and 5 the domestic departures, 3 the international departures, and 8 represents local exit to ground transportation. Transit connections are indicated by segments in the graph. We assume that input flows to nodes 1, 2, 6, and 7 are, respectively, 150, 220, 1100, and 1500 people per hour and that output flows at nodes 3, 4, 5, and 8 are 185, 200, 1800, and 785 people per hour. Assume that no one waits in the terminal for over an hour. Write the system of linear equations governing the flow.

Figure (3.2.9).

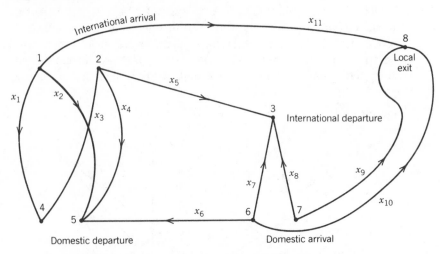

3. Voting behavior studies show that, in the long run, voting patterns tend to shift in cyclical fashion, due to material and perceptual changes in interest patterns. However, the changes can be conveniently understood as "conversions" from one ideological category to another, with fixed percentages of each category "converting" to each other. The following table is based on five ideological categories:

(a) Left liberal.

(b) Liberal.

(c)   Center.

(d)   Conservative.

(e)   Ultraconservative.

The "from/to" conversion factors are based on a 4-year (i.e., presidential election) cycle:

Table of Conversion Factors

To Category \ From Category	1	2	3	4	5
1	0.70	0.05	0.05	0.01	0.01
2	0.10	0.85	0.20	0.04	0.01
3	0.10	0.05	0.50	0.20	0.03
4	0.09	0.04	0.20	0.60	0.15
5	0.01	0.01	0.05	0.15	0.80

Write Eqs. (3.2.4) for the division of the electorate into constant fractions. (In a parliamentary system, this could serve as an allocation policy for representation.)

4.   The economy of a small developing country is divided into five major sectors: agriculture, mining, manufacturing, service, and foreign trade 5. To promote development, the outputs of the various sectors are to be used in the rest of the economy as follows:

Agriculture.   40% to agriculture, 10% each to mining, manufacturing, and service, and 30% to export.

Mining.   30% to agriculture and to manufactoring, 20% to mining, and 10% each to services and export.

Manufacturing.   30% to agriculture, 10% to services, 20% each to mining, manufacturing, and export.

Services.   20% to each sector.

Foreign trade.   30% to agriculture, 20% each to services, manufacturing, and mining, and 10% to export.

Construct the exchange matrix (3.2.7) for this economy and write the equilibrium price equations which will enable outputs to be used as desired.

5. Let A be an $n \times n$ matrix whose columns each sum to one. Prove that there is a solution $x \neq 0$ to $Ax = x$. Is this a consequence of Theorem (3.2.5)?

3.3 ROW REDUCING MATRICES WITH LINPACK

In this section we take up the problem of actually row reducing an m by n matrix in practice, using the computer. Our methods will use the LINPACK linear algebra procedures or, to be more accurate, will use the BLAS vector operation subroutines attached to LINPACK. We end up with a program whose basic algorithm is quite similar to the LINPACK factoring routine SGECO studied in Section 2.4. Indeed, one of the purposes of constructing the program in the way it will be done here is to provide some insight into how the LINPACK factoring procedure operates.

To begin, we assume an $m \times n$ matrix A is given, and that A is to be row reduced by row interchanges and subtracting multiples of rows from other rows, using the matrix version of the row-reduction process (3.1.11). Whenever it is necessary to do a row interchange to get a nonzero element in some position, we will always switch in the available element of largest absolute value, and the first of these if we have a choice. This rule is adopted for reasons of numerical stability whose proof is hard, but we can at least suggest why it is so: we need nonzero elements to divide by. Dividing by small numbers can cause dangerous overflow, so we want to divide by as large a number as possible.

Before we begin to code the reduction process (3.1.11), we will look at the various steps from a point of view somewhat different than usual. One of the main features of FORTRAN that we will want to take advantage of is the way it treats matrices as long vectors [see Section (1.4)], in which columns, or parts of them, are easily accessible. To do things efficiently, then, we copy a LINPACK device of doing *row operations as (partial) column operations*. Here's how this is done if we need, for example, to subtract multiples of a given row from all rows below it (we assume here we are at a stage in row reduction where we have rows 1 to $k - 1$ in correct form and that the entry in position q of row k is the appropriate nonzero one):

$$(3.3.1) \qquad \begin{bmatrix} u_{11} & & \cdots & & u_{1n} \\ & \ddots & & & \\ & & a_{kq} & \cdots & a_{kn} \\ & & \vdots & & \vdots \\ & & a_{mq} & \cdots & a_{mn} \end{bmatrix}$$

In (3.3.1), row k is to be multiplied by $l_i = -a_{iq}/a_{kq}$ and added to row i, for $i = k + 1, \ldots, m$. This means the submatrix of (3.3.1) made up of rows k to m and columns q to n becomes

$$(3.3.2) \qquad \begin{bmatrix} a_{k,q} & \cdots & a_{k,j} & \cdots & a_{k,n} \\ \vdots & & & & \\ 0 & \cdots & l_i a_{k,j} + a_{i,j} & \cdots & a_{i,n} \\ \vdots & & & & \\ 0 & \cdots & l_m a_{k,j} + a_{m,j} & \cdots & a_{m,n} \end{bmatrix}$$

Column q of (3.3.2) is determined by its first entry, $a_{k,q}$. For j from $q + 1$ to n, the jth column of (3.3.2) can be described as follows: we know its first entry, and the remaining have the vector form:

$$(3.3.3) \qquad \begin{bmatrix} l_{k+1} a_{k,j} + a_{k+1,j} \\ \vdots \\ l_m a_{k,j} + a_{m,j} \end{bmatrix} = a_{k,j} \begin{bmatrix} l_{k+1} \\ \vdots \\ l_m \end{bmatrix} + \begin{bmatrix} a_{k+1,j} \\ \vdots \\ a_{m,j} \end{bmatrix}$$

Notice that this is a column operation: we are adding a multiple of one column to another.

(3.3.4) Now we back up slightly to consider the sequence in which we need to do these various steps. Suppose we found the appropriate nonzero entry to switch into position (k, q) in (3.3.1) in position (i, q) $(i \geq k)$. Rather than switch rows i and k completely at this stage, let us just swap the k and i entries of column q. As we noted, the rest of column q in (3.3.2) will be all zeros at the end of the operations with row k. Temporarily, however, we can use those positions to hold the numbers $l_{k+1}, \ldots, l_m$. [This makes the entries from $k + 1$ to m of column q look like the first vector on the right in (3.3.3).] Now as j goes from $q + 1$ to n we can swap the i and k entries of column j, then add $a_{k,j}$ times column q to column j (just the rows $k + 1$ to m, of course) to accomplish (3.3.3). After having done this for column n we can replace the entries $l_{k+1}, \ldots, l_m$ of column q with zeros and we are in the position of (3.3.2).

The steps in the preceding paragraph are vital for understanding the method used in this section for row reduction. Here's an example to help. Assume in (3.3.1) that $k = 1$, $m = 3$, $n = 4$ and we have

$$\begin{bmatrix} 0 & 1 & -1 & 2 \\ 1 & 3 & 1 & -1 \\ 2 & 2 & 0 & 1 \end{bmatrix}$$

We are going to switch rows 1 and 3 to get a nonzero $(1, 1)$ entry (remember we want largest absolute value, which is why we don't use row 2). So we switch the $(1, 1)$ and $(3, 1)$ entries:

$$\begin{bmatrix} 2 & 1 & -1 & 2 \\ 1 & 3 & 1 & -1 \\ 0 & 2 & 0 & 1 \end{bmatrix}$$

Now we replace the $(2, 1)$ entry by $l_2 = -\frac{1}{2}$ and the $(3, 1)$ entry by $l_3 = -\frac{0}{2} = 0$, giving

$$\begin{bmatrix} 2 & 1 & -1 & 2 \\ -\frac{1}{2} & 3 & 1 & -1 \\ 0 & 2 & 0 & 1 \end{bmatrix}$$

For $j = 2$, we switch the first and third entries to get

$$\begin{bmatrix} 2 & 2 & -1 & 2 \\ -\frac{1}{2} & 3 & 1 & -1 \\ 0 & 1 & 0 & 1 \end{bmatrix}$$

and then add 2 [the $(1, 2)$ entry] times column 1 to column 2:

$$\begin{bmatrix} 2 & 2 & -1 & 2 \\ -\frac{1}{2} & 2 & 1 & -1 \\ 0 & 1 & 0 & 1 \end{bmatrix}$$

For $j = 3$ we switch and sum similarly

$$\begin{bmatrix} 2 & 2 & 0 & 2 \\ -\frac{1}{2} & 2 & 1 & -1 \\ 0 & 1 & -1 & 1 \end{bmatrix}$$

and also for $j = 4$

$$\begin{bmatrix} 2 & 2 & 0 & 1 \\ -\frac{1}{2} & 2 & 1 & -\frac{3}{2} \\ 0 & 1 & -1 & 2 \end{bmatrix}$$

and finish by setting l_2 and l_3 to zero:

$$\begin{bmatrix} 2 & 2 & 0 & 1 \\ 0 & 2 & 1 & -\frac{3}{2} \\ 0 & 1 & -1 & 2 \end{bmatrix}$$

These "row operations by columns" of paragraph (3.3.4) are designed to be easy to implement in FORTRAN, using the BLAS vector operations presented in (2.5.6). So we now proceed to construct FORTRAN code which does them.

We assume we have an M by N matrix stored in the 50 by 50 array A, and that in the course of row reduction we have arrived at row IE ("E" for "equation"), and that in column IV ("V" for variable) we have located the element, which is to occupy the (IE, IV) position, in row I. [In the terms of (3.3.4) we have $k = IE$, $q = IV$, and $i = I$.] We denote this selected element by X, and swap it with the element in the (IE, IV) position:

$$X = A(I,IV)$$
$$A(I,IV) = A(IE,IV)$$
$$A(IE,IV) = X$$

Now we replace the elements in column IV from row $IE + 1$ to row M by the l's:

$$RX = -1.0/X$$
$$IEP1 = IE + 1$$
$$DO\ 40\ L = IEP1,M$$
$$A(L,IV) = RX * A(L,IV)$$
$$40\quad CONTINUE$$

We are now set to do the column operations in columns $IV + 1$ to N. These column operations are symbolized in (3.3.3); the length of the columns is $M - IE$, which we will denote MLEN, and they are stored as follows: the column of l's [the first one on the right in (3.3.3)] is stored as a vector of length MLEN, and increment 1, whose first entry is in position $A(IEP1, IV)$, and the second column on the right in (3.3.3) is stored as a vector of length MLEN, and increment 1, whose first entry is in position $A(IEP1, J)$. We carry out the operation in (3.3.3) by using the BLAS procedure SAXPY, which adds a multiple of a vector to another [see (2.5.6) for a description]. The multiplier in (3.3.3) still has to be swapped from row I to row IE, which, following (3.3.4), we do a column at a time. In FORTRAN, this looks like the following:

$$MLEM = M - IE$$
$$IVP1 = IV + 1$$
$$DO\ 50\ J = IVP1,N$$
$$Y = A(I,J)$$
$$A(J,J) = A(IE,J)$$
$$A(IE,J) = Y$$

(We've swapped the row I and row IE entries of column J.)

CALL SAXPY (MLEN,Y,A(IEP1,IV),1,A(IEP1,J),1)

[Remember that the ultimate (IE, J) entry is still in Y so we can use Y to denote the multiplier instead of $A(IE, J)$.]

50 CONTINUE

Finally, we need to replace the column of "1's" (entries $IE + 1$ to M of column IV) with zeros. We do this by multiplying that whole column by 0, using the BLAS scalar multiplication procedure SSCAL [see (2.5.6)]:

60 CALL SSCAL(MLEN,0.0,A(IEP1,IV),1)

We have now translated the operation steps of (3.3.4) into FORTRAN. To complete the program, we need to explain how to transition from each stage of row reduction to the next. We still have our matrix stored the same way, and still use IE and IV as row and column counters indicating where we are in the row reduction. To start, we set them both to zero and then increment the row counter by 1 to advance to the next row:

$$IE = 0$$
$$IV = 0$$
$$20 \quad IE = IE + 1$$

(This step is numbered, since we will return to it each time we complete a stage, ending in step 60.) When we reach row M, if we do, we go directly to output, which will begin with a step numbered 99. Otherwise, we increment the column counter to get to the next column. If there is no next column, that is, if the next one would be $N + 1$, we go to output also:

$$IF\ (IE.EQ.M)\ GO\ TO\ 99$$
$$30 \quad IV = IV + 1$$
$$IF\ (IV.EQ.N + 1)\ GO\ TO\ 99$$

(Step 30 is numbered since we will need to go back to it every time we need to advance to another column.)

Now we search column IV from row IE to row M for a nonzero element. We do this by locating the index of the element of largest absolute value using the BLAS procedure ISAMAX [see (2.5.6)], since the elements we are searching lie in a vector of length $M - IE + 1$ whose first entry is in $A(IE, IV)$ and whose increment is 1. We call this index I, and the corresponding element X, in anticipation of steps of the first part of the program. If $X = 0$, we go back to 30 and try the next column:

```
MLEN = M - IE
I = ISAMAX (MLEN + 1,A(IE,IV),1)
X = A(I,IV)
IF (X.EQ.0.0) GO TO 30
```

If we happen to be in the last column, that is, if $IV = N$, then all we want to do is swap the (I, N) and (IE, N) entries and put in zeros below. So we need to skip from the switching step directly to step 60. That is, right after the command A(IE,IV) = X we insert

```
IF (IV.EQ.N) GO TO 60
```

To complete the program we need to add input and output. These are similar to those of Chapter 2: we need to input both the row and column indexes M and N, and since the reduction procedure overwrites the matrix we need to print the matrix as we input it to see it. Here's a complete program [Fig. (3.3.5)]:

Figure (3.3.5).

```
C   ROW REDUCES M BY N MATRIX A
C      FIRST CARD M,N
C      NEXT CARDS A BY ROWS
 1000 FORMAT('0')
  100 FORMAT('0 MATRIX A OF SIZE ',I2,2X,'BY',I2)
  110 FORMAT('0 ROW REDUCED FORM OF A')
      DIMENSION A(50,50)
      READS(5,*) M,N
      WRITE(6,100) M,N
      WRITE(6,1000)
      DO 10 I=1,M
      READ(5,*) (A(I,J),J=1,N)
      WRITE(6,*) (A(I,J),J=1,N)
   10 CONTINUE
      IE=0
      IV=0
   20 IE=IE+1
      IF(IE.EQ.M) GO TO 99
   30 IV=IV+1
      IF(IV.EQ.(N+1)) GO TO 99
      MLEN=M-IE
```

Figure (3.3.5) (continued).

```
    I=ISAMAX(MLEN+1,A(IE,IV),1)
    I=I+IE-1
    X=A(I,IV)
    IF(X.EQ.0.0) GO TO 30
    IF(IV.EQ.N) GO TO 60
    A(I,IV)=A(IE,IV)
    A(IE,IV)=X
    RX= -1.0/X
    IEP1=IE+1
    DO 40 L=IEP1,M
    A(L,IV)=RX*A(L,IV)
 40 CONTINUE
    IVP1=IV+1
    DO 50 J=IVP1,N
    Y=A(I,J)
    A(I,J)=A(IE,J)
    A(IE,J)=Y
    CALL SAXPY(MLEN,Y,A(IEP1,IV),1,A(IEP1,J),1)
 50 CONTINUE
 60 CALL SSCAL (MLEN,0.0,A(IEP1,IV),1)
    GO TO 20
 99 WRITE(6,110)
    WRITE(6,1000)
    DO 70 I=1,M
    WRITE(6,*) (A(I,J),J=1,N)
 70 CONTINUE
    STOP
    END
```

As a sample application of the program, we will use it to solve the system of Example (3.1.12). This is a system of four equations in six unknowns. We will take the right-hand sides to be 1, 2, 3, 7:

$$3x_4 + 5x_5 + 2x_6 = 1$$

$$x_1 - x_2 + 2x_3 + x_4 + x_5 \qquad = 2$$

$$2x_1 - 2x_2 + 4x_3 + 5x_4 + 7x_5 + 6x_6 = 3$$

$$3x_1 - 3x_2 + 6x_3 + 6x_4 + 8x_5 + 2x_6 = 7$$

To solve, we use the method of row reduction of the augmented matrix (3.1.23). Our input matrix is the 4×6 matrix of coefficients augmented by adding the right-hand sides as a final column. A run of the program yields:

MATRIX A OF SIZE 4 BY 7

0.0	0.0	0.0	3.0	5.0	2.0	1.0
1.0	−1.0	2.0	1.0	1.0	0.0	2.0
2.0	−2.0	4.0	5.0	7.0	6.0	3.0
3.0	−3.0	6.0	6.0	8.0	2.0	7.0

ROW REDUCED FORM OF A

3.0	−3.0	6.0	6.0	8.0	2.0	7.0
0.0	0.0	0.0	3.0	5.0	2.0	1.0
0.0	0.0	0.0	0.0	0.0	4.0	−2.0
0.0	0.0	0.0	0.0	0.0	0.0	0.0

This means our original system is equivalent to the system

$$3x_1 - 3x_2 + 6x_3 + 6x_4 + 8x_5 + 2x_6 = 7$$

$$3x_4 + 5x_5 + 2x_6 = 1$$

$$4x_6 = -2$$

[Note that this is not quite the outcome of Example (3.1.12); the program always switches for largest absolute values.]

From this form we have the free variables x_2, x_3, and x_5. In terms of the free variables we have:

$$x_1 = \tfrac{8}{3} + x_2 - 2x_3 + \tfrac{2}{3}x_5$$

$$x_4 = \tfrac{2}{3} - \tfrac{5}{3}x_5$$

$$x_6 = -\tfrac{1}{2}$$

If we change the right-hand side of the first equation from 7 to 8, then in the row reduction A becomes

3.0	−3.0	6.0	6.0	8.0	2.0	8.0
0.0	0.0	0.0	3.0	5.0	2.0	1.0
0.0	0.0	0.0	0.0	0.0	4.0	−2.7
0.0	0.0	0.0	0.0	0.0	0.0	−0.3

This means that the final equation of our reduced system is

$$0 = -0.3$$

and hence our changed system is inconsistent.

Suppose we add the equation $x_1 - x_2 + 2x_3 + x_4 + x_5 = 1$ to the system. Now we are looking at the system

$$3x_4 + 5x_5 + 2x_6 = 1$$

$$x_1 - x_2 + 2x_3 + x_4 + x_5 = 2$$

$$2x_1 - 2x_2 + 4x_3 + 5x_4 + 7x_5 + 6x_6 = 3$$

$$3x_1 - 3x_2 + 6x_3 + 6x_4 + 8x_5 + 2x_6 = 8$$

$$x_1 - x_2 + 2x_3 + x_4 + x_5 = 1$$

When we run the row reduction of the augmented matrix, we obtain

3.0	−3.0	6.0	6.0	8.0	2.0	8.0
0.0	0.0	0.0	3.0	5.0	2.0	1.0
0.0	0.0	0.0	0.0	0.0	4.0	−2.7
0.0	0.0	0.0	0.0	0.0	0.0	−1.3
0.0	0.0	0.0	0.0	0.0	0.0	0.0

Notice the last row is all zeros. The program does not distinguish between the last column of the matrix and any others. In effect, at the penultimate stage the row reduction enters the last column with the matrix looking like

$$\begin{bmatrix} 3 & -3 & 6 & 6 & 8 & 2 & 8 \\ & & & 3 & 5 & 2 & 1 \\ & & & & & 4 & -2.7 \\ & & & & & & -0.3 \\ & & & & & & -1.3 \end{bmatrix}$$

interchanges the last two rows, and uses the $(4, 7)$ entry, -1.3, to put a zero in the $(5, 7)$ position. This is equivalent to operating on the system of equations

$$0 = -0.3$$

$$0 = -1.3$$

to obtain the equivalent system

$$0 = -1.3$$

$$0 = 0$$

This points out the fact that, when we are checking for consistency by row reducing the augmented matrix, *only one inconsistent equation will happen.* On the other hand, because of our switching rules, it will be the "most inconsistent" in the sense of having the right-hand side of largest absolute value.

EXERCISES 3.3

Problems 1 to 7 should be solved using the program of Figure (3.3.5).

1. Row reduce the matrices of problem 1 of Exercises 3.1.
2. Use the augmented matrix of coefficients (3.1.23) to find the solution (if any) of the systems of equations in problem 3 of Exercises 3.1.
3. Row reduce the system of problem 1 of Exercises 3.2. What is the effect if a dam interrupts the flow from nodes 6 to 8?
4. Row reduce the system of problem 2 of Exercises 3.2. What is the effect if concourse 4 (and its connecting links) are temporarily closed?
5. Solve the constant-allocation equations (3.2.4) for Example (3.2.3).
6. Solve the constant-allocation equations of problem 3 of Exercises 3.2.
7. Solve the equilibrium price equations of problem 4 of Exercises 3.2.
8. (Programming problem) Modify the program of Figure (3.3.5) so that the rank of A and bases for its range and null spaces are also computed and printed.

4

OVERDETERMINED SYSTEMS

4.1 VECTOR GEOMETRY AND OVERDETERMINED SYSTEMS OF EQUATIONS

Not every system of linear equations has a solution: some are just inconsistent. There are situations, however, when we want to try to solve such systems anyway. For example, suppose we are studying an applied problem where we expect one variable we are measuring to be a linear function of another measurable variable, and our goal is to determine the linear function on the basis of the measurements. To be concrete, it is known that within reasonable limits a vertical steel beam under strain lengthens proportionally to the stretching force applied. If the beam's unstressed length is L and the proportionality constant is k, then as the result of applying a stretching force x the beam's length y can be computed as $y = L + kx$. Neither L nor k, we assume, is known in advance. (This is realistic: k needs to be determined by experiment, and L, the unstressed length, would have to be measured without gravity.) So experiments are performed: various stretching forces $x_1, x_2, \ldots, x_m$ are applied and the corresponding lengths

118

$y_1, y_2, \ldots, y_m$ are measured. Since for each experiment we have $y_i = L + kx_i$, we end up with a system of m equations for the two unknown constants L and k:

$$\begin{cases} L + kx_1 = y_1 \\ L + ky_2 = y_2 \\ \vdots \\ L + kx_m = y_m \end{cases}$$

Intuitively, we expect that the larger m is, that is, the more experiments performed, then the better chance we have of computing L and k correctly. But the larger m is, the more likely it becomes that the system is inconsistent. The following numerical data illustrates this point. Suppose in three experiments we have found the results tabulated in (4.1.1):

(4.1.1)

Test Number	Applied Stress (lb)	Measured Length (ft)
1	10	11.15
2	15	11.85
3	20	12.25

Our system of equations is then

$L + 10k = 11.60$ $\qquad\qquad$ $L + 10k = 11.60$

$L + 15k = 11.85$ $\quad$ which row reduces to $\quad$ $5k = 0.25$

$L + 20k = 12.25$ $\qquad\qquad$ $0 = 0.15$

So the system is inconsistent. This we attribute to experimental error. If the third test is discarded, then we can solve the system, of course, and find $L = 11.1$ and $k = 0.05$, or we could discard the second test and find $L = 10.95$ and $k = 0.065$, or discard the first and find $L = 10.65$ and $k = 0.08$. There is no reason, however, to suppose that two of the tests are exactly accurate, and even if we do make that assumption there is no way to know in advance which two to choose. It is much more reasonable to expect that every measurement has some error in it, and that what we should choose to do is to use all three.

As this example shows, there are situations in which a scientific theory leads to a system of linear equations, which needs to be solved, but the numerical coefficients in the system may be inaccurate due to data collection errors, making the system inconsistent. Since the scientific theory predicts a solution, we want to develop a procedure for producing the "best" candidate for a solution. Of course "best" is not a mathematical term, and whatever mathematical definition we choose to assign it will determine our procedure for solving inconsistent systems.

The definition we choose is geometrically based: to solve a (possibly inconsistent) system $Ax = b$, with $m \times n$ matrix of coefficients, we select the n-vector $\bar{x}$ such that $A\bar{x}$ is closest to the vector b, among all the possible choices of n-vectors. To make sense of this definition, and to create a procedure based on it, we need to review some vector geometry.

There are two basic notions in metric plane and solid geometry: distance and direction. The distance between two points is the length of a line segment joining them, and the direction of a line segment joining the points can be specified in terms of the angles that line segment makes with the horizontal and vertical reference directions. So to do metric geometry, it is enough to be able to measure distances and angles.

Consider these measurements in plane analytic geometry: assume we are given two points $P = (a, b)$ and $Q = (c, d)$ with coordinates as indicated. Then the length of the line segment from P to Q is, by the Pythagorean formula, $\sqrt{(c - a)^2 + (d - b)^2}$ [see Fig. (4.1.2a)], and the angle between this line segment and the line segment from P to $R = (e, f)$ is given by the law of cosines, $\cos \theta = \{[(c - a)^2 + (d - b)^2][(e - a)^2 + (f - b)^2]\}^{-1/2}[(c - a)(e - a) + (d - b)(f - b)]$ [see Fig. (4.1.2b)]. These quantities are much easier to describe in vector notation. Let x be the vector

Figure (4.1.2a).

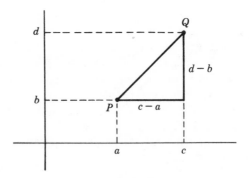

Figure (4.1.2b).

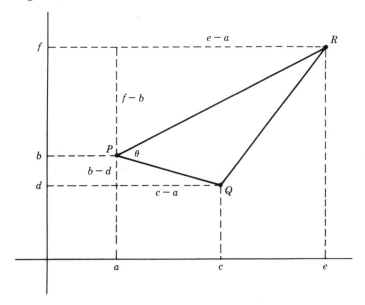

$\begin{bmatrix} a \\ b \end{bmatrix}$, y the vector $\begin{bmatrix} c \\ d \end{bmatrix}$, and z the vector $\begin{bmatrix} e \\ f \end{bmatrix}$. Then the length of the line segment from P to Q is simply $\sqrt{(y - x)^T (y - x)}$, while $\cos \theta$ is given by $\{[(y - x)^T(y - x)][(z - x)^T(z - x)]\}^{1/2}[(y - x)^T(z - x)]$. (Similar computations apply in 3-space.) So all the necessary geometry of direction and angles can be expressed in terms of the vector operation $u^T v$, the dot product. So to introduce metric geometry in higher dimension, we take as definitions formulas based on the above vector formulas for the plane. To simplify, we put the point P at the origin:

(4.1.3) Let x and y be n-vectors:

1. The dot product of x and y is the number $x^T y$.
2. The length of the vector x, denoted $\|x\|$, is $\sqrt{x^T x}$.
3. If $\|x\| \neq 0$ and $\|y\| \neq 0$, then the angle θ between them is given by

$$\cos \theta = \frac{x^T y}{\|x\| \|y\|}$$

A number of the properties of the definitions (4.1.3) are explored in the exercises. In particular, you are asked to show:

(4.1.4)   Let x and y be n-vectors:

1.   (Law of cosines for vectors) $\|x - y\|^2 = \|x\|^2 + \|y\|^2 - 2\|x\|\,\|y\|\cos\theta$.
2.   (Pythagorean theorem for vectors) If $x^Ty = 0$, then $\|x + y\|^2 = \|x\|^2 + \|y\|^2$.

Since $\cos(\pi/2) = 0$, from item 2 of (4.1.3) vectors with $x^Ty = 0$ are said to be perpendicular or orthogonal, and this also applies to vectors of zero length. Unit vectors are length one vectors. We record this and some associated terminology:

(4.1.5)

1. n vectors x and y are *orthogonal* if $x^Ty = 0$.
2. n vectors $x_1, \ldots, x_m$ are an *orthogonal set* if $x_i^Tx_j = 0$ for each pair $i \neq j$.
3.   An n vector x is a *unit vector* if $\|x\| = 1$.
4. n vectors $x_1, \ldots, x_m$ are an *orthonormal set* if $x_i^Tx_j = 0$ for each pair $i \neq j$ and $\|x_i\| = 1$ for each i.

Property 4 says that $x_1, \ldots, x_m$ are a set of mutually perpendicular unit vectors. The condition of orthonormality can be given a more uniform description when we note that $\|x_i\| = 1$ means the same as $x_i^Tx_j = 1$:

(4.1.6) n-vectors $x_1, \ldots, x_m$ are an *orthonormal set* exactly when the $n \times m$ matrix Q with columns $x_1, \ldots, x_m$ satisfies $Q^TQ = I_m$ (the $m \times m$ identity).

To see (4.1.6), we note that the (i, j) entry of Q^TQ is $x_i^Tx_j$, and that the set is orthonormal if and only if $x_i^Tx_j = 0$ for $i \neq j$ and $x_i^Tx_i = 1$.

As will become clear shortly, these concepts of angle and orthogonality will be relevant to our work of finding the closest approximation to a solution of an inconsistent system of linear equations. We recall that our problem specifies an $m \times n$ matrix A and an m-vector b and asks for an n-vector $\bar{x}$ such that $A\bar{x}$ is as close to b as possible. We are now in a position to formulate this problem precisely:

(4.1.7)   Let A be an $m \times n$ matrix and let b be an m-vector. An n-vector $\bar{x}$ is called a *least squares*[†] *approximate solution of* $Ax = b$ if $\|A\bar{x} - b\|$ is less than or equal to $\|Ay - b\|$ for all n-vectors y.

[†] This name will be explained in (4.2.4).

The location of a least-squares solution $\bar{x}$ turns out to be a linear problem, again. It is a little easier to understand why if (4.1.7) is recast in a slightly more general form. In (4.1.7) the vectors $A\bar{x}$ and Ay that enter into the defining property of $\bar{x}$ are in the range space of A. In fact, from (3.1.20), range(A) is the set of all m-vectors of the form Az for some n-vector z. Now range(A) is a subspace of the space of m-vectors, so we might think of the problem, for an arbitrary subspace W, that corresponds to (4.1.7):

(4.1.8) Let W be a subspace of m-vectors and let b be an m-vector. An m-vector p in W is said to be a *best W-approximation to b* if $\|p - b\| \leq \|w - b\|$ for all w in W.

In the terminology of (4.1.8), $\bar{x}$ is a least-squares approximate solution of $Ax - b$ if $A\bar{x}$ is a best range(A)-approximation in b.

We want to consider the problem of finding a best W-approximation to b, given a subspace W and a vector b. Suppose, to get started, that it is possible to find a vector p in W such that $b - p$ is orthogonal to every vector in W. Then it turns out that p is a best W-approximation to b. For if z is any vector in W, then $z - b = (p - z) + (b - p)$ and $p - z$ and $b - p$ are orthogonal since $p - z$ is in W. So by item 2 of (4.1.4), $\|z - b\|^2 = \|p - z\|^2 + \|b - p\|^2$. This shows us that $\|z - b\| \geq \|b - p\| = \|p - b\|$, and if $z \neq p$ then $\|z - b\| > \|p - b\|$. So if there is a vector p in W with $b - p$ orthogonal to W, then p is the unique best W-approximation to b.

In case $W = $ range(A) for some $m \times n$ matrix A, we can guarantee the existence of the vector p using (3.1.22). For in that case we know that there is a basis $x_1, \ldots, x_r, y_1, \ldots, y_{m-r}$ for the space of m-vectors such that x_i is in range(A) for $1 \leq i \leq r$ and $y_j \in $ null(A^T) for $1 \leq j \leq m - r$. So we can write $b = a_1 x_1 + \cdots + c_r x_r + d_1 y_1 + \cdots + d_{m-r} y_{m-r}$ for some scalars $c_1, \ldots, c_r, d_1, \ldots, d_{m-r}$. Let $p = c_1 x_1 + \cdots + c_r x_r$. Then p is in range(A), and $b - p = d_1 y_1 + \cdots + d_{m-r} y_{m-r}$. Since $b - p$ is in null(A^T), $b - p$ is orthogonal to range(A).

Moreover, the case $W = $ range(A) is completely general: if W is any subspace and $x_1, \ldots, x_n$ is any spanning set for W then W is the range of the $m \times n$ matrix with columns $x_1, \ldots, x_n$.

What we have just done not only shows that the vector p in W with $b - p$ orthogonal to W exists, but suggests a procedure to find it, at least in the case of $W = $ range(A): we try to find p in W with $b - p$ in null(A^T), that is, with $A^T(b - p) = 0$. This is just a purely linear problem, as we shall now see.

First we streamline our language:

(4.1.9) Let W be a subspace of m-vectors and b an m-vector. A vector p in W with $b - p$ orthogonal to W is called the *projection* of b into W. (As we have seen, p is uniquely determined by b.)

To compute a projection of b into W, we assume that we are given a set of m-vectors $A_1, \ldots, A_n$ in W such that every vector in W can be written as a linear combination of $A_1, \ldots, A_n$. Then $b - p$ will be orthogonal to W if $A_i^T(b - p) = 0$ for $i = 1, \ldots, n$. Now p is required to be in W, so $p = x_1 A_1 + \cdots + x_n A_n$ for some numbers $x_1, \ldots, x_n$. Thus we are trying to solve the equations $A_i^T(b - \Sigma x_j A_j) = 0$ $(1 \le i \le n)$ for $x_1, \ldots, x_n$. This is a linear problem, if we phrase it properly. That means, of course, to get the correct matrix problem. The matrix needed here is the $m \times n$ matrix A whose ith column is A_i and the needed vector is the n-vector x whose ith entry is x_i. Then $p = Ax$ and the equations $A_i^T(b - p) = 0$ $(1 \le i \le n)$ become the single matrix equation $A^T(b - p) = 0$. Since $p = Ax$, this becomes $A^T(b - Ax) = 0$ or $A^TAx = A^Tb$. This is an important formula that we record for future reference.

(4.1.10) Let W be a subspace of m-vectors and let b be an m-vector. Suppose the m-vectors $A_1, \ldots, A_n$ span W and let $A = [A_1 \cdots A_n]$. Then the projection p of b into W can be written as $p = Ax$ where $A^TAx = A^Tb$.

We are especially interested in the case where W is the range space of an $m \times n$ matrix. In that case the columns of A span W, so the matrix produced in (4.1.10) will be our original matrix. Since the projection of p in W is a best range(A)-approximation to b, we now have a method from (4.1.10) for locating a least-squares approximate solution:

(4.1.11) Normal Equations for Least Squares. Let A be an $m \times n$ matrix and b an m-vector. Then a solution $\bar{x}$ of

$$A^TA\bar{x} = A^Tb \quad \text{(normal equations)}$$

is a least-squares approximate solution to $Ax = b$. Moreover, the normal equations always have at least one solution.

We haven't yet verified the final assertion of (4.1.11): this will be a consequence of our discussion of the orthonormalization process, which will prove that b always has a projection into any subspace. It is important to remember that the normal equations are *always consistent*, even if they have no unique solution. [There is only one projection $p = A\bar{x}$ of b into range(A), but we could have $p = A\bar{x} = A\bar{z}$ where $\bar{x} \neq \bar{z}$.] So row reduction will always lead to a solution of the normal equations. For efficiency, in our automated versions of solving the normal equations we will always try first to use the methods of Chapter 2 on the square matrix A^TA, but if it turns out to be singular we can always use the methods of Chapter 3.

Here are some examples of least-squares solutions:

Example (4.1.12) The system based on Table (4.1.1) has matrix form

$$\begin{bmatrix} 1 & 10 \\ 1 & 15 \\ 1 & 20 \end{bmatrix} \begin{bmatrix} L \\ k \end{bmatrix} = \begin{bmatrix} 11.60 \\ 11.85 \\ 12.25 \end{bmatrix}$$

So the normal equations are

$$\begin{bmatrix} 3 & 45 \\ 45 & 725 \end{bmatrix} \begin{bmatrix} \overline{L} \\ \overline{k} \end{bmatrix} = \begin{bmatrix} 35.7 \\ 538.75 \end{bmatrix}$$

which has the solution

$$\overline{L} = 10.925$$

$$\overline{k} = 0.065$$

Example (4.1.13) Consider the 4×3 system, in matrix form

$$\begin{bmatrix} 1 & 1 & 2 \\ 1 & -1 & 0 \\ 0 & 1 & 1 \\ 1 & -1 & 0 \end{bmatrix} \begin{bmatrix} x_1 \\ x_2 \\ x_3 \end{bmatrix} = \begin{bmatrix} 2 \\ 0 \\ 1 \\ 0 \end{bmatrix}$$

Here the normal equations are

$$\begin{bmatrix} 3 & -1 & 2 \\ -1 & 4 & 3 \\ 2 & 3 & 5 \end{bmatrix} \begin{bmatrix} \overline{x}_1 \\ \overline{x}_2 \\ \overline{x}_3 \end{bmatrix} = \begin{bmatrix} 2 \\ 3 \\ 5 \end{bmatrix}$$

Row reduction of the augmented matrix

$$\begin{bmatrix} 3 & -1 & 2 & 2 \\ -1 & 4 & 3 & 3 \\ 2 & 3 & 5 & 5 \end{bmatrix}$$

yields the matrix

$$\begin{bmatrix} 3 & -1 & 2 & 2 \\ 0 & \frac{11}{3} & \frac{11}{3} & \frac{11}{3} \\ 0 & 0 & 0 & 0 \end{bmatrix}$$

so that the system of normal equations for least squares is

$$\begin{cases} 3\bar{x}_1 - \bar{x}_2 + 2\bar{x}_3 = 2 \\ \phantom{3\bar{x}_1} \bar{x}_2 + \bar{x}_3 = 1 \end{cases}$$

Here the free variable is $\bar{x}_2$, and in terms of $\bar{x}_3$ we have for the dependent variables

$$\bar{x}_1 = 1 - \bar{x}_3$$

$$\bar{x}_2 = 1 - \bar{x}_3$$

This means, in vector form, that every solution $\bar{x}$ of the normal equations can be written as

(4.1.14) $$\bar{x} = \begin{bmatrix} 1 \\ 1 \\ 0 \end{bmatrix} + t \begin{bmatrix} -1 \\ -1 \\ 1 \end{bmatrix}$$

for some scalar t, and conversely every t gives a solution.

Example (4.1.13) shows how the normal equations for least squares can be singular. Here we have infinitely many solutions $\bar{x}$ to the normal equations $A^T A \bar{x} = A^T b$. [The projection $p = A\bar{x}$ of b in range(A) is the same for all choices of $\bar{x}$, since this projection is uniquely determined by b.] In cases like this, it is still possible to make some choices to select a unique $\bar{x}$. We are tempted to say, for example, in (4.1.14) that taking $t = 0$ is the easiest choice. However, the form of (4.1.14) depended on a choice of solution pattern for the normal equations. It is conceivable that different sequences of operations would lead to different forms of the solution. So we need a selection criterion which is independent of the method of obtaining a solution. As it happens, the key to this criterion is the projection device we used to solve for least-squares approximations.

(4.1.15) Let A be an $m \times n$ matrix, b an m-vector, and $\bar{x}$ and $\bar{x}'$ n-vectors such that $A^T A \bar{x} = A^T b$ and $A^T A \bar{x}' = A^T b$. Let q and q' be the projections of $\bar{x}$ and $\bar{x}'$ into range(A^T). Then $q = q'$. Moreover, $\|q\| \le \|\bar{x}\|$, $\|q\| \le \|\bar{x}'\|$, $A\bar{x} = Aq$, and $A^T A q = A^T b$.

If we are to prove (4.1.15), we need to see that $A\bar{x} - Aq = 0$, or that $A(\bar{x} - q) = 0$. Since q is the projection of $\bar{x}$ into range(A^T), we know that $\bar{x} - q$ is orthogonal to range(A^T). This means that if z is any m-vector, we have $(A^T x)^T (\bar{x} - q) = 0$, or $0 = z^T (A(\bar{x} - q))$. Letting z be, in turn, the m-vector whose ith component is one and the rest zero, as i goes from 1 to

m, we see that all m components of $A(\bar{x} - q)$ are zero. This proves that $A\bar{x} = Aq$. Similarly, we have $A\bar{x}' = Aq'$. Since $A\bar{x}$ and $A\bar{x}'$ are both the projections of b into range(A), they are equal, so $Aq = Aq'$. This means that $q - q'$ is in the null space of A. We also know that q and q', and hence $q - q'$, is in the range space of A^T. But from (3.1.22) this means that $(q - q')^T(q - q') = 0$, so that $q - q' = 0$. To complete the proof of (4.1.15) we use $\bar{x} = q + (\bar{x} - q)$ with q and $\bar{x} - q$ orthogonal to show that $\|x\|^2 = \|q\|^2 + \|\bar{x} - q\|^2$ by item 2 of (4.1.4) so that $\|q\| \leq \|\bar{x}\|$, and we use $A^TA\bar{x} = A^Tb$ to pass from $A\bar{x} = Aq$ to $A^TAq = A^Tb$ by left multiplication by A^T.

The vector q produced in (4.1.15) will be our unique choice for a least-squares approximate solution. There are really two equivalent selection criteria contained in (4.1.15), which will now be made explicit:

(4.1.16)   Unique Choice of Least-Squares Approximations.   Let A be an $m \times n$ matrix and let b be an m-vector. Then there is a unique least-squares approximate solution to $Ax = b$ which lies in range(A^T). We can also characterize this solution as the one of shortest length among all the least-squares solutions.

To prove (4.1.16), we appeal to (4.1.15): the projection into range(A^T) of all least-squares solutions $\bar{x}$ yield the same vector q, and q is itself a least-squares solution, so it's the only one inside range(A^T). If $\bar{x}$ is not in range(A^T), $\bar{x} - q$ is not zero, and so $\|\bar{x} - q\|$ is positive. Since $\|\bar{x}\|^2 = \|q\|^2 + \|\bar{x} - q\|^2$, we must have $\|\bar{x}\| > \|q\|$. This means that if $\bar{x}$ is any least-squares solution other than q, its length exceeds that of q, so q is indeed the shortest.

Example (4.1.13) (Continued).   In (4.1.14) we wrote all the least-squares solutions to (4.1.13). Here

$$\|\bar{x}\| = \sqrt{2 - 4t + 3t^2}$$

Since $(2 - 4t + 3t^2) = 3(t - \frac{2}{3})^2 + \frac{14}{9}$, $\bar{x}$ is minimal where $t = \frac{2}{3}$, that is, for

$$(4.1.17) \qquad \bar{x} = \begin{bmatrix} \frac{1}{3} \\ \frac{1}{3} \\ \frac{2}{3} \end{bmatrix}$$

This is using the "shortest-length" criterion of (4.1.16). To use the "range(A^T)" criterion, we need to compute this subspace. The transposed matrix of coefficients is

$$\begin{bmatrix} 1 & 1 & 0 & 1 \\ 1 & -1 & 1 & -1 \\ 2 & 0 & 1 & 0 \end{bmatrix}$$

which row reduces to

$$\begin{bmatrix} 1 & 1 & 0 & 1 \\ 0 & -2 & 1 & -2 \\ 0 & 0 & 0 & 0 \end{bmatrix}$$

This means that columns one and two of the matrix A^T are a basis of range(A^T). So if $\bar{x}$ is to lie in range(A^T), we need to find scalars u, v, and t with

$$(4.1.18) \qquad \begin{bmatrix} 1 \\ 1 \\ 0 \end{bmatrix} + t \begin{bmatrix} -1 \\ -1 \\ 1 \end{bmatrix} = u \begin{bmatrix} 1 \\ 1 \\ 2 \end{bmatrix} + v \begin{bmatrix} 1 \\ -2 \\ 0 \end{bmatrix}$$

[The left-hand side of (4.1.18) expresses the fact that the vector is a least-squares solution and the right-hand side that it lies in the range space of A^T.] We can rewrite (4.1.18) as

$$\begin{bmatrix} 1 & 1 & 1 \\ 1 & -2 & 1 \\ 2 & 0 & -1 \end{bmatrix} \begin{bmatrix} u \\ v \\ t \end{bmatrix} = \begin{bmatrix} 1 \\ 1 \\ 0 \end{bmatrix}$$

to which the solution is

$$\begin{bmatrix} u \\ v \\ t \end{bmatrix} = \begin{bmatrix} \frac{1}{3} \\ 0 \\ \frac{2}{3} \end{bmatrix}$$

so that the unique least-squares approximate solution that lies in range(A^T) is again determined to be

$$\begin{bmatrix} 1 \\ 1 \\ 0 \end{bmatrix} + \frac{2}{3} \begin{bmatrix} -1 \\ -1 \\ 1 \end{bmatrix} = \begin{bmatrix} \frac{1}{3} \\ \frac{1}{3} \\ \frac{2}{3} \end{bmatrix}$$

as in (4.1.17).

We are now adequately prepared to obtain all the least-squares approximate solutions we need: we just form the normal equations and solve them by the methods of Chapters 2 and 3. There is, however, another approach to the least-squares problem, which uses a method of matrix factorization of the coefficient matrix in order to make the normal equations especially easy to solve. We will get to the factorization by performing a geometric process—orthonormalization—on the columns of the coefficient matrix.

We start with a subspace W of m-vectors and search for a computational way of determining the projection p of an m-vector b into W. "Determining p" will mean expressing p as a linear combination of a basis $A_1, \ldots, A_k$ of W. As we will see, this computation will be especially simple if the vectors $A_1, \ldots, A_k$ form an *orthogonal set*; that is, if $A_i^T A_j = 0$ for $i \neq j$ [item 2 of (4.1.5)]. We are looking to write $p = x_1 A_1 + \cdots + x_k A_k$ for some scalars $x_1, \ldots, x_k$ such that $b - p$ is orthogonal to W. This latter means that for each i, $1 \leq i \leq k$, we have $A_i^T(b - p) = 0$. Since $A_i^T p = \Sigma x_j A_i^T A_j = x_i A_i^T A_i$, we have $A_i^T b - x_i A_i^T A_i = 0$, so $x_i = A_i^T b / A_i^T A_i$.

(4.1.19)   The projection p of b into the subspace W with orthogonal basis $A_1, \ldots, A_k$ is given by

$$(1) \qquad p = \sum_{i=1}^{k} \frac{A_i^T b}{A_i^T A_i} A_i$$

If $A_1, \ldots, A_k$ is orthonormal, we have

$$(2) \qquad p = \sum_{i=1}^{k} A_i^T b A_i$$

[The second assertion of (4.1.19) just records the fact that if $A_1, \ldots, A_k$ is orthonormal then $A_i^T A_i = 1$ for $i = 1, \ldots, k$.]

Of course the subspace W may not come equipped with an orthogonal basis. As we will now see, we can use the projection formula [Eq. (1) of (4.1.19)] to *create* an orthogonal basis for W. For suppose we begin with a basis $A_1, \ldots, A_k$ of a subspace W. The vector A_1, by itself, forms an orthogonal set. The scalar multiples of A_1 form a subspace W_1 into which we can consider the projections of vectors. In particular, we can take the projection of A_2 into W_1. By Eq. (1) of (4.1.19), this projection is the vector $p_2 = (A_1^T A_2 / A_1^T A_1) A_1$. By construction, we know that the vector $A_2 - p_2$ is orthogonal to W_1. Moreover, the subspace W_2 formed of the linear combinations of A_1 and $A_2 - p$ has an orthogonal basis, and since p is just a multiple of A_1 this subspace is the same as that spanned by A_1 and A_2. Using the orthogonal basis A_1, $A_2 - p_2$ of W_2 we can compute the projection p_3 of A_3 into this subspace:

$$p_3 = \left(A_1^T A_3 / A_1^T A_1\right) A_1 + \left[(A_2 - p_2)^T A_3 / (A_2 - p_2)^T (A_2 - p_2)\right](A_2 - p_2)$$

Then $A_3 - p_3$ is orthogonal to W_2, so the subspace W_3 spanned by A_2, $A_2 - p_2$, $A_3 - p_3$ has an orthogonal basis, and this subspace is the same as that spanned by A_1, A_2, A_3. We continue this process up to stage k, producing an orthogonal basis for the subspace spanned by $A_1, \ldots, A_k$, namely, W itself. Formally, we have

(4.1.20) Gram–Schmidt Process. Let W be a subspace with a basis $A_1, \ldots, A_k$. For $i = 1$ to k define, inductively:

1. Vectors B_i by

$$B_1 = A_1$$

$$B_{i+1} = A_{i+1} - \left(\frac{B_1^T A_{i+1}}{B_1^T B_1}\right) B_1 - \left(\frac{B_2^T A_{i+1}}{B_2^T B_2}\right) B_2 - \cdots - \left(\frac{B_i^T A_{i+1}}{B_i^T B_i}\right) B_i$$

2. Vectors Q_i by

$$Q_i = \frac{1}{\|B_i\|} B_i \qquad 1 \le i \le k$$

Then $B_1, \ldots, B_k$ is an orthogonal basis of W and $Q_1, \ldots, Q_k$ is an orthogonal basis of W.

To verify (4.1.20), we define subspaces $W_1, \ldots, W_k$ by letting W_i be the space spanned by $A_1, \ldots, A_i$, so that W_1 consists of the multiples of A_1 while W_k equals W. Obviously, W_1 also has B_1 as a basis and B_1 is trivially an orthogonal basis of W_1. Suppose we have shown that $B_1, \ldots, B_i$ is an orthogonal basis of W_i. Since W_{i+1} is spanned by W_i and A_{i+1}, we have that $B_1, \ldots, B_i, A_{i+1}$ is a basis of W_{i+1}. Since B_{i+1} differs from A_{i+1} by an element of W_i, we also have that $B_1, \ldots, B_{i+1}$ is a basis of W_{i+1}. From Eq. (1) of (4.1.19) we have that $B_{i+1} = A_{i+1} - p$ where p is the projection of a_{i-1} into W_i, so that B_{i+1} is orthogonal to W_i. So the vectors $B_1, \ldots, B_{i+1}$ are mutually orthogonal, and we have now shown that $B_1, \ldots, B_{i+1}$ is an orthogonal basis of W_{i+1}. So we climb, a step at a time, to $W_k = W$. Of course once we have the orthogonal basis $B_1, \ldots, B_k$ if we adjust each to be of length one by dividing each B_i by its length, we obtain the orthonormal basis $Q_1, \ldots, Q_k$. This completes the proof of (4.1.20).

The formulas in (4.1.20) have an interesting matrix formulation: first, we rewrite Eq. (1) of (4.1.20) solving for the A's:

$$A_1 = B_1$$

(4.1.21)
$$A_2 = \frac{B_1^T A_2}{B_1^T B_1} B_1 + B_2$$

$$\vdots$$

$$A_k = \frac{B_1^T A_k}{B_1^T B_1} B_1 + \cdots + \frac{B_{k-1}^T A_k}{B_{k-1}^T B_{k-1}} B_{k-1} + B_i$$

and then we solve Eq. (2) of (4.1.20) for the B's:

$$B_i = \|B_i\| Q_i$$

This latter means that $(B_i^T A_j / B_i^T B_i) B_i = Q_i^T A_j Q_i$. We let $r_{ij} = Q_i^T A_j$ for $i < j$ and let $r_{ii} = \|B_i\|$. Then we can rewrite (4.1.21) as

$$(4.1.22) \quad A_i = r_{1i} Q_1 + r_{2i} Q_2 + \cdots + r_{i-1,i} Q_{i-1} + r_{ii} Q_i \qquad \text{for } 1 \le i \le k$$

Equations (4.1.22) admit an easy matrix formulation, named after the matrices which appear in its factorization.

(4.1.23)   Q-R Factorization. Let $A = [A_1 \cdots A_k]$ be a matrix with linearly independent columns. Let $Q_1, \ldots, Q_k$ be the orthonormal basis for range(A) produced by the Gram–Schmidt process and let $Q = [Q_1 \cdots Q_k]$ be the matrix with the Q's as columns. Define numbers r_{ij} for $1 \le i \le j \le k$ by

$$r_{ii} = \|A_i - (Q_1^T A_i) Q_1 - \cdots - (Q_{i-1}^T A_i) Q_{i-1}\|$$

and

$$r_{ij} = Q_i^T A_j \qquad \text{for } i < j$$

and let R be the $k \times k$ matrix

$$R = \begin{bmatrix} r_{11} & r_{12} & \cdots & r_{1k} \\ & r_{12} & \cdots & r_{2k} \\ & & \ddots & \vdots \\ & & & r_{kk} \end{bmatrix}$$

Then

1. R is upper triangular with all positive diagonal elements.
2. Q satisfies $Q^TQ = I_k$ (the $k \times k$ identity).
3. $A = QR$.

All the assertions of (4.1.23) have already been observed, except for item 3, which is just the matrix form of Eqs. (4.1.22). To illustrate (4.1.23), we will do the Q-R factorization of the matrix of Example (4.1.12):

Example (4.1.24). Let

$$A = \begin{bmatrix} 1 & 10 \\ 1 & 15 \\ 1 & 20 \end{bmatrix} \quad \text{so} \quad A_1 = \begin{bmatrix} 1 \\ 1 \\ 1 \end{bmatrix} \quad \text{and} \quad A_2 = \begin{bmatrix} 10 \\ 15 \\ 20 \end{bmatrix}$$

Applying (4.1.20) we have

$$B_1 = A_1 = \begin{bmatrix} 1 \\ 1 \\ 1 \end{bmatrix} \quad B_2 = A_2 - \frac{B_1^T A_2}{B_1^T B_1} B_1 = \begin{bmatrix} 10 \\ 15 \\ 20 \end{bmatrix} - \frac{45}{3} \begin{bmatrix} 1 \\ 1 \\ 1 \end{bmatrix} = \begin{bmatrix} -5 \\ 0 \\ 5 \end{bmatrix}$$

$$\|B_1\| = \sqrt{3} \qquad \|B_2\| = 5\sqrt{2}$$

$$Q_1 = \frac{1}{\sqrt{3}} \begin{bmatrix} 1 \\ 1 \\ 1 \end{bmatrix} \qquad Q_1 = \frac{1}{\sqrt{2}} \begin{bmatrix} -1 \\ 0 \\ 1 \end{bmatrix}$$

$$Q = \frac{1}{\sqrt{6}} \begin{bmatrix} 2 & -\sqrt{3} \\ 2 & 0 \\ 2 & \sqrt{3} \end{bmatrix} \qquad R = \begin{bmatrix} \sqrt{3} & 15\sqrt{3} \\ 0 & 5\sqrt{2} \end{bmatrix}$$

And, indeed, $A = QR$.

There is a point to calculating the Q-R factorization of a matrix associated to a least-squares problem. Suppose we intended to find the least-squares approximate solution to $Ax = b$, and that we have available the factorization $A = QR$ of A satisfying (4.1.23). Then the normal equations simplify as follows:

$$A^T A \bar{x} = A^T b$$

$$(QR)^T (QR) \bar{x} = (QR)^T b$$

$$R^T Q^T Q R \bar{x} = R^T Q^T b$$

$$R \bar{x} = Q^T b$$

[To obtain the last step we multiplied on both sides by $(R^T)^{-1}$ and then replaced $Q^T Q$ by I.] So we have:

(4.1.25) Normal Equations for Least Squares with Q-R Factorization. If the matrix A factors as $A = QR$ as in (4.1.23), then the normal equations for the least-squares approximate solutions to $Ax = b$ become

$$R\bar{x} = Q^T B$$

The advantage of (4.1.25), of course, is that the matrix R on the left-hand side is upper triangular, so the system can be solved by back substitution. We apply this in the case of (4.1.24).

Example (4.1.24) (Continued). Let

$$\bar{x} = \begin{bmatrix} \bar{L} \\ \bar{k} \end{bmatrix} \quad \text{and} \quad b = \begin{bmatrix} 11.66 \\ 11.85 \\ 12.25 \end{bmatrix}$$

as in (4.1.12). Then using the Q-R decomposition of

$$A = \begin{bmatrix} 1 & 10 \\ 1 & 15 \\ 1 & 20 \end{bmatrix}$$

obtained in (4.1.24) the normal equations for $\bar{x}$ in the form (4.1.25) become

$$\begin{bmatrix} \sqrt{3} & 15\sqrt{3} \\ 0 & 5\sqrt{2} \cdot \end{bmatrix} \begin{bmatrix} \bar{L} \\ \bar{k} \end{bmatrix} = \frac{1}{\sqrt{6}} \begin{bmatrix} (35.7) & \sqrt{2} \\ (0.65) & \sqrt{3} \end{bmatrix}$$

from which we obtain

$$\bar{L} = 10.925$$

$$\bar{k} = 0.065$$

as we did in (4.1.12).

In an example like (4.1.24), forming the Q-R decomposition of the matrix of coefficients seems to involve more computation than simply solving the normal equations by Gaussian elimination. In general, however, the two computations are of about the same complexity: forming the Q-R factorization of A and using the normal equations in the form (4.1.25) and then backsolving is about the same as obtaining the normal equations in the form (4.1.11), forming the L-U decomposition of $A^T A$ and then backsolving. This equivalence of complexity is not so apparent in hand computation, as will be borne out by experimenting with nearly any 4×4 or larger square matrix A. Here Gaussian elimination is usually much easier to do, in part because the L-U decomposition is not actually formed, but instead some manipulations are performed, transforming the system to the triangular system for backsolving. The Gram–Schmidt process, as we have so far seen it, has none of this transformational character. There is, however, an alternative approach to the Q-R decomposition which does have this property, and which we will now examine. This approach has more than intellectual interest: it turns out to be more numerically reliable than the Gram–Schmidt process, and is also much easier to program. The basic idea behind this transformational approach to the Q-R decomposition is the following elementary fact about vectors in 2-space.

(4.1.26)   Let $v = \begin{bmatrix} a \\ b \end{bmatrix}$ be a 2-vector not equal to zero. Then there is a unique number θ, $-\pi \le t \le \pi$, such that $a = (\cos t)\|v\|$ and $b = (\sin t)\|v\|$. (This just expresses the fact that $a^2 + b^2 = \|v\|^2$.) Then we have

$$\begin{bmatrix} \cos t & \sin t \\ -\sin t & \cos t \end{bmatrix}\begin{bmatrix} a \\ b \end{bmatrix} = \begin{bmatrix} \|v\| \\ 0 \end{bmatrix}$$

This formula also makes sense for $v = 0$, where by convention we take $\theta = 0$.

   The formula of (4.1.26) can be applied to 2-vectors occurring in parts of m-vectors:

(4.1.27)   Let a be an m-vector with entries $a_1, \ldots, a_m$, and let θ be chosen as in (4.1.26) relative to the 2-vector v with entries a_i, a_{i+r}. Let $T = T_{i, i+r, \theta}$ denote the $m \times m$ matrix

$$T = \begin{bmatrix} 1 & & & & & & & & \\ & \ddots & & & & & & & \\ & & 1 & & & & & & \\ & & & \cos\theta & & & \sin\theta & & & i \\ & & & & 1 & & & & \\ & & & & & \ddots & & & \\ & & & & & & 1 & & \\ & & & -\sin\theta & & & \cos\theta & & & i+r \\ & & & & & & & 1 & \\ & & & & & & & & \ddots \\ & & & & & & & & & 1 \end{bmatrix}$$

Then

$$
Tx = \begin{bmatrix} a_1 \\ \vdots \\ \|v\| \\ \vdots \\ 0 \\ \vdots \\ a_n \end{bmatrix} \begin{matrix} \\ \\ i \\ \\ i+r \\ \\ \\ \end{matrix}
$$

[The entries in Tx are $\|v\|$ in position i, 0 in position $i + r$ and a_k in position k for $k \neq i$, $i + r$. The entries in T are $\cos\theta$ in position (i, i) and $(i + r, i + r)$, $\sin\theta$ in position $(i, i + r)$, $-\sin\theta$ in position $(i + r, i)$, 0 elsewhere off the diagonal, and 1 elsewhere on the diagonal.]

The matrices $T = T_{i,j,\theta}$ with $i < j$ of (4.1.27) have orthonormal columns, so $T^T T = I_m$. We will use them, suitably chosen, to form the "Q" in a Q-R decomposition. For convenience we assume we begin with an $m \times k$ matrix with properties which are typical of least-squares problems:

(4.1.28) Q-R Factorization by Matrix Multiplication.   Let A be an $m \times k$ matrix such that $m \geq k$ and such that A has rank(k).

Stage 1.   There is a nonzero entry in column 1, say in position i. For suitable choice of θ we have $T_{1,i,\theta}A$ with a nonzero positive entry in position 1 of column 1. (This step is not necessary if $i = 1$.) Now for each position i from 2 to m we multiply the matrix successively by matrices of the form T_{1,i,θ_i} to put zeros in positions 2 through m, and still leaving a positive entry in position 1.

From Stage j to Stage $j + 1$.   Assume that columns 1 through j of our transformed matrix have positive diagonal entries and zeros below the diagonal. Since each transformation was multiplication by an invertible matrix, the rank of the matrix at this stage is still k. This means there must be a nonzero entry in column $j + 1$ on or below the diagonal. So by multiplication by a suitable matrix of the form $T_{j+1,i,\theta}$ with $j + 1 < i$ we get a positive entry on the diagonal in column $j + 1$. Then for positions i from $j + i$ to m we again multiply successively by matrices of the form T_{j+1,i,θ_i} to put zeros in positions $j + 1$ through m. By (4.1.27), none of these products affect columns 1 through j. So now we have columns 1 through $j + 1$ with positive diagonals and zeros below the diagonals.

When we complete stage k, the matrix has the following form:

$$B = \begin{matrix} k \\ m-k \end{matrix} \begin{Bmatrix} \begin{bmatrix} R \\ 0 \end{bmatrix} \\ \end{Bmatrix} \qquad R = \begin{bmatrix} x_{11} & & * \\ & \ddots & \\ & & r_{kk} \end{bmatrix} \qquad x_{ii} > 0 \quad (R \text{ is } k \times k)$$

$$0 = \begin{bmatrix} 0 & \cdots & 0 \\ \vdots & & \vdots \\ 0 & \cdots & 0 \end{bmatrix} \quad [0 \text{ is } (m-k) \times k]$$

If we let S denote the product of all the $m \times m$ matrices T used in the various stages, we have $S^T S = I_m$, since the same property holds for all factors T making up S. We then have $SA = B$, or, multiplying by S^T, that $A = S^T B$. Since $S^T = S^{-1}$, we have that $SS^T = I_m$, or that $(S^T)^T S^T = I_m$, so that the columns of S^T are an orthonormal set. We put the first k of these columns into an $m \times k$ matrix Q and the last $m - k$ into an $m \times (m - k)$ matrix P. Then the equation $A = S^T B$ becomes

$$[Q \quad P]\begin{bmatrix} R \\ 0 \end{bmatrix} = A$$

so that $QR = A$, where:

1. R is upper triangular with all positive diagonal elements.
2. Q satisfies $Q^T Q = I_k$.

This is, of course, as the notation implies, the Q-R factorization of the matrix A.

Although we will not carry out any hand Q-R factorizations using (4.1.28), it is the method which underlies the LINPACK implementation of the factorization, so we will be using it in principle.

As we will see in the examples of the next section, it is often the case that forming the normal equations for a least-squares problem is a lengthy computation. Fortunately, it can be done automatically. For later use, we record the principles of this computation here.

(4.1.29) Forming the Normal Equations for Least Squares. Let $A = [A_1 \cdots A_n]$ be an $n \times n$ matrix with columns $A_1, \ldots, A_n$ and

$$b = \begin{bmatrix} b_1 \\ \vdots \\ b_m \end{bmatrix}$$

be an m-vector. Then the normal equations for least-squares $A^TAx = A^Tb$ are formed as follows:

1. The (i, j) entry of A^TA is $(A_i)^TA_j$.
2. The ith entry of A^Tb is $(A_i)^Tb$.

Both assertions follow from the fact that the rows of A^T are given by

$$A^T = \begin{bmatrix} A_1^T \\ \vdots \\ A_n^T \end{bmatrix}$$

Note also that number 1 of (4.1.29) implies that A^TA is a *symmetric* matrix, that is, its (i, j) and (j, i) entry are equal for all pairs (i, j).

EXERCISES 4.1

1. Prove the following properties of the dot product:
   (a) $x^Ty = y^Tx$ (symmetry).
   (b) $(x + y)^Tz = x^Tz + y^Tz$ and (bilinearity) $(ax)^Ty = x^T(ay) = ax^Ty$ for scalar a.
   (c) $x^Tx \geq 0$ for all x and if $x \neq 0$, $x^Tx > 0$ (positive definiteness).
2. Prove the following properties of the length of a vector:
   (a) $\|ax\| = |a|\,\|x\|$ for scalar a.
   (b) $\|x + y\| \leq \|x\| + \|y\|$.
   (c) $|\,\|x\| - \|y\|\,| \leq \|x - y\|$.
   (d) Law of cosines (item 1 of 4.1.4).
   (e) Pythagorean theorem (item 2 of 4.1.4).
   (f) $\|x\| = 0$ if and only if $x = 0$.
   (g) If $x \neq 0$, $\|\,\|x\|^{-1}x\| = 1$.
3. (Orthogonal matrices) An $n \times n$ matrix Q is called *orthogonal* if the columns of Q are an orthonormal set. By (4.1.6), this means $Q^TQ = I_n$. Prove:
   (a) If Q is orthogonal, transposes of the rows of Q is an orthonormal set.
   (b) Q is orthogonal if and only if it is invertible with $Q^T = Q^{-1}$.
   (c) If Q, Q' are orthogonal so is QQ'.
   (d) If Q is orthogonal so is Q^{-1}.

(e)   Any $n \times n$ matrix can be regarded as an element of the space of real n^2-tuples. Prove that the set of orthogonal matrices is a closed and bounded subset.

4.   Let A be an $m \times n$ matrix of rank(r). Show that:

   (a)   Null(A) = null($A^T A$).

   (b)   Rank($A^T A$) = r.

5.   For the following matrices A, form the normal equations for least squares, determine all the solutions, and find the unique one of shortest length:

   (a) $\begin{bmatrix} 1 & 1 \\ 1 & 2 \\ 1 & 3 \end{bmatrix} \begin{bmatrix} x_1 \\ x_2 \end{bmatrix} = \begin{bmatrix} 4 \\ 7 \\ 11 \end{bmatrix}$

   (b) $\begin{bmatrix} 1 & 0 & 7 \\ 2 & 4 & -2 \\ 1 & -2 & 15 \end{bmatrix} \begin{bmatrix} x_1 \\ x_2 \\ x_3 \end{bmatrix} = \begin{bmatrix} 1 \\ 2 \\ 4 \end{bmatrix}$

   (c) $\begin{bmatrix} 1 & 0 & 1 \\ 2 & -1 & 2 \\ 3 & -1 & 3 \\ 5 & -2 & 5 \end{bmatrix} \begin{bmatrix} x_1 \\ x_2 \\ x_3 \end{bmatrix} = \begin{bmatrix} 6 \\ 2 \\ 2 \\ 7 \end{bmatrix}$

6.   Find the Q-R factorization of the matrix in (a) of problem 4 and solve the system of that exercise using that factorization.

4.2   FITTING EQUATIONS TO DATA BY LEAST SQUARES

In many scientific problems which can be modeled by functions with a single input and output, the form the function is supposed to take may be supplied in advance by scientific theory, while specific parameters associated to the particular problem being studied can only be estimated by experiment. Since slight errors are likely to occur in the experiments, they will be repeated several times. The resulting data will be slightly inconsistent, due to the variation in the experimental results. It is possible to use least-squares approximations to solve the inconsistent problem to obtain an estimate for the unknown parameters. Here's how:

   The problem is to estimate a function $f(t)$. Some theory says that the function f can be represented as

$$(4.2.1) \qquad f(t) = a_1 f_1(t) + \cdots + a_m f_m(t)$$

where $f_1, \ldots, f_m$ are some specified functions. For example, we might have $f_i(t) = t^{i-1}$ or $f_i(t) = \sin(b_i t)$, or any other collection of functions that the relevant theory suggests. As a result of a number of experiments a sequence of data points (t_i, s_i), $1 \le i \le n$, are collected. Ideally, we are supposed to have $f(t_i) = s_i$, $1 \le i \le n$, so that

(4.2.2) $s_i = f(t_i) = a_1 f_1(t_i) + \cdots + a_m f_m(t_i)$, $1 \le i \le n$, or

$$\begin{bmatrix} f_1(t_1) & \cdots & f_m(t_1) \\ \vdots & & \vdots \\ f_1(t_n) & \cdots & f_m(t_n) \end{bmatrix} \begin{bmatrix} a_1 \\ \vdots \\ a_m \end{bmatrix} = \begin{bmatrix} s_1 \\ \vdots \\ s_n \end{bmatrix}$$

Since the data points may involve experimental errors, the system of equations (4.2.2) may be inconsistent. By using the methods of Section 4.1, a least-squares approximate solution $\bar{a}$ is obtained. If the entries of this solution are $\bar{a}_1, \ldots, \bar{a}_m$, then the *estimated* choice for f is

(4.2.3) $\bar{f}(t) = \bar{a}_1 f_1(t) + \cdots + \bar{a}_m f_m(t)$

It is important to understand exactly in what sense $\bar{f}$ is the chosen estimate. For this, we need to return to the definition of least-squares approximate solution, as given in (4.1.7): the term $\|A\bar{x} - b\|$ of that definition translates here to

(4.2.4) $\sqrt{\displaystyle\sum_{i=1}^{n} \left[\bar{a}_1 f_1(t_i) + \cdots + \bar{a}_m f_m(t_i) - s_i \right]^2}$

The fact that $\bar{a}$ is a least-squares approximate solution means that the number (4.2.4) has been minimized among all possible choices for the multipliers a_i of the functions f_i. The term

(4.2.5) $\left[\bar{a}_1 f_1(t_i) + \cdots + \bar{a}_m f_m(t_i) - s_i \right]^2$

represents the square of the vertical distance from the point $(t_i, \bar{f}(t_i))$ on the graph of (4.2.3) to the point (t_i, s_i) which was ideally supposed to be on the graph. Since we have minimized the sum of all the squares (4.2.4), we call $\bar{a}$ a least-squares solution. The justification of the method of least squares for linear problems as presented in Section 4.1 was based on geometry: if we can't have $Ax = b$, we choose $\bar{x}$ so that $A\bar{x}$ comes as close to b as possible, using the geometric sense of "close" given by vector length. But now we are applying this method in a different context. The method does give an estimate of parameters, but it is up to us to decide how realistic the estimate is. Here is an example to illustrate both the method and its limitations.

Example (4.2.6). A manufacturer has discovered from experience that the cost of producing a unit of a new product declines at a constant rate with respect to the total number of units of the new product made. This means that the total cost $f(t)$ of producing t units of the new product is given by

$$f(t) = a_0 + a_1 t + a_2 t^2$$

where $a_0 = $ the startup cost prior to producing any of the new product; $a_1 + 2a_2 t = $ the marginal cost of producing one additional unit after t have been manufactured; and $2a_2 = $ the rate of decline of the unit cost.

These constants are such that $a_1 < 0$ (so cost declines), $a_1 > 0$ (marginal cost positive), and $a_0 > 0$ (positive startup cost). Factoring out $|a_2|$ and completing the square we have

$$ f(t) = |a_2|^{-1}\left\{\left[4a_0|a_2| + (a_1)^2\right]\left(4|a_2|^2\right)^{-1} - \left[t - a_1(2|a_2|)^{-1}\right]\right\}^2 $$

which means that the total production cost will peak when

$$ t = a_1 2|a_2|^{-1} $$

Based on an analysis of early production data, it is desired to predict this peak, that is, to determine the parameters a_1 and a_2.

To keep scales within reasonable bounds, we assume that we measure production in dozen-gross units ($= 1728$) and costs in thousands of dollars. The early production figures are then given by Table (4.2.7):

(4.2.7)

	Number of Units Produced/1728	Total Cost/$1000
1.	0	25
2.	2	70
3.	5	130
4.	6	150
5.	8	187

Each of the five lines of Table (4.2.7) gives us a data point (t_i, s_i), $1 \le i \le 5$:

Data Points

1. $(0, 25)$
2. $(2, 70)$
3. $(5, 130)$
4. $(6, 150)$
5. $(8, 187)$

and our goal is to find a parabolic function $f(t) = a_0 + a_1 t + a_2 t^2$ which passes nearest to them, in the sense of minimizing the squares of vertical distances between the points and the graph of the parabola [see Fig. (4.2.8)].

Figure (4.2.8).

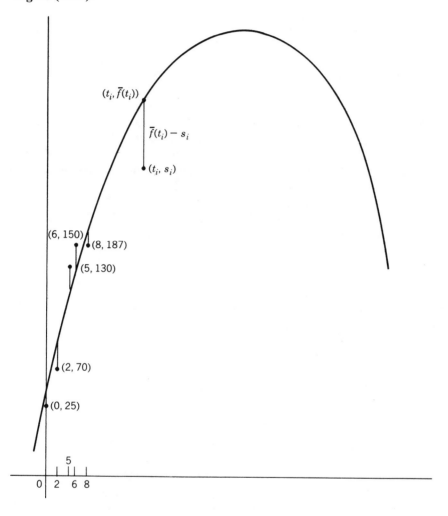

We do this by the methods of this section. Our reference functions are $f_0(t) = 1$, $f_1(t) = t$, and $f_2(t) = t^2$, so $f(t) = a_0 f_0(t) + a_1 f_1(t) + a_2 f_2(t)$. Then (4.2.2) becomes

$$\begin{bmatrix} 1 & 0 & 0 \\ 1 & 2 & 4 \\ 1 & 5 & 25 \\ 1 & 6 & 36 \\ 1 & 8 & 64 \end{bmatrix} \begin{bmatrix} a_0 \\ a_1 \\ a_2 \end{bmatrix} = \begin{bmatrix} 25 \\ 70 \\ 130 \\ 150 \\ 187 \end{bmatrix}$$

to which we will apply least squares to obtain a solution. (The actual application of least squares will be done after the computer methods are introduced in Section 4.3.)

It is worthwhile to reflect, now, on the appropriateness of the measure of fit used here. Referring to Figure (4.2.8) again, the clustering of the data in the interval from 0 to 8, and then the use of the vertical separation as a measure of fit, may seem a little risky. The usefulness of the prediction depends on two strong assumptions: (1) that the model is accurate, namely, that rate of decline of unit production cost is constant; and (2) that the pointwise least-squares fit is a reasonable measure of which choice of parameters cause the model to most accurately reflect the data. The method of least squares doesn't provide any insight into the validity of the two assumptions in the example, or elsewhere. This is important to remember: least squares will always give an answer. How good an answer it is, and how useful, depends on how carefully the situation was modeled to begin with.

It is possible to use least squares to fit equations to data when the equations are not necessarily graphs of functions, as we now see:

Example (4.2.9) A newly discovered asteroid in orbit around the sun has had its position determined, in the plane of its orbit, and in reference to a suitable coordinate system, at 10 observations:

Observation Number i	X_i	Y_i
1	-1.02494	-0.389269
2	-0.949898	-0.322894
3	-0.866114	-0.265256
4	-0.773392	-0.216557
5	-0.671372	-0.177152
6	-0.559524	-0.1475821
7	-0.437067	-0.128618
8	-0.302909	-0.121353
9	-0.155493	-0.127348
10	-0.007464	-0.148885

Theory tells us that the asteroid is in an elliptical orbit with the sun at one focus [see Fig. (4.2.10)]. The equation of such an ellipse can be written

$$(4.2.11) \qquad X^2 = AY^2 + BXY + CX + DY + E$$

If the data point (X_i, Y_i) is put into (4.2.11) for $1 \leq i \leq 10$ we have the 10 linear equations for A, B, C, D, E given by

$$Y_i^2 A + X_i Y_i B + C Y_i + D Y_i + E = X_i^2 \qquad 1 \leq i \leq 10$$

Figure (4.2.10).

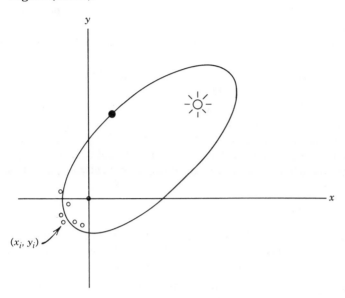

which, in matrix form, becomes

$$(4.2.12) \quad \begin{bmatrix} Y_1^2 & X_1Y_1 & X_1 & Y_1 & 1 \\ & & \vdots & & \\ Y_{10}^2 & X_{10}Y_{10} & X_{10} & Y_{10} & 1 \end{bmatrix} \begin{bmatrix} A \\ B \\ C \\ D \\ E \end{bmatrix} = \begin{bmatrix} X_1^2 \\ \vdots \\ X_{10}^2 \end{bmatrix}$$

This system of 10 equations in five unknowns can be solved for a least-squares approximate solution $\bar{A}, \bar{B}, \bar{C}, \bar{D}, \bar{E}$ giving an approximation to the orbit equation (4.2.11).

It is, of course, conceivable that the object whose orbit is to be determined in (4.2.9) is not an asteroid at all, but some object (a space probe from some other planetary system?) on a parabolic orbit with the sun as focus. The tight spacing of the data points in (4.2.9) certainly allows for this possibility. Our method of solving (4.2.9) via Eq. (4.2.11) rules out some potential parabolas by making the coefficient of X^2 nonzero. We can try for other parabolic fits by setting the X^2 coefficient to 0, and assuming that the Y^2 coefficient is nonzero, replacing (4.2.11) by $Y^2 = aXY + bX + cY + d$, which will represent a parabola. The judgment of whether a parabolic fit or an elliptic fit is better is entirely a question of the nature of the orbit, and is not something that the least-squares method addresses. Once again, least squares can help find the parameters of a good model. It is not a method to create the model from the data.

The systems of linear equations in (4.2.6) and (4.2.9) are 5×3 and 10×5, respectively. This means the resulting systems of normal equations will be 3×3 and 5×5. These are not especially large systems, although they are large enough to warrant solution by the computer methods of Section 2.4 (if these normal equations are nonsingular) or by Section 3.3 (if the normal equations are singular). *Forming* the normal equations, however, is going to be a tedious process: there are nine (respectively 25) inner products to compute just to form the matrix of coefficients of the normal equations. We will discuss how to do this automatically in the next section.

EXERCISES 4.2

1. Assume $f(t) = a + bt$ is linear, and that n data points (t_i, s_i), $i = 1, \ldots, n$, have been collected for f. Solve the least-squares equations (4.2.2) explicitly for the least-squares line $f(t) = \bar{a} + \bar{b}t$.

2. Timber growth is cubic in time (volume increases in all three axes) with quadratic decay (bark surface degradation), so the growth function has the form $f(t) = a_1 + a_2 t^2 + a_3 t^3$. Form the least-squares equations (4.2.2) based on the data points given in the following table:

Year t	Timber Volume s (in 10^3 ft^3)
1	0.5
5	0.1
7	5.9
8	10.3
10	22.1

3. Find Eqs. (4.2.2) for a degree-four least-squares polynomial equation $f(x) = a_0 + a_1 x + a_2 x^2 + a_3 x^3 + a_4 x^4$ to the following functions $F(x)$ by considering the eight points $(\pm 0.8, F(\pm 0.81))$, $(\pm 0.6, F(\pm 0.61))$, $(\pm 0.4, F(\pm 0.4))$, $(\pm 0.2, F(\pm 0.2))$ for $F(x) =$
    (a) e^x.
    (b) $\sin(x)$.
    (c) $\cos(x)$.
    [Determine the values of $F(x)$ in the data, using a calculator or tables, to eight-digit accuracy].

4. The following five points all lie on the unit circle (to four-digit accuracy). Set up the least-squares equations to fit these points to:
   (a) A parabola $y = (x - a)^2 + b$.
   (b) An ellipse $(x/a)^2 + (y/b)^2 = 1$.
   (c) A hyperbola $(y/a)^2 - (x/b)^2 = 1$
        $(-0.7, -0.7141)$, $(-0.5, -0.8660)$, $(0, -1)$, $(0.3, -0.9539)$, $(0.6, -0.8)$.

5. A Fourier series is an infinite sum of the form

$$f(t) = a_1\cos(t) + b_1\sin(t) + a_2\cos(2t) + b_2\sin(2t) + \cdots$$

$$+ a_n\cos(nt) + b_n\sin(nt) + \cdots.$$

Every periodic function $f(t)$ with period 2π [i.e., with $f(t) = f(t + 2\pi)$] can be expressed as such a series. The sum of the first $2n$ terms, which is called a level n trigonometric polynomial, can be taken as an approximation to $f(t)$.

Waves (of sound or electromagnetic radiation) in appropriate units are specified by periodic functions (of period 2π) giving their amplitudes at time t. Set up the least-squares equation to find the level-3 trigonometric polynomial best approximating the wave with amplitude function $f(t)$ of period 2π having the values:

t	$f(t)$
0.1	0.0993
0.2	0.1947
0.3	0.2823
0.5	0.4207
1.1	0.4042
1.3	0.2578
1.6	-0.0292
2.1	-0.4358
2.9	-0.2323
3.2	0.0583

4.3 LEAST-SQUARES APPROXIMATE SOLUTIONS USING LINPACK

A least-squares approximate solution to the system

$$(4.3.1) \hspace{3cm} Ax = b$$

is a solution $\bar{x}$ to the system of normal equations for least squares

$$(4.3.2) \qquad A^T A \bar{x} = A^T b$$

In a sense, the program developed in Section 2.4 is already perfectly adequate for the solution of (4.3.2): if A is $m \times n$, then $A^T A$ is $n \times n$ and we can run the program of Figure (2.4.4a) with matrix $A^T A$ and vector $A^T b$. (If the matrix turns out to be singular, we may be forced to use the methods and programs of 3.3 instead.)

However, it is often the case that the passage from (4.3.1) to (4.2.3) involves a considerable amount of computation: in practice, the number of rows, m, of A often greatly exceeds the number of columns, n, so that the computations involved in forming $A^T A$ and $A^T b$ are possibly lengthier than those involved in solving (4.3.2). For example, if (4.3.1) comes from a problem of fitting equations to data by least squares, as in Section 4.2, then m corresponds to the number of data points while n corresponds to the number of parameters to be estimated. Since more data means more accuracy, it would not be unusual for m to exceed n by a couple of orders of magnitude. Therefore, this section will introduce a program that accepts the data A and b from (4.3.1) as input and returns the vector $\bar{x}$ as output. In outline, the program is to:

1. Input A and b.
2. Form $A^T A$ and $A^T b$.
3. Solve $A^T A \bar{x} = A^T b$.
4. Output $\bar{x}$.

Step 1 can be carried out exactly as in the program of Figure (2.4.4a); it is in step 2 that some new ideas are needed. In (4.1.2a) it was noted that if

$$A = [A_1 \cdots A_n] \quad \text{and} \quad b = \begin{bmatrix} b_1 \\ \vdots \\ b_m \end{bmatrix}$$

then $A^T A$ has (i, j) entry $(A_i)^T A_j$ and $A^T b$ has ith entry $(A_i)^T b$. So accomplishing step 2 requires forming a number of dot products, of vectors and of columns of matrices. As has been noted several times, it is easy in FORTRAN to regard columns of matrices as vectors. So the problem of forming $(A_i)^T A_j$, for example, is just the problem of forming the dot product of two FORTRAN vectors.

Within the BLAS library of basis linear algebra subroutines, there is a function which computes dot products:

(4.3.3) Let v and w be N-vectors stored in the FORTRAN arrays X and Y, with first entries in positions X(initial) and Y(initial) and with increments IX and IY, respectively. Then:

The BLAS function SDOT (N,X(initial),IX,Y(initial),IY) gives the number $v^T w$.

For example, if the $M \times N$ matrix A is stored in an array of the same name, and we want to compute the dot product of the Ith and Jth columns, we can obtain this dot product as the value of the function SDOT(M,A(1,I),1,A(1,J),1): the Ith column of A is a vector of length M (the number of rows), and increment 1, whose initial entry is in position $A(1, I)$, and similarly for the Jth column.

Carrying out step 2 requires, in principle, determining n^2 inner products to form $A^T A$. Actually, since $(A_i^T)A_j = (A_j)^T A_i$, only $n + \frac{1}{2}(n^2 - n)$ distinct ones are required. It is possible to form these, say for $i \leq j$, and then for $j < i$ copy the (j, i) into the (i, j) position. There is, however, a feature in LINPACK which makes it possible to avoid the copying: LINPACK has versions of the factor and solve procedures which work with symmetric matrices. To use these procedures, we do not need to supply the full matrix of coefficients, but only the entries on or above the diagonal [the (i, j) entries with $i \leq j$]. So in forming $A^T A$ in step 2 we will only compute the dot products $A_i^T A_j$ with $i \leq j$.

We assume that A is stored in an array $A(50, 50)$ and b is stored in an array $B(50)$, and that A is M by N. As we form $A^T A$ and $A^T b$ we store them in arrays $C(50, 50)$ and $D(50)$. We are only going to form $A_i^T A_j$ with $i \leq j$. This will be done, using the BLAS function SDOT of (4.3.3), by the following program segments:

```
        DO 40 I = 1,N
        DO 50 J = I,N
        C(I,J) = SDOT(M,A(1,I),1,A(1,J),1)
   50   CONTINUE
   40   CONTINUE
        DO 60 I = 1,N
        D(I) = SDOT(M,A(1,I),1,B,1)
   60   CONTINUE
```

To accomplish step 3, we use the two LINPACK procedures SSICO and SSISL. The first, SSICO, is analogous to SGECO, except it works with symmetric indefinite (SI) matrices, and the second is analogous to SGESL. Both require the same parameter lists as the corresponding "GE" procedures (see Section 2.4), the only difference being that only the upper triangles of the matrices C are used. So step 3 is done exactly as in the program of Figure (2.4.4a): first, SSICO is called to produce the L-U decomposition of A^TA, and to supply the condition number as a check for singularity. If this condition number is nonzero, then the procedure SSISL is called to solve the normal equations. These procedures, like their GE analogs, include in their parameter lists a work array Z, an integer array IPVT to record row interchanges, and the leading dimension LDC of the array C. The program segment using these procedures then looks as follows (using the contents of C and D, and the value of N, obtained in step 2):

```
CALL SSICO(C,LDC,N,IVPT,RCOND,Z)
(print the condition number)
T = 1.0 + RCOND
IF (T.EQ.1.0) GO TO   (print that equations are singular)
CALL SSISL(C,LDC,N,IPVT,D)
```

Step 4 is then done as previously. A complete program, with input and output, now looks like the following [Fig. (4.3.4)] (We are still echo-printing A and b on input; this is not strictly necessary here since A and b are not lost in the calls to SSICO and SSISL but was kept to make this program conform to our earlier ones):

Figure (4.3.4).

```
C     SOLVES AX=B BY LEAST SQUARES
C     A M BY N MATRIX B AN N VECTOR
C        FIRST CARD M,N
C        NEXT CARDS A BY ROWS
C        NEXT CARDS B BY ENTRIES
 9999    FORMAT('0 THE NORMAL EQUATIONS ARE SINGULAR')
 1000    FORMAT('0')
  110    FORMAT('1 LEAST SQUARES SOLUTION OF AX=B')
  120    FORMAT('0 MATRIX A OF SIZE ',I2,2X,'BY ',I2)
  130    FORMAT('0 RCOND= ',E10.3)
  140    FORMAT('0 THE VECTOR B OF CONSTANTS')
```

Figure (4.3.4) (continued).

```
150     FORMAT('0 THE SOLUTION VECTOR X')
        REAL A(50,50),C(50,50),B(50),Z(50),D(50)
        INTEGER IPVT(5)
        DATA LDC/50/
        WRITE(6,110)
        READ(5,*) M,N
        WRITE(6,1000)
        DO 10 I=1,M
        READ(5,*)(A(I,J),J=1,N)
        WRITE(6,*)(A(I,J),J=1,N)
10      CONTINUE
        WRITE(6,140)
        WRITE(6,1000)
        DO 20 I=1,M
        READ(5,*) B(I)
        WRITE(6,*) B(I)
20      CONTINUE
        DO 40 I=1,N
        DO 50 J=I,N
        C(I,J)=SDOT(M,A(1,I),1,A(1,J),1)
50      CONTINUE
40      CONTINUE
        DO 60 I=1,N
        D(I)=SDOT(M,A(1,I),1,B,1)
60      CONTINUE
        CALL SSICO(C,LDC,N,IPVT,RCOND,Z)
        WRITE(6,130) RCOND
        T=1.0+RCOND
        IF(T.EQ.1.0) GO TO 90
        CALL SSISL(C,LDC,N,IPVT,D)
        WRITE(6,150)
        WRITE(6,1000)
        DO 70 I=1,N
        WRITE(6,*) D(I)
70      CONTINUE
        STOP
90      WRITE(6,9999)
        STOP
        END
```

The program of Figure (4.3.4) will solve least-squares approximate solutions problems by solving the normal equations via the L-U decomposition and back substitution. As we saw in (4.1.25), however, there is another theoretical alternative: we can take the Q-R decomposition of the matrix of coefficients and use that to prepare the normal equations so that they are directly solvable by back substitution. LINPACK also contains procedures to implement these concepts.

We still seek a least-squares approximate solution to the system (4.3.1). We assume we have a factorization, as in (4.1.23),

$$(4.3.5) \qquad\qquad A = QR$$

with R upper triangular with positive diagonal and $Q^TQ = I$. Then the normal equations (4.3.2) have the equivalent form (4.1.25)

$$(4.3.6) \qquad\qquad R\bar{x} = Q^Tb$$

which can be solved for $\bar{x}$ by back substitution.

In outline, to obtain the least-squares solution via a Q-R factorization, we need to:

1. Input A.
2. Form the factorization $A = QR$.
3. Input b.
4. Solve $R\bar{x} = Q^Tb$.
5. Write $\bar{x}$.

This outline follows quite closely that of Section 2.4, which solves systems via an L-U factorization of the matrix of coefficients. So will our program. The main new steps are step 2 and step 4. Both represent complex tasks, but each may be carried out by a single LINPACK procedure.

The procedure which will accomplish step 2 is called SQRDC: "S" stands for single precision, "QR" for Q-R factorization, and "DC" stands for decomposition. To use it, we need an array A, of dimension LDA $\times$ P, containing an $M \times N$ matrix whose Q-R decomposition is to be calculated, a vector QRAUX of length P, an integer vector JPVT and a vector WORK (of length P if a column interchange option is used), and an integer JOB which is to be 1 if column interchange is desired and 0 if not. The procedure is called by a FORTRAN statement

CALL SQRDC(A,LDA,M,N,QRAUX,JPVT,WORK,JOB)

Since we will not need the column interchange feature, we will set JOB to be 0 and put in length 1 vectors DUM and JDUM for WORK and JPVT so that the statement looks like

CALL SQRDC(A,LDA,M,N,QRAUX,JDUM,DUM,0)

This has the effect of obtaining, for internal LINPACK use, the Q-R decomposition of A. As with the other space-conserving LINPACK procedures, the matrix in A is lost. In its place will be R in the upper triangle, and part of the data to construct Q in the lower triangle. The rest of the data for Q is in the vector QRAUX.

In principle, the call of SQRDC has produced a Q-R factorization. In fact, the matrices Q and R are not really available anywhere. As in the case with a call to SGECO to do an L-U decomposition, what is being stored is a record of the operations necessary to do the Q-R factorization. [In this case the operations follow the method of (4.1.28).] But it is precisely this version of a Q-R decomposition that the LINPACK procedure to do step 4 requires.

This procedure is called SQRSL: "S" and "QR" have the same meaning as above in SQRDC, while "SL" stands for solve. This procedure takes the data for the decomposition of A as passed by SQRDC (namely, the contents of A and QRAUX), plus a vector B containing the right-hand side b of (4.3.1), and solves (4.3.6) for $\bar{x}$. Actually, it can solve for many things: QB = Qb, QTB = Q^Tb, XBAR = $\bar{x}$, RSD = $\bar{x} - Ab$, and P = $A\bar{x}$. Which of these is actually obtained is controlled by an integer JOB. In such cases, it also returns an integer INFO which is zero, unless R is singular. A complete call to SQRSL would thus take the form

CALL SQRSL(A,LDA,M,N,QRAUX,B,QB,QTB,XBAR,RSD,P,JOB,INFO)

We will just be interested in obtaining $\bar{x}$ and $\bar{x} - Ab$. This can be done by setting JOB = 110. For QB and P we can put the dummy vector DUM and we use the same vector RSD for $\bar{x} - Ab$ and in place of QTB. So our call looks like

CALL SQRSL(A,LDA,M,N,QRAUX,B,DUM,RSD,XBAR,RDS,DUM,110,INFO)

A call like this does step 4 of our outline program. If for some reason A^TA were singular, this would be reflected in the singularity of R. This possibility doesn't cause SQRSL to stop, but it means the result XBAR is not really the desired $\bar{x}$. So before we print $\bar{x}$, we need to check if INFO is zero. If it isn't, XBAR is unreliable, so we want to announce that the normal equations are singular and not print XBAR. Otherwise, we advance to step 5. Thus steps 2 and 4 are done by single calls of LINPACK procedures; steps 1 and 3 are combined in our usual way; and step 5 is also done as it has been in our other LINPACK-based programs.

All that remains is to declare the various arrays needed in the procedure calls and input–output segments. A complete program is listed below [Fig. (4.3.7)]:

Figure (4.3.7).

```
C    SOLVES AX=B BY LEAST SQUARES
C    USES QR FACTORIZATION OF A
C    A M BY N MATRIX B AN N VECTOR
C        FIRST CARD M,N
C        NEXT CARDS A BY ROWS
C        NEXT CARDS B BY ENTRIES
9999    FORMAT('0 THE NORMAL EQUATIONS ARE SINGULAR')
1000    FORMAT('0)
110     FORMAT('1 LEAST SQUARES SOLUTION OF AX=B')
120     FORMAT('0 MATRIX A OF SIZE ',I2,2X,'BY ',I2)
140     FORMAT('0 THE VECTOR B OF CONSTANTS')
150     FORMAT('0 THE SOLUTION VECTOR X')
        REAL A(50,50),QRAUX(50),B(50),XBAR(50),RSD(50),DUM(1)
        INTEGER JDUM(1)
        DATA LDA/50/
        INFO=0
        WRITE(6,110)
        READ(5,*) M,N
        WRITE(6,120) M,N
        WRITE(6,1000)
        DO 10 I=1,M
        READ(5,*)(A(I,J),J=1,N)
        WRITE(6,*)(A(I,J),J=1,N)
10      CONTINUE
        WRITE(6,140)
        WRITE(6,1000)
        DO 20 I=1,M
        READ(5,*) B(I)
        WRITE(6,*) B(I)
20      CONTINUE
        CALL SQRDC(A,LDA,M,N,QRAUX,JDUM,DUM,0)
        CALL SQRSL(A,LDA,M,N,QRAUX,B,DUM,RSD,XBAR,RSD,DUM,110,INFO)
        IF(INFO.NE.0) GO TO 90
        WRITE(6,150)
        WRITE(6,1000)
        DO 30 I=1,N
        WRITE(6,*) XBAR(I)
30      CONTINUE
        STOP
90      WRITE(6,9999)
        STOP
        END
```

EXERCISES 4.3

In problems 1 through 6 use both the programs of Figures (4.3.4) and (4.3.7). In problems 7 through 9 use either.

1. Find the least-squares solution to the system of linear equations of problem 2(b) of Exercises 2.1 and compare the answers with the solution to problem 1 of Exercises 2.4.

2. Find the least squares to the systems of Example (4.1.12) and compare the answers obtained to those calculated in the text.

3. Find the least-squares solutions to the systems of problems 4(a) and 4(b) of Exercises 4.1.

4. Find the least-squares solution to Example (4.2.6).

5. Find the least-squares solution to Example (4.2.9).

6. Find the least-squares solutions to the systems of problem 3 of Exercises 4.2.

7. Find the least-squares solutions to the systems of problem 4 of Exercises 4.2. Is there any reason to suspect any of the three curves to be the best?

8. Find the least-squares solution to the system of problem 2 of Exercises 4.2.

9. Find the least-squares solution to the system of problem 5 of Exercises 4.2.

10. (Programming problem) Adjoin the program of Figure (3.3.5) to that of Figure (4.3.4) to obtain a program which produces a least-squares solution by row reducing an augmented matrix. Test the program on the systems of Example (4.1.13) and problem 4(c) of Exercises 4.1. Further adapt the program to calculate the best least-squares solution (4.1.16). (The resulting program is then applicable to all systems of linear equations of all sizes with unique, infinitely many, or no solutions—a "universal" linear equation solver.)

4.4   MORE FITTING EQUATIONS TO DATA[†]

The general problem of fitting equations to data, as covered in Section 4.2, runs as follows:

(4.4.1)   Fitting Problem.   The function f is to be written as a combination of given functions $f_1, \ldots, f_n$: $f = a_1 f_1 + \cdots + a_n f_n$. A large number of

---

[†] This optional section is intended for readers who have studied some calculus.

approximate values of f have been found by experiment. These are recorded as pairs (t_i, s_i), $1 \le i \le m$, where it is intended that $f(t_i) = s_i$. The problem is to choose values $\bar{a}_1, \ldots, \bar{a}_n$ of the parameters so that the graph of $\bar{f} = a_1 f_1 + \cdots + \bar{a}_n f_n$ fits as close as possible to the data points $(t_1, s_2), \ldots, (t_m, s_m)$.

At the heart of the fitting problem is the question of what is meant by "close." In Section 4.2, the pointwise least-squares solution was chosen. This had the effect of minimizing the sum of the squares of the vertical distances from the data points to the graph of $\bar{f}$ [see (4.2.4)]. This is illustrated in Figure (4.4.2).

Figure (4.4.2).

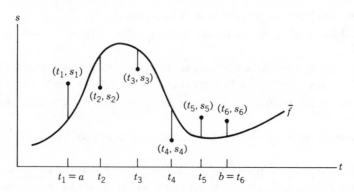

But there are other possible interpretations of "close." Suppose we assume that there is a true function f that actually goes through our data points, and that what we want to find is a function $\bar{f}$ such that the area between the graph of $\bar{f}$ and that of f is as small as possible. This is illustrated in Figure (4.4.3). Note that in the figure we are limiting t to the

Figure (4.4.3).

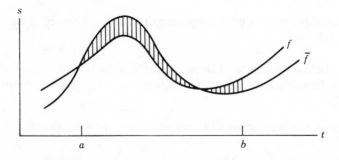

interval from a to b. In this case the area involved, between the graphs of f and $\bar{f}$ for $a \leq t \leq b$, is given by the integral

(4.4.4)
$$\int_a^b |f(t) - \bar{f}(t)| \, dt$$

The integral in (4.4.4), while not terribly hard to compute for any given choice of the parameters $\bar{a}_1, \ldots, \bar{a}_n$ in $\bar{f}$, is difficult to deal with conceptually. Since for numbers c we have $|c| = \sqrt{c^2}$, it is possible to show that the integral in (4.4.4) is reasonably approximated by the following integral

(4.4.5)
$$\sqrt{\int_a^b [f(t) - \bar{f}(t)]^2 \, dt}$$

In general, for a function $g(t)$ on the interval $a \leq t \leq b$ whose square is integrable over that integral we write

(4.4.6)
$$\sqrt{\int_a^b g(t)^2 \, dt} = \|g\|_2$$

and we call the number $\|g\|_2$ the L^2-norm of g. (L^2 is pronounced "el two.") Thus the alternative measure of closeness in the fitting problem can be rephrased, in terms of this notation, as follows:

(4.4.7) $\bar{f} = \bar{a}_1 f_1 + \cdots + \bar{a}_n f_n$ is the *best* L^2 *approximation* to f on the interval $a \leq t \leq b$ if $\|f - \bar{f}\|_2$ is minimal; that is, if $\|f - \bar{f}\|_2 \leq \|f - \Sigma a_i f_i\|_2$ for all choices of $a_1, \ldots, a_n$.

The problem is still to find a certain n-tuple $\bar{a}_1, \ldots, \bar{a}_n$ of numbers. So perhaps it is not too surprising that this is still a linear problem. Here is how to make the translation: What we seek to minimize is $\|f - \Sigma \bar{a}_i f_i\|_2$, which of course can be done by minimizing its square

(4.4.8) $\int_a^b (f - \Sigma \bar{a}_i f)^2 \, dt = \int_a^b [f^2 - 2f\Sigma \bar{a}_i f_i + (\Sigma \bar{a}_i f_i)^2] \, dt$

We can ignore the contribution from the integral of f^2, because this constant is the same for all choices of $a_1, \ldots, a_n$. Using this, and the linearity of the integral, we have that minimizing (4.4.8) is equivalent to finding the minimum of

(4.4.9)
$$\sum_{i,j} \bar{a}_i \left(\int_a^b f_i f_j \, dt \right) \bar{a}_j - \sum_i \bar{a}_i \left(\int_a^b f_i f \, dt \right)$$

It is a simple matter to write (4.4.9) in matrix form:

(4.4.10) Matrix Form of the Equations for Best L^2-Approximation

$$C_{ij} = \int_a^b f_i f_j \, dt \quad 1 \le i, j \le n \quad B_i = \int_a^b f_i f \, dt \quad 1 \le i \le n$$

$$C = \begin{bmatrix} C_{11} & \cdots & C_{1n} \\ \vdots & & \vdots \\ C_{n1} & \cdots & C_{nn} \end{bmatrix} \quad b = \begin{bmatrix} B_1 \\ \vdots \\ B_n \end{bmatrix} \quad \bar{a} = \begin{bmatrix} \bar{a}_1 \\ \vdots \\ \bar{a}_n \end{bmatrix}$$

(4.4.11) $\quad \bar{a}^T C \bar{a} - 2 \bar{a}^T b \quad$ [This is the matrix form of (4.4.9).]

We still have to minimize the expression (4.4.11). In the following lemma we have a theoretical tool to do that.

(4.4.12) Let C be an n by n matrix such that for every nonzero n-vector z we have $z^T C z > 0$, and let b be an n-vector. Then

1. There is a unique n-vector y with $Cy = b$.
2. If x is any other n-vector, then $(x^T C x - 2x^T b) > (y^T C y - 2y^T b)$.

The proof of number 1 is easy: if $Cz = 0$ for some n-vector z, then $z^T C z = 0$, so $z = 0$. This proves that C has a nonzero determinant, so we can solve $Cy = b$ for a vector y. To prove number 2, we calculate $(x^T C x - 2x^T b) - (y^T C y - 2y^T b)$, replacing b by Cy to find $x^T C x - 2x^T C y + y^T C y = (x - y)^T C (x - y)$ which is greater than zero, by assumption, if x and y are different.

To apply (4.4.12) to minimize (4.4.11), we need to know that the matrix C of (4.4.10) satisfies the assumption of (4.4.12), namely, that $z^T C z > 0$ for $z \ne 0$. It usually does: Suppose z has components $z_1, \ldots, z_n$. Then

$$z^T C z = \sum_{i,j} z_i C_{ij} z_j = \int_a^b \left(\sum z_i f_i \right)^2 dt$$

and the function $g = (\sum z_i f_i)^2$ is a nonnegative function on the interval $a \le t \le b$. The only way that g can have zero integral over the interval is if g is identically zero. Thus we have:

(4.4.13) Assume that no linear combination $\sum z_i f_i$ of the functions $f_1, \ldots, f_n$ is identically zero on the interval $a \le t \le b$. Then for C as in (4.4.10) we have $z^T C z > 0$ for any nonzero vector t. In particular, by (4.4.12), the best

L^2-approximation $\bar{f} = \bar{a}_1 f_1 + \cdots + \bar{a}_n f_n$ to f is given by the unique vector $\bar{a}$ with $C\bar{a} = b$.

In applications of (4.4.13), usually n is small, so that *solving* $C\bar{a} = b$ for $\bar{a}$ is not terribly difficult (at least in principle; it may happen that the reciprocal condition number of C is small so that it may be difficult to get an accurate solution numerically); the problem is usually in *forming* the matrix C and especially the vector b. For the most part, one would use standard choices of $f_1, \ldots, f_n$, so that C could be predetermined, but b must be estimated. A reasonable way to estimate the integrals involved is via the trapezoidal rule. This takes the following form here [remember that we assume $s_i = f(t_i)$ for $1 \le i \le m$ and we further assume that $t_1 = a$ and $t_m = b$]:

$$(4.4.14) \quad B_i = \frac{1}{2}\left[\left(\sum_{j=1}^{n}\left[s_{j+1}f_i(t_{j+1}) - s_j f_i(t_j)\right](t_{j+1} - t_j)\right)\right]$$

Similarly, C_{ij} can be estimated by

$$(4.4.15) \quad C_{ij} = \frac{1}{2}\left(\sum_{k=1}^{m-1}\left\{\left[f_i(t_{k+1})f_j(t_{k+1}) - f_i(t_k)f_j(t_k)\right](t_{k+1} - t_k)\right\}\right)$$

Once a choice of the function $f_1, \ldots, f_n$ has been made, it is certainly possible to compute C and b using (4.4.14) and (4.4.15) and then to solve $Cx = b$ by means of Section 2.4.

There are still several things to be wary of in this method:

1. The answer must be expressed in terms of the functions $f_1, \ldots, f_n$, so that there must be solid theoretical grounds for choosing those functions.

2. The best L^2-approximation is a particular selection of what is meant by "close," so that any conclusions drawn about the values of parameters must be understood with respect to this choice of close.

With these warnings stated, we proceed to consider an example:

Example (4.4.16) To good approximation, many biological phenomena may be described in terms of "simple harmonic emitters": functions of the form

$$f(t) = \begin{cases} A\cos\left[\dfrac{\pi}{b-a}\left(t - \dfrac{a+b}{2}\right)\right] & \text{for } a \le t \le b \\ 0 & \text{for } t < a \quad \text{and} \quad t > b \end{cases}$$

[see Figure (4.4.17)]. Here the independent variable t represents time and

Figure (4.4.17).

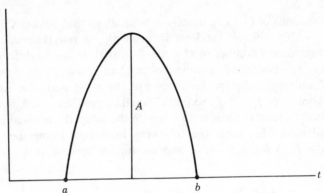

the function $f(x)$ gives the magnitude of the emission at time x. The emitter fires at time $t = a$, rises to a maximum amplitude A at time $(a + b)/2$, and returns to 0 at time $t = b$. Let us suppose that a particular organism has been observed to have an ion concentration in its gut cavity that is to be analyzed in terms of simple harmonic emitters. On the basis of dissection studies, it is suspected that the concentration levels are produced by a pair of sites, whose secretion levels are simple harmonic emitters. Each site fires twice a minute, and peaks as the other site fires. The amplitudes of each emission are independent, but repeat on a minute cycle. Data has been collected on concentration levels every 0.02 min, and the firing amplitudes are desired.

In Figure (4.4.18) we have drawn the emission levels of emitter one (solid line) and emitter two (dashed line) and indicated the amplitude levels $\bar{A}_1$,

Figure (4.4.18).

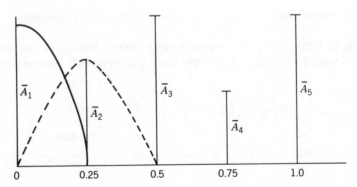

$\overline{A}_2$, $\overline{A}_3$, $\overline{A}_4$, and $\overline{A}_5$. We want to choose these amplitude levels to fit the data on concentration levels, which we assume is given by a function $f(t)$. We will use a best L^2-approximation on the interval $0 \le t \le 1$ of the form

$$\bar{f}(t) = \overline{A}_1 f_1(t) + \overline{A}_2 f_2(t) + \overline{A}_3 f_3(t) + \overline{A}_4 f_4(t) + \overline{A}_5 f_5(t)$$

where

$$f_1(t) = \cos(2t) \qquad\qquad 0 \le t \le 0.25, \qquad 0 \text{ otherwise}$$

$$f_2(t) = \cos[2(t - 0.25)] \qquad 0 \le t \le 0.5, \qquad 0 \text{ otherwise}$$

$$f_3(t) = \cos[2(t - 0.5)] \qquad 0.25 \le t \le 0.75, \qquad 0 \text{ otherwise}$$

$$f_4(t) = \cos[2(t - 0.75)] \qquad 0.5 \le t \le 1, \qquad 0 \text{ otherwise}$$

$$f_5(t) = \cos[2(t - 1)] \qquad 0.75 \le t \le 1, \qquad 0 \text{ otherwise}$$

We would like to apply the solution method (4.4.13). First, we need to check that if $z_1 f_1 + \cdots + z_5 f_5 = 0$, then all $z_1, \ldots, z_5$ are 0: for, evaluating at $t = 0, 0.25, 0.5, 0.75,$ and 1, we have that $z_1 = z_2 = \cdots = z_5 = 0$. Next, we need to calculate the matrix C. This can be done by the trapezoidal-rule approximation (4.4.15), or, since the functions involved are directly integrable, we may appeal to the definition (4.4.10): for the first row of C, we have

$$C_{1j} = \int_0^1 f_1(t) f_j(t)\, dt = \begin{cases} 0 & j \ne 1, 2 \\ \frac{1}{4}\pi & j = 1 \\ \frac{4}{\pi} & j = 2 \end{cases}$$

and similar formulas for the other rows, giving

$$(4.4.19) \qquad C = \begin{bmatrix} \frac{1}{4}\pi & 4/\pi & & & \\ 4/\pi & \frac{1}{2}\pi & 4/\pi & & \\ & 4/\pi & \frac{1}{2}\pi & 4/\pi & \\ & & 4/\pi & \frac{1}{2}\pi & 4/\pi \\ & & & 4/\pi & \frac{1}{4}\pi \end{bmatrix}$$

In Figure (4.4.20) we have given a table of the data values (t_i, s_i) as t_i varies from 0.0 to 1.00 in steps of 0.02. Using this data and the trapezoidal approximations (4.4.14), the terms $B_1, \ldots, B_5$ can be computed. Then the

Figure (4.4.20).

I	T(I)	S(I)
0	0.0	2.5000
1	0.02	2.7310
2	0.04	2.9188
3	0.06	3.0607
4	0.08	3.1543
5	0.10	3.1981
6	0.12	3.1915
7	0.14	3.1346
8	0.16	3.0282
9	0.18	2.8741
10	0.20	2.6747
11	0.22	2.4330
12	0.24	2.1530
13	0.26	2.0588
14	0.28	2.1520
15	0.30	2.2111
16	0.32	2.2354
17	0.34	2.2245
18	0.36	2.1785
19	0.38	2.0981
20	0.40	1.9846
21	0.42	1.8398
22	0.44	1.6660
23	0.46	1.4660
24	0.48	1.2428
25	0.50	1.0000
26	0.52	1.0548
27	0.54	1.0929
28	0.56	1.1138
29	0.58	1.1172
30	0.60	1.1029
31	0.62	1.0712
32	0.64	1.0227
33	0.66	0.9580
34	0.68	0.8782
35	0.70	0.7845
36	0.72	0.6785
37	0.74	0.5618
38	0.76	0.5932
39	0.78	0.7722
40	0.80	0.9391
41	0.82	1.0911
42	0.84	1.2259
43	0.86	1.3414
44	0.88	1.4357
45	0.90	1.5074
46	0.92	1.5553
47	0.94	1.5787
48	0.96	1.5772
49	0.98	1.5508
50	1.00	1.5000

160

Figure (4.4.21).

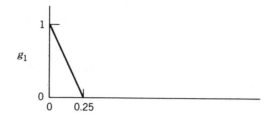

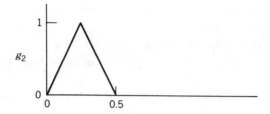

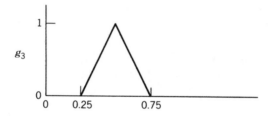

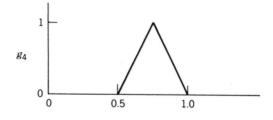

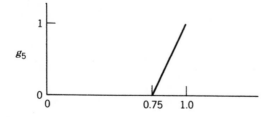

equation

$$(4.4.21) \qquad\qquad\qquad Cy = b$$

can be solved for y and by (4.4.13) the entries of y will be the desired coefficients $\bar{A}_1, \ldots, \bar{A}_5$. The solution of (4.4.21) can be carried out using the LINPACK-based program of Figure (2.4.4a).

EXERCISES 4.4

1. Verify the computation of C in (4.4.19) by calculating the integrals C_{ij}.
2. Use the data of Figure (4.4.20) and formula (4.4.14) to compute the vector b. Then solve the system (4.4.21) for $\bar{A}_1, \ldots, \bar{A}_n$.
3. If $f_1, \ldots, f_5$ are as in Example (4.4.16) and $t_1 = 0$, $t_2 = 0.25$, $t_3 = 0.5$, $t_4 = 0.75$, and $t_5 = 1.0$, verify that $f_i(t_j) = 0$ if $i \neq j$ and $f_i(t_i) = 1$. [From this it follows that if $f = z_1 f_1 + z_2 f_2 + \cdots + z_5 f_5$, then $z_i = f(t_i)$.] Show that if $f_1, \ldots, f_n$ are any functions on the interval $a \leq t \leq b$ such that no linear combination $\Sigma z_i f_i$ of them is identically zero on the interval, then there are numbers $a \leq t_1 < t_2 < \cdots < t_n \leq b$ such that $f_i(t_i) = 0$ if $i \neq j$ and $f_i(t_i) = 1$. Deduce as a consequence that if $f = \Sigma z_i f_i$ then $z_i = f(t_i)$.
4. Define the functions $g_1, \ldots, g_5$ on the interval $0 \leq t \leq 1$ so that their graphs are as in Figure (4.4.21). Using the data of Figure (4.4.20), find the best L^2-approximation $\bar{f} = \bar{A}_i g_i$.

PART 2

DYNAMIC MODELS

5

DISCRETE TIME
SYSTEM
EVOLUTION

5.1 ITERATIVE INHOMOGENEOUS LINEAR MODELS

The models considered in previous chapters were static, or steady state, in the sense that the solution sought was always a particular set of values of some unknowns. It is often the case, however, that the question of interest with a given system is not a solution but the long-range behavior over time. In this chapter and the next we will begin the investigation of such systems.

What qualifies as a "system" is a matter of some interest. As we will use the term here, a system is something which is determined by its states, and the states are n-tuples of numbers. To be precise:

(5.1.1) An n-dimensional system has its *state* at time t determined by an n-tuple of numbers $x_1(t), \ldots, x_n(t)$. The state at time t is thus an n-vector

$$x(t) = \begin{bmatrix} x_1(t) \\ \vdots \\ x_n(t) \end{bmatrix}$$

and the system is completely determined by the function sending t to $x(t)$.

We want further that the next state of the system is to be determined by its previous state. This "historical determinancy" has several possible meanings. Many systems change their states continuously, so the determinancy may have to refer to the previous instant, or the system may change in discrete jumps, so the determinancy may refer to the state at some fixed interval of time in the past. Continuously changing systems will be studied in Chapter 6. Here, we will restrict our attention to discretely changing systems. (Actuallly, even continuously changing systems can be studied by sampling them at discrete time intervals.) Formally:

(5.1.2)   An n-dimensional *discrete time system*, with initial time t_0 and time interval Δt, is specified by the sequences of states

$$x^{(0)} = x(t_0) \quad \text{and} \quad x^{(k)} = x(t_0 + k\Delta t)$$

The system is *linear* if there is an n by n matrix A and an n-vector b such that:

(5.1.3) $$x^{(k+1)} = Ax^{(k)} + b$$

If $b \neq 0$, the system is inhomogeneous; if $b = 0$ the system is homogeneous.

The evolution equation (5.1.3) reflects the fact that the next state is to be determined by the previous one. As we will see in our examples, this is not to be taken too literally: we may have the condition of the physical system determined by the conditions at several previous times; but by introducing some additional formal variables, we can bring such a system into the form (5.1.3). Here is an example:

Example (5.1.4)   A 4-year medical school plans to adopt the following admission and retention policies:

1.   100 new freshmen and 20 new juniors will be admitted each year.
2.   80% of each class will be promoted to the next year (or graduate, in the case of seniors).
3.   10% of each class will not continue in school (or leave without graduating, in the case of seniors).
4.   5% of each class will be asked to repeat that year.
5.   5% of each class will be asked to repeat that year after a year's furlough.

Suppose that the program starts in a year with 100 freshmen, 80 sophomores,

90 juniors, and 85 seniors, with no students currently furloughed. We would like to predict how many students there are in each class, and how many graduate, after the program has been operating for 15 years.

The condition of the school is the number of students in each class, but because of the furlough policy, it will be necessary to keep track of the number of students in each class in the previous year. Thus the state will be 8-vectors

$$x^{(n)} = \begin{bmatrix} a_n \\ b_n \\ c_n \\ d_n \\ e_n \\ f_n \\ g_n \\ h_n \end{bmatrix}$$

where a_n = the number of freshmen in year n
b_n = the number of freshmen in year $n-1$
c_n = the number of sophomores in year n
d_n = the number of sophomores in year $n-1$
e_n = the number of juniors in year n
f_n = the number of juniors in year $n-1$
g_n = the number of seniors in year n
h_n = the number of seniors in year $n-1$

These change as follows:

$$a_{n+1} = 0.05a_n + 0.05b_n + 100$$

$$(5\% \text{ repeaters, } 5\% \text{ furloughed repeaters, } 100 \text{ new})$$

$$b_{n+1} = a_n$$

$$c_{n+1} = 0.8a_n + 0.05c_n + 0.05d_n$$

$$(80\% \text{ promotees, } 5\% \text{ repeaters, } 5\% \text{ furloughed})$$

$$d_{n+1} = c_n$$

$$e_{n+1} = 0.8c_n + 0.05e_n + 0.05f_n + 20$$

$$f_{n+1} = e_n$$

$$g_{n+1} = 0.8e_n + 0.05g_n + 0.05h_n$$

$$h_{n+1} = g_n$$

In matrix terms (5.1.3) this means $x^{(n+1)} = Ax^{(n)} + b$ where

$$A = \begin{bmatrix} 1.05 & 0.05 & 0 & 0 & 0 & 0 & 0 & 0 \\ 1 & 0 & 0 & 0 & 0 & 0 & 0 & 0 \\ 0.8 & 0 & 0.05 & 0.05 & 0 & 0 & 0 & 0 \\ 0 & 0 & 1 & 0 & 0 & 0 & 0 & 0 \\ 0 & 0 & 0.8 & 0 & 0.05 & 0.05 & 0 & 0 \\ 0 & 0 & 0 & 0 & 1 & 0 & 0 & 0 \\ 0 & 0 & 0 & 0 & 0.8 & 0 & 0.05 & 0.05 \\ 0 & 0 & 0 & 0 & 0 & 0 & 1 & 0 \end{bmatrix} \quad b = \begin{bmatrix} 100 \\ 0 \\ 0 \\ 0 \\ 20 \\ 0 \\ 0 \\ 0 \end{bmatrix}$$

Initially we have

$$x^{(0)} = \begin{bmatrix} 100 \\ 0 \\ 80 \\ 0 \\ 90 \\ 0 \\ 85 \\ 0 \end{bmatrix}, \text{ then } x^{(1)} = \begin{bmatrix} 105 \\ 100 \\ 84 \\ 80 \\ 88.5 \\ 90 \\ 76.25 \\ 85 \end{bmatrix},$$

$$x^{(2)} = \begin{bmatrix} 110.25 \\ 105 \\ 92.2 \\ 84 \\ 96.125 \\ 88.5 \\ 78.8625 \\ 76.25 \end{bmatrix}, \text{ and so on}$$

(The number of graduates is 68 at the end of year 0, 61 at the end of year 1, 63 at the end of year 2, and so on —80% of the seniors graduate.)

To carry this process through to year 10 (and beyond, if desired), it is convenient to carry out the calculations by computer. Such a program needs to input A, B, and $x^{(0)}$ and carry out the iteration step (5.1.3) as many times as desired. The key step is of course the iteration. In Section 2.5, a subroutine AXPB was developed with the following features [see Figure (2.5.7)]:

AXPB(N,A,X,B,Y): on entry, X, B, Y are N-vectors and A is an N by N matrix; on return, X contains AX + B and Y contains X.

Using this subroutine we obtain a program which carries out (5.1.3) until a desired $x^{(k)}$ is reached [Fig. (5.1.5)]:

Figure (5.1.5).

```
C       COMPUTES X(K+1)=AX(K)+B
C       A IS N BY N
C           FIRST CARD N
C           NEXT CARDS A BY ROWS
C           NEXT CARDS B BY ENTRIES
C           NEXT CARDS XO BY ENTRIES
C           NEXT CARD NUMBER OF ITERATES
 1000      FORMAT('0')
  120      FORMAT('0 MATRIX A OF SIZE ',I2,2X,'BY ',I2)
  130      FORMAT('0 THE VECTOR B')
  140      FORMAT('0 THE VECTOR X0')
  150      FORMAT('0 THE VECTOR X(K) FOR K= ',I3)
           REAL A(50,50),B(50),X(50),Y(50)
           READ(5,*) N
           WRITE(6,120) N,N
           WRITE(6,1000)
           DO 10 I=1,N
           READ(5,*)(A(I,J),J=1,N)
           WRITE(6,*)(A(I,J),J=1,N)
   10      CONTINUE
           WRITE(6,130)
           WRITE(6,1000)
           DO 20 I=1,N
           READ(5,*) B(I)
           WRITE(5,*) B(I)
   20      CONTINUE
           WRITE(6,140)
           WRITE(6,1000)
           DO 30 I=1,N
           READ(5,*) X(I)
           WRITE(6,*) X(I)
   30      CONTINUE
           READ(5,*) ITER
           DO 40 I=1,ITER
           CALL AXPB(N,A,X,B,Y)
   40      CONTINUE
           WRITE(6,150) ITER
           WRITE(6,1000)
           DO 50 I=1,N
           WRITE(6,*) X(I)
   50      CONTINUE
           STOP
           END
C       **********************************************************************
           SUBROUTINE AXPB(N,A,X,B,Y)
C       ON ENTRY A IS N BY N,X,B,Y ARE N VECTORS
C       ON RETURN X CONTAINS AX+B AND Y CONTAINS X
           REAL A(50,50),B(50),X(50),Y(50)
           INTEGER N
           CALL SCOPY(N,X,1,Y,1)
           CALL SCOPY(N,B,1,X,1)
           DO 10 I=1,N
           T=Y(I)
           CALL SAXPY(N,T,A(1,I),1,X,1)
   10      CONTINUE
           RETURN
           END
```

In the exercises, the computations completing Example (5.1.4), and some other similar problems, are asked for. These computations are straightforward applications of the program of Figure (5.1.5).

EXERCISES 5.1ˋ

All computations are to be done using the program of Figure (5.1.5).

1. Calculate the enrollment in each class in the medical school of Example (5.1.4) in years (a) 5, (b) 10, (c) 20 after the new enrollment policy is instituted.

2. A company has five classifications of employees: (a) worker, (b) skilled workers, (c) professionals, (d) managers, and (e) senior mangers. Employees are hired only in classification (a) and (c) and all promotions are from within. Promising individuals are tested for advancement by trial periods in higher classifications: each year 5% of the workers are given a 1-year trial as skilled workers, 5% of the skilled workers and professionals are given a 1-year trial as managers, and 5% of the managers begin a 2-year trial as senior managers. At the end of the trial period half of the employees are retained in their new classification and half return to their former classification (they can also be reconsidered for trial advancement then or in the future). Retirements and resignations, voluntary or otherwise, cause each classification to lose 4% of its employees annually. Suppose that in a given year there are 1000 workers, 250 skilled workers, 300 professionals, 175 managers, and 80 senior managers, and that over the next 15 years 90 workers and 30 professionals are to be added annually. What will be the number of employees in each classification at the end of the 15-year period?

3. Olives at harvest are graded by size into five categories: large, super, giant, mammoth, and colossal. As each day of their season passes, the olives increase in size, but as they do so the chances that they will be lost to crop damage also increases. Precisely, with each day, 10% of each category increases in size to the next category (the colossal remain in their category), and the losses per category are 10% for large and super, 15% for giant and mammoth, and 18% for colossal. Every 3 days the grove is harvested of 100 kg each of large and super, 60 kg of giant, 40 kg of mammoth, and 20 kg of colossal. At the beginning of the season the grove contains 600 kg of mammoth and 100 kg of colossal. The grove is then harvested three times and on the tenth day all remaining olives are picked. What is the total yield in each category? If no harvest

was done on intermediate days and all olives were picked on the tenth day what would the total yields be?

4. (Programming problem) Adapt the program of Figure (5.1.5) so that $X(K)$ is printed for each K from 1 to ITER. Use the adapted program to obtain the class-by-class enrollments for Example (5.1.4) in each year from year 1 to year 20.

5. (Programming problem) Further adapt the program of Figure (5.1.5) to allow changes in the vector B in the course of the computation. Recompute problem 4 where at the end of the tenth year the admission policy is changed to 75 new freshmen and 10 new juniors per year.

5.2 EIGENVECTORS AND EIGENVALUES

The iteration equation (5.1.3)

$$x^{(k+1)} = Ax^{(k)} + b$$

is the same equation that we considered back in Section 2.5. There, it was shown that, in terms of $x^{(0)}$, we have

(5.2.1) $\qquad x^{(k+1)} = A^{k+1}x^{(0)} + A^k b + A^{k-1}b + \cdots + Ab + b$

In general, there is no easy way to find $x^{(k+1)}$ except by iterating (5.1.3), as we did in Section 5.1. This is acceptable if all we want to do is examine $x^{(k)}$ for some specific value of k. Suppose, however, that we are interested in predicting the long-term behavior of $x^{(k)}$ for all large k. The best we can do by iteration is to look at some representative values of $x^{(k)}$ for some chosen k's and guess. The difficulty of detecting patterns this way leads us to the consideration of the analysis of (5.2.1) for some special matrices A.

The easiest special case is when A is *diagonal*:

(5.2.2) $\quad A = \begin{bmatrix} \lambda_1 & & & \\ & \lambda_2 & & \\ & & \ddots & \\ & & & \lambda_n \end{bmatrix} \qquad x^{(0)} = \begin{bmatrix} a_1 \\ \vdots \\ a_n \end{bmatrix} \qquad b = \begin{bmatrix} b_1 \\ \vdots \\ b_n \end{bmatrix}$

Then we have

$$A^k = \begin{bmatrix} \lambda_1^k & & & \\ & \lambda_2^k & & \\ & & \ddots & \\ & & & \lambda_1^k \end{bmatrix}$$

so that (5.2.1) becomes

$$(5.2.3) \qquad x^{(k+1)} = \begin{bmatrix} \vdots \\ \lambda_i^{k+1} a_0 + \left(\lambda_i^k + \lambda_i^{k-1} + \cdots + \lambda_i + \lambda \right) b_i \\ \vdots \end{bmatrix}$$

This looks much simpler to evaluate than the general form (5.2.1). It is in fact even simpler than it looks now: the ith entry of $x^{(k+1)}$ is $\lambda_i^{k+1} a_0 + (\lambda_i^k - 1)(\lambda_i - 1)^{-1} b_i$ (if $\lambda_i \neq 1$) and $a_0 + (k+1)b$ (if $\lambda_i = 1$). And it is a simple matter to use these formulas to study the long-term behavior of $x^{(k)}$.

Most matrices are not diagonal, of course. But it is not as rare to be *diagonalizable*; that is, to have

$$(5.2.4) \qquad A = PDP^{-1} \text{ where } D = \begin{bmatrix} \lambda_1 & & \\ & \ddots & \\ & & \lambda_n \end{bmatrix}$$

is diagonal and P is invertible. Then $A^k = PDP^{-1}PDP \cdots PDP^{-1} = PD^kP^{-1}$, so (5.2.1) becomes $x^{(k+1)} = PD^{k+1}P^{-1}x^{(0)} + PD^kP^{-1}b + \cdots + PDP^{-1}b + b$, or

(5.2.5)

$$P^{-1}x^{(k+1)} = D^{k+1}(P^{-1}x^{(0)}) + D^k(P^{-1}b) + \cdots + D(P^{-1}b) + (P^{-1}b)$$

Using (5.2.5), we can compute $P^{-1}x^{(k+1)}$ from $P^{-1}x^{(0)}$ and $\lambda_1, \ldots, \lambda_n$ by (5.2.3) and then obtain $x^{(k+1)}$ as $P(P^{-1}x^{(k+1)})$.

Since most matrices are in fact diagonalizable—in fact a matrix chosen at random is diagonalizable with probability one in the sense of Section 1.3 —the most sensible way to carry out the long-term analysis of (5.2.1) is to try to write it in the form (5.2.4) This leads us to the theory of eigenvectors and eigenvalues.

We begin with Eq. (5.2.4), which can be written in the form

(5.2.6) $$AP = PD$$

If P has columns $P_1, \ldots, P_n$, then (5.2.6) implies that

(5.2.7) $$AP_i = \lambda_i P_i \qquad i = 1, \ldots, n$$

Conversely, if we are given vectors $P_1, \ldots, P_n$ and numbers $\lambda_1, \ldots, \lambda_n$ satisfying (5.2.7), then $P = [P_1 \cdots P_n]$ satisfies (5.2.6) with D the diagonal matrix with entries $\lambda_1, \ldots, \lambda_n$. If in addition the matrix P is invertible, then A can be written in the form (5.2.4). Thus the important step in obtaining Eq. (5.2.4) is finding vectors satisfying (5.2.7). Since our hope is to invert the matrix P made up from these vectors, it is important to stay away from the trivial cases $P_i = 0$. This leads to the following definitions:

(5.2.8) Let A be an n by n matrix. A nonzero n-vector v is called an *eigenvector* of A if there is a number λ with $Av = \lambda v$. Since v is nonzero, the number λ is uniquely determined by this equation and is called the *eigenvalue* corresponding to the eigenvector v.

A number λ is an eigenvalue of the n by n matrix A if there is a nonzero vector v with $Av = \lambda v$. Another way to write this is to say that the equation $(A - \lambda I_n)x = 0$ has a nonzero solution x, which in turn is equivalent to saying that $\det(A - \lambda I_n) = 0$. So λ is an eigenvalue of A exactly when $\det(A - \lambda I_n) = 0$. This characterization of eigenvalues has the following formalization:

(5.2.9) Let A be an n by n matrix, and let t be an indeterminate. The polynomial $\mathrm{char}(A, t) = \det(A - tI_n)$ is called the *characteristic polynomial* of A. The eigenvalues of A are precisely the roots of $\mathrm{char}(A, t)$.

Finding eigenvectors is a two-step process: (1) we find the roots of the characteristic polynomial; this *nonlinear* problem locates the eigenvalues; then (2) for each eigenvalue λ we solve the equation $(A - \lambda I)x = 0$ for a nonzero solution x; this *linear* problem locates the eigenvectors. The linear problem always has a solution. The nonlinear problem is more complicated: it has solutions in principle, but they may be difficult to locate. We will return to these points after considering some simple (2 by 2) examples:

Example (5.2.10)

$$A = \begin{bmatrix} 2 & 2 \\ -2 & -3 \end{bmatrix}$$

Then

$$\text{char}(A,t) = \det\left(\begin{bmatrix} 2 & 2 \\ -2 & -3 \end{bmatrix} - t\begin{bmatrix} 1 & 0 \\ 0 & 1 \end{bmatrix}\right) = \det\begin{pmatrix} 2-t & 2 \\ -2 & -3-t \end{pmatrix}$$

$$= t^2 + t - 2$$

Step 1. The eigenvalues are the roots of $\text{char}(A,t) = 0$:

$$t^2 + t - 2 = 0$$

$$(t-1)(t+2) = 0$$

$$t = 1, -2$$

There are two eigenvalues: $\lambda_1 = 1$, $\lambda_2 = -2$.

Step 2. For each eigenvalue λ the eigenvectors are solutions of $(A - \lambda I)x = 0$:

$$\lambda_1 = 1: (A - \lambda_1 I_2)x = 0$$

$$\begin{bmatrix} 1 & 2 \\ -2 & -4 \end{bmatrix}\begin{bmatrix} x_1 \\ x_2 \end{bmatrix} = \begin{bmatrix} 0 \\ 0 \end{bmatrix}$$

We solve this with x_2 as the free variable, finding

$$\begin{bmatrix} x_1 \\ x_2 \end{bmatrix} = x_2\begin{bmatrix} -2 \\ 1 \end{bmatrix} \qquad v_1 = \begin{bmatrix} -2 \\ 1 \end{bmatrix}$$

$$\lambda_1 = -2: (A - \lambda_2 I_2)x = 0$$

$$\begin{bmatrix} 4 & 2 \\ -2 & -1 \end{bmatrix}\begin{bmatrix} x_1 \\ x_2 \end{bmatrix} = \begin{bmatrix} 0 \\ 0 \end{bmatrix}$$

We solve this with x_2 as the free variable, finding

$$\begin{bmatrix} x_1 \\ x_2 \end{bmatrix} = x_2\begin{bmatrix} -\frac{1}{2} \\ 1 \end{bmatrix} \qquad v_2 = \begin{bmatrix} -\frac{1}{2} \\ 1 \end{bmatrix}$$

In summary the eigenvectors corresponding to the eigenvalue $\lambda_1 = 1$ are all multiples of v_1 and those corresponding to $\lambda_2 = -2$ are all multiples of v_2.

Example (5.2.11)

$$A = \begin{bmatrix} 2 & 1 \\ -1 & 4 \end{bmatrix}$$

Then $\text{char}(A, t) = t^2 - 6t + 9 = (t - 3)^2$.

Step 1. The only eigenvalue of A is $\lambda_1 = 3$.

Step 2. The eigenvectors of A:

$$(A - \lambda_1 I_2)x = 0$$

$$\begin{bmatrix} -1 & 1 \\ -1 & 1 \end{bmatrix}\begin{bmatrix} x_1 \\ x_2 \end{bmatrix} = \begin{bmatrix} 0 \\ 0 \end{bmatrix}$$

so

$$\begin{bmatrix} x_1 \\ x_2 \end{bmatrix} = x_2 \begin{bmatrix} -1 \\ 1 \end{bmatrix} \qquad v_1 = \begin{bmatrix} -1 \\ 1 \end{bmatrix}$$

The only eigenvectors of A are the multiples of v_1.

Example (5.2.12)

$$A = \begin{bmatrix} 0 & 1 \\ -1 & 0 \end{bmatrix}$$

Then $\text{char}(A, t) = t^2 + 1$.

Step 1. This example presents a new phenomenon. The polynomial $t^2 + 1$ has no *real* number roots. It has, however, two distinct *complex* roots $\lambda_1 = i$ and $\lambda_2 = -i$ (where $i = \sqrt{-1}$). We proceed to step 2 using these eigenvalues:

Step 2.

$$\lambda_1 = i \qquad (A - \lambda_1 I_2)x = 0$$

$$\begin{bmatrix} -i & 1 \\ -1 & i \end{bmatrix}\begin{bmatrix} x_1 \\ x_2 \end{bmatrix} = \begin{bmatrix} 0 \\ 0 \end{bmatrix}$$

This yields the system of linear equations

(1) $$-ix_1 + x_2 = 0$$

(2) $$-x_1 + ix_2 = 0$$

Multiplying Eq. (1) by $-1/-i = -i$ and subtracting from Eq. (2) yields

$$-ix_1 + x_2 = 0$$

$$0 = 0$$

Using x_2 as the free variable we have

$$\begin{bmatrix} x_1 \\ x_2 \end{bmatrix} = x_2 \begin{bmatrix} -i \\ 1 \end{bmatrix} \qquad v_1 = \begin{bmatrix} -i \\ 1 \end{bmatrix}$$

So all eigenvectors corresponding to the eigenvalue $\lambda_1 = i$ are multiples of v_1.

$$\lambda_2 = -i \qquad (A - \lambda_2 I_2) = 0$$

$$\begin{bmatrix} i & 1 \\ -1 & i \end{bmatrix} \begin{bmatrix} x_1 \\ x_2 \end{bmatrix} = \begin{bmatrix} 0 \\ 0 \end{bmatrix}$$

As before, we solve to find

$$\begin{bmatrix} x_1 \\ x_2 \end{bmatrix} = x_2 \begin{bmatrix} i \\ 1 \end{bmatrix} \qquad v_2 = \begin{bmatrix} i \\ 1 \end{bmatrix}$$

So all eigenvectors corresponding to the eigenvalue $\lambda_2 = -i$ are multiples of v_2.

There are several lessons to draw from these examples: we recall that our goal is to find eigenvectors of A which, when put in as columns of a matrix P, will give a diagonalization (5.2.4). What is needed, then, are linearly independent eigenvectors. That is exactly what we have in Example (4.2.10): if we let $P = [v_1, v_2]$, then since v_1 and v_2 are independent, P is invertible and we get (5.2.4). A similar situation obtains with Example (5.2.12), except here we note that the matrix P (as well as the diagonal matrix D) have complex entries, even though A was a real matrix to start with. In the case of Example (5.2.11), however, all eigenvectors are multiples of the single eigenvector v_1. In this case there is no way to make a matrix P (whose columns are eigenvectors) which is invertible. So there is no possibility for an equation of the form (5.2.4).

Of course, in the case of Examples (5.2.10) and (5.2.12) we still have to compute P^{-1} to write A in the form (5.2.4). For 2 by 2 matrices this is an easy matter, and for completeness we record the results here:

Example (5.2.10) in form (5.2.4)

$$\begin{bmatrix} 2 & 2 \\ -2 & -3 \end{bmatrix} = \begin{bmatrix} -2 & -\frac{1}{2} \\ 1 & 1 \end{bmatrix} \begin{bmatrix} 1 & \\ & -2 \end{bmatrix} \begin{bmatrix} -\frac{2}{3} & -\frac{1}{3} \\ \frac{2}{3} & \frac{4}{3} \end{bmatrix}$$

Example (5.2.12) in form (5.2.4)

$$\begin{bmatrix} 0 & 1 \\ -1 & 0 \end{bmatrix} = \begin{bmatrix} -i & i \\ 1 & 1 \end{bmatrix}\begin{bmatrix} i & \\ & -i \end{bmatrix}\begin{bmatrix} \frac{1}{2}i & \frac{1}{2} \\ -\frac{1}{2}i & \frac{1}{2} \end{bmatrix}$$

In both of our successful examples we found a pair of distinct eigenvalues for the 2 by 2 matrix A, and then it turned out that we had, in fact, linearly independent eigenvalues. As we shall now see, this phenomenon also occurs in larger matrices, and is moreover the typical case.

(5.2.13) Independence of Eigenvectors with Distinct Eigenvalues. Let A be an n by n matrix. Suppose $\lambda_1, \ldots, \lambda_k$ are eigenvalues of A with $\lambda_i \neq \lambda_j$ for $i \neq j$, and suppose $v_1, \ldots, v_k$ are corresponding eigenvectors. Then $x_1, \ldots, x_k$ are linearly independent.

To prove (5.2.13), assume that $a_1 v_1 + \cdots + a_k v_k = 0$ for some numbers $a_1, \ldots, a_k$. Then $0 = A(a_1 v_1 + \cdots + a_k v_k) = a_1 A v_1 + \cdots + a_k A v_k = a_1 \lambda_1 v_1 + \cdots + a_k \lambda_k v_k$, and also $0 = \lambda_1(a_1 v_1 + \cdots + a_k v_k) = a_1 \lambda_1 v_1 + \cdots + a_k \lambda_k v_k$. Subtracting, we have $0 = (a_1 \lambda_1 v_1 + \cdots + a_k \lambda_k v_k) - (a_1 \lambda_1 v_1 + \cdots + a_k \lambda_k v_k)$, or

$$(5.2.14) \qquad 0 = a_2(\lambda_2 - \lambda_1)v_2 + \cdots + a_k(\lambda_k - \lambda_k)v_k$$

Multiplying (5.2.14) by first A, then by λ_2, and subtracting gives

$$(5.2.15) \quad 0 = a_3(\lambda_3 - \lambda_1)(\lambda_3 - \lambda_2)v_3 + \cdots + a_k(\lambda_k - \lambda_1)(\lambda_k - \lambda_2)v_k$$

Continuing with $\lambda_3, \lambda_4, \ldots, \lambda_{k-1}$ gives a sequence of new equations, ending with:

$$(5.2.16) \qquad 0 = a_{k-1}(\lambda_{k-1} - \lambda_1) \cdots (\lambda_{k-1} - \lambda_{k-2})v_{k-1}$$
$$+ a_k(\lambda_k - \lambda_1) \cdots (\lambda_k - \lambda_{k-2})v_k$$

$$(5.2.17) \qquad 0 = a_k(\lambda_k - \lambda_1) \cdots (\lambda_k - \lambda_{k-1})v_k$$

Since $v_k \neq 0$ and all the differences $\lambda_k - \lambda_1, \ldots, \lambda_k - \lambda_{k-1}$ are nonzero (all λ_i are different), from (5.2.17) we have $a_k = 0$. Then (5.2.16) becomes $0 = a_{k-1}(\lambda_{k-1} - \lambda_1) \cdots (\lambda_{k-1} - \lambda_{k-2})v_{k-1}$, and since $v_{k-1} \neq 0$ and the differences $\lambda_{k-1} - \lambda_1, \ldots, \lambda_{k-1} - \lambda_{k-2}$ are nonzero, $a_{k-1} = 0$ also. Climbing back up through all the equations we find $a_k = a_{k-1} = \cdots = a_2 = 0$. Then our original equation $a_1 v_1 + \cdots + a_k v_k = 0$ implies $a_1 v_1 = 0$, so $a_1 = 0$ also.

Because of (5.2.13), the most convenient situation to have for the eigenvalue/eigenvector problem is when the n by n matrix A has n distinct eigenvalues. For brevity, we describe these circumstances as saying that A has *distinct eigenvalues*. Since to each eigenvalue there always is a corresponding eigenvector, and (5.2.13) implies that these eigenvectors are automatically linearly independent, if A has distinct eigenvalues it is diagonalizable. In the form (5.2.4), the diagonal entries $\lambda_1, \ldots, \lambda_n$ of D are the distinct eigenvalues of A.

How likely is it that the n by n matrix A has distinct eigenvalues? This, as it turns out, is a question in polynomial algebra. It is always the case that the characteristic polynomial $\text{char}(A, t)$ can be written as a product of complex polynomials of the form $(\alpha_i - t)$, $i = 1, \ldots, n$, [so $\text{char}(A, t) = (\alpha_1 - t) \cdots (\alpha_n - t)$] for some complex numbers $\alpha_1, \ldots, \alpha_n$. The numbers α_i are the eigenvalues of A, but not all the α_i need to be distinct. To tell if they are distinct, we look at the t-derivative of $\text{char}(A, t)$: this is just a sum of terms, each a product of the factors $(\alpha_i - t)$ with one deleted. Putting a caret over the omitted factor we have

$$\frac{d}{dt}(\text{char}(A, t)) = - \sum_{i=1}^{n} (\alpha_1 - t) \cdots \widehat{(\alpha_i - t)} \cdots (\alpha_n - t)$$

If we evaluate $(d/dt)(\text{char}(A, t))$ at α_i, we obtain $-(\alpha_1 - \alpha_i) \cdots \widehat{(\alpha_i - \alpha_i)} \cdots (\alpha_n - \alpha_i)$ which is zero if $\alpha_j = \alpha_i$ for some $i \neq j$ and nonzero if no α_j equals α_i. So we conclude: A doesn't have distinct eigenvalues exactly when $\text{char}(A, t)$ and its derivative have a root in common.

Now $\text{char}(A, t)$ is a polynomial of degree n, say

$$\text{char}(A, t) = a_n t^n + a_{n-1} t^{n-1} + \cdots + a_1 t + a_0$$

For any polynomial $f(t) = b_n t^n + \cdots + b_1 t + b_0$ of degree n, there is a certain polynomial expression $d(b_0, \ldots, b_n)$ in the coefficients of f, called the *discriminant* of f, such that f and $(d/dt)f$ have a common root exactly when $d(b_0, \ldots, b_n) = 0$. (The discriminant is the resultant of f and its derivative; this resultant is a certain determinant. The theory of this sort of polynomial algebra is explained in advanced algebra texts.[†])

Now suppose the (i, j) entry of A is a_{ij}. Then, since $\text{char}(A, t) = \det(A - tI)$, the coefficients of the characteristic polynomial are polynomial functions of $a_{11}, \ldots, a_{nn}$. This means, finally, that for A to fail to have distinct eigenvalues a certain polynomial expression in the entries of A is zero, so A has distinct eigenvalues if $d(a_0(a_{11}, \ldots, a_{nn}), \ldots,$

[†]See, for example, B. L. van der Waerden, *Modern Algebra*, Ungar, New York, 1950, Chapter 11.

$a_n(a_{11}, \ldots, a_{nn})) \neq 0$. So having distinct eigenvalues means that a polynomial in the entries of A is nonzero. By the general theory of polynomial inequalities from Section 1.3, we have:

(5.2.18) An n by n matrix chosen at random has n distinct eigenvalues with probability one. In particular, it is diagonalizable.

This fact of likely diagonalizability is at the heart of all mechanical computational schemes for finding eigenvectors and eigenvalues: we don't make many mistakes assuming diagonalizability and distinct eigenvalues, and even if we run across a nondiagonalizable matrix by accident, only slight changes in entries will make it diagonalizable.

But of course all matrices are not diagonalizable, despite the assumptions of the computer routines for eigenvalues and eigenvectors. When using these programs, we need to keep this in mind, since the machine computations and round-off will indeed change matrix entries slightly and hence convert the assumptions to self-fulfilling prophecies. Thus (5.2.18) contains an important lesson: before an eigenvector machine computation is begun, we need to ask whether the assumption of distinct eigenvalues is a reasonable one.

With these caveats in mind, we return to our study of iteration equations. Our study of diagonalizability (5.2.4) was applied to the iteration equation to obtain Eq. (5.2.5). Actually, this equation is a bit awkward, as we have to produce the matrix P^{-1}, multiply it by various vectors, and then eliminate it with multiplication by P. There are more convenient ways of using eigenvectors to study the iteration equations, as we shall now see.

This time we will confine our attention to the homogeneous iteration equation [$b = 0$ in (5.1.3)]:

(5.2.19) $x^{(k+1)} = Ax^{(k)}$ where A is n by n and $x^{(0)}$ is a given n-vector.

Assume in (5.2.19) that A has linearly independent eigenvectors $v_1, \ldots, v_n$ with eigenvalues $\lambda_1, \ldots, \lambda_n$. Then there are numbers $a_1, \ldots, a_n$ such that

$$(5.2.20) \qquad x^{(0)} = a_1 v_1 + \cdots + a_n v_n$$

Multiplying (5.2.20) by A, and repeating, gives

$$x^{(1)} = Ax^{(0)} = a_1 \lambda_1 v_1 + \cdots + a_n \lambda_n v_n$$

$$(5.2.21) \qquad x^{(2)} = Ax^{(1)} = a_1 \lambda_1^2 v_1 + \cdots + a_n \lambda_n^2 v_n$$

$$\vdots$$

$$x^{(k)} = Ax^{(k-1)} = a_1 \lambda_1^k v_1 + \cdots + a_n \lambda_n^k v_n$$

Remember that, in general, the eigenvalues $\lambda_1, \ldots, \lambda_n$ of A are distinct (complex) numbers. In many cases, this means that there is one, say λ_1, of largest absolute value. So $|\lambda_1| > |\lambda_i|$ if $i \neq 1$, which means that the quotient $\lambda_i^k/\lambda_1^k = (\lambda_i/\lambda_1)^k$, which has absolute value $(|\lambda_i|/|\lambda_1|)^k$, is approximately zero for large k. If we divide (5.2.21) by λ_1^k, we obtain

$$\lambda_1^{-k} x^{(k)} = a_1 v_1 + a_2 (\lambda_2/\lambda_1)^k v_2 + \cdots + a_n (\lambda_n/\lambda_n)^k v_n$$

and for large k the right-hand side is approximately $a_1 v_1$ (the other coefficients being approximately zero). So:

(5.2.22) If $|\lambda_1| > |\lambda_i|$ for $i \neq 1$, then (5.2.21) becomes $x^{(k)} = a_1 \lambda_1^k v_1$ (approximately) for large k. There are three conclusions to draw from (5.2.22):

1. If $a_1 \neq 0$ and $|\lambda_1| > 1$, then some entries of $x^{(k)}$ become arbitrarily large as k gets large.
2. If $a_1 \neq 0$ and $|\lambda_1| < 1$, then all entries of $x^{(k)}$ go to zero as k gets large.
3. If $a_1 \neq 0$ and $|\lambda_1| = 1$, then all entries of $x^{(k)}$ stay approximately constant in absolute value as k gets large.

Other conclusions can be drawn from (5.2.22) also, the most important of which is that for large k, since $x^{(k)} = a_1 \lambda_1^k v_1$ (approximately) and $x^{(k+1)} = a_1 \lambda_1^{k+1} v_1$ (approximately) then

(5.2.23) If $|\lambda_1| > |\lambda_i|$ for $i \neq 1$, then (5.2.19) becomes $x^{(k+1)} = \lambda_1 x^{(k)}$ (approximately).

Equation (5.2.23) has two important implications for eigenvalue problems. First, it tells us that if there is an eigenvalue of maximal absolute value for the matrix, then it comes to dominate the long-term change of any system modeled by the matrix, in the sense that the state change becomes just multiplication by the eigenvalue (approximately). Second, it suggests that a possible way to discover this dominating eigenvalue (if there is one) is by tracking the ratio of corresponding components in the vectors $x^{(0)}, x^{(1)}, x^{(2)}, \ldots$.

Under certain circumstances, both implications are used together. Suppose we are studying a "mature" system; that is, a system modeled by the homogeneous iteration equation (5.2.19) where we are observing $x^{(k)}$ and can assume k is large. Then we should see the change from time k to time $k + 1$ in the form (5.2.23), and we can understand the change ratio λ_1 as the largest eigenvalue of the modeling matrix A.

The second implication also suggests a method for finding, approximately, an eigenvalue of A. Actually, the problem of finding eigenvalues, approximately, can be done more directly, at least for matrices of moderate size: by (5.2.9), the eigenvalues of A are the roots of $\text{char}(A, t)$. If this polynomial can be computed, then there are various standard procedures for finding the roots of it, approximately. (For example, if all the roots are real numbers we can use Newton's method, as explained in any calculus text.)

Finding eigenvectors, however, is a subtler problem. Suppose a number μ has been found which is known to be an approximate root of $\text{char}(A, t)$, in the sense that $0 < |\text{char}(A, \mu)| < \varepsilon$ for some small number ε. This means that μ is *close* to an eigenvalue λ of A. But μ *isn't* an eigenvalue, so there is no nonzero vector v with $Av = \mu v$. That is, the linear system $(A - \mu I)x = 0$ is of no help in finding an eigenvector, even if μ is close to an eigenvalue.

There are various solutions to these dilemmas. One involves using Eq. (5.2.22): it says that for large k the vector $x^{(k)} = A^k x^{(0)}$ is, approximately, an eigenvector (every multiple of the eigenvector v_1 is also an eigenvector with the same eigenvalue) corresponding to the dominant eigenvalue. For this to be true, we need, in the notation of (5.2.22), that $a_1 \neq 0$. This will be true with probability one for an $x^{(0)}$ chosen at random, so we can essentially choose anything for $x^{(0)}$. If we choose $x^{(0)}$ to be the jth column of A, then $x^{(k)}$ will be the jth column of A^k, so we could even proceed by just computing A^k for large k. In that case, we would expect the columns of A^k to all be multiples of each other. This is a method that has some practical use, at least in certain cases, and we will use a variant of it in Section 5.5.

The "matrix power" method for eigenvectors of the preceding paragraph is only going to discover the eigenvector v_1 corresponding to the dominant eigenvalue λ_1. Methods that yield all the eigenvectors and eigenvalues are based on an incremental version of the diagonalization equation (5.2.4): if we have $A = PDP^{-1}$ for D diagonal, then $P^{-1}AP = D$. That is, the matrix A is modified by operating on it with the invertible matrix P to get a diagonal matrix D. What we will do is consider operating on the matrix A by invertible matrices with the goal of just making A closer to a diagonal matrix. Our basic operation is called conjugation:

(5.2.24) Let A be an n by n matrix and T an invertible n by n matrix. The matrix $T^{-1}AT$ is called the *conjugate* of A by T.

We want to focus especially on the effect of conjugation on eigenvalues and eigenvectors:

(5.2.25) Suppose that A is an n by n matrix with eigenvectors $v_1, \ldots, v_k$ and corresponding eigenvalues $\lambda_1, \ldots, \lambda_k$, and that T is an invertible n by n matrix. Then $T^{-1}AT$ has eigenvectors $T^{-1}v_1, \ldots, T^{-1}v_k$ with corresponding eigenvalues $\lambda_1, \ldots, \lambda_k$.

Now we prove (5.2.25): let v be an eigenvector of A with eigenvalue λ. Then $T^{-1}AT(T^{-1}v) = T^{-1}Av = T^{-1}\lambda v = \lambda(T^{-1}v)$, so $T^{-1}v$ is an eigenvector of $T^{-1}AT$ of eigenvalue λ. This shows that $T^{-1}v_1, \ldots, T^{-1}v_k$ are eigenvectors of $T^{-1}AT$ with eigenvalues $\lambda_1, \ldots, \lambda_k$. If w is an eigenvector of $T^{-1}AT$ of eigenvalue μ, then $T^{-1}ATw = \mu w$, so $A(Tw) = \mu(Tw)$ (after multiplying both sides by T) which means Tw is an eigenvector of A and so $Tw = v_i$ for some i. This means $w = T^{-1}v_i$ and $\mu = \lambda_i$, so the only eigenvectors and eigenvalues of $T^{-1}AT$ are $T^{-1}v_1, \ldots, T^{-1}v_k$ and $\lambda_1, \ldots, \lambda_k$.

From (5.2.25), we know that conjugation moves the eigenvectors but keeps the same eigenvalues. The strategy is to conjugate towards a diagonal matrix. We need to ask how problems can arise. One possible problem is to get eigenvectors too close to each other to be numerically distinct. Since the relevant thing about eigenvectors is the direction they point (changing an eigenvector by a scalar multiple just gives another eigenvector with the same eigenvalue), what we need to guard against is changing the angles between eigenvectors. In terms of the conjugation (5.2.25), and the definition of angle between vectors (4.1.3), we can see that these angles will all be preserved if we have

$$(5.2.26) \qquad v_i^T(v_j) = \left(T^{-1}v_i\right)^T\left(T^{-1}v_j\right) \qquad \text{for } 1 \le i, j \le k.$$

Because of problem 6 Exercises 5.2, we know that (5.2.26) will hold if $T^TT = I$. Thus the most desirable type of conjugation to make is by an *orthogonal* matrix T; that is, by a matrix satisfying $T^TT = I$ (4.1.6). This is also an easy conjugation, since $T^{-1} = T^T$.

If we start with a matrix A, then there is an orthogonal matrix Q_1 associated to A, namely, the matrix in the Q-R decomposition $A = Q_1R_1$ [see (4.1.23)]. (We will explain the subscripts shortly.) The conjugation of A by Q_1 gives $Q_1^{-1}AQ_1 = Q_1^{-1}Q_1R_1Q_1 = R_1Q_1$. The matrix R_1Q_1 also has an orthogonal matrix associated to it, from its Q-R decomposition $R_1Q_1 = Q_2R_2$. Conjugation of R_1Q_1 by Q_2 gives $Q_2^{-1}R_1Q_1Q_2 = R_2Q_2$, which has a Q-R decomposition $R_2Q_2 = Q_3R_3$; conjugation by Q_3 gives $R_3Q_3 = Q_4R_4$; and so on. At each stage the eigenvectors change according to (5.2.25), with the eigenvalues staying the same. Moreover, we know that the angles between eigenvectors are being preserved. It is a remarkable fact that this procedure leads to a method for calculating eigenvectors and eigenvalues. It is called the *Q-R algorithm*. To see why it works requires a deep study of the numerical analysis of matrices. (A proof can be found, e.g., in *Computational Methods for Matrix Eigenproblems*[†].) That it does work, however, will be part of our subsequent experience, since it is the mathematical basis for

---

[†] By A. R. Gourlay and G. A. Watson, Wiley, London, 1973, Chapter 10.

the eigenvector/eigenvalue procedures that we will use for computer solution.

Formally, the Q-R algorithm amounts to the following process:

(5.2.27) Q-R algorithm. Let A be an n by n matrix.

Step 1 (preparation). An n by n orthogonal matrix U is found so that $A_1 = U^{-1}AU$ has all its entries zero in positions (i, j) where $i > j + 1$.[†]

Step k to step $k + 1$. Let λ_k be the (complex) eigenvalue of the 2 by 2 matrix made up of the last two rows and columns of A_k which is closest in absolute value to the (k, k) entry of A_k. Form the Q-R factorization of $A_k - \lambda_k I_n = Q_k R_k$. Then define $A_{k+1} = \lambda_k I_n + R_k Q_k$.

Then the following facts hold for the sequence of matrices $A_1, A_2, A_3, \ldots$:

1. Each of the matrices A_k has only zero entries in positions (i, j) where $i > j + 1$.
2. For each k, $Q_k^{-1} A_k Q_k = A_{k+1}$.
3. As k gets large, the entries in positions $(i, i + 1)$, $i = 1, \ldots, n - 1$ approach zero.

From (5.2.7), we have a sequence of orthogonal conjugations leading from A to a matrix A_k which, for large k, is (approximately) an upper triangular matrix. Since the eigenvalues and eigenvectors of a triangular matrix can readily be found, we have found (approximately) the eigenvectors and eigenvalues of A.

There is one final topic in the theory of eigenvectors and eigenvalues that we will need subsequently: since eigenvectors and eigenvalues can be complex numbers, the general theory works just as well with complex matrices as with real ones. In the case where the matrix is real, there is a slight simplification in the way complex eigenvalues and eigenvectors occur; since some eigenvalue routines take advantage of this simplification, we will need to know it.

(5.2.28) Let A be an n by n (real) matrix. Suppose A has distinct eigenvalues. As $\text{char}(A, t) = \det(A - tI)$ is a real polynomial, its roots are either real or occur in complex conjugate pairs. Assume

$$\lambda_k = a + ib$$

$$a, b \text{ real numbers}$$

$$\lambda_{k+1} = a - ib$$

[†]See Gourlay and Watson, *Computational Methods*, pp. 102–105.

are a pair of complex conjugate eigenvalues of A. Then corresponding eigenvectors can be found in the form

$$v_k = r + is$$

$$r, s \text{ real } n\text{-vectors}$$

$$v_{k+1} = r - is$$

To verify (5.2.28), we first observe that any eigenvector v_k of eigenvalue λ_k can be written in the form $v_k = r + is$, r, s real vectors. Then the eigenvalue formula

$$Av_k = \lambda_k v_k$$

becomes

$$Ar + iAs = (a + ib)(r + is) = (ar - bs) + i(br + as)$$

or, since A, k, r, s are all real,

$$Ar = (ar - bs) \quad \text{and} \quad As = (br + as)$$

Hence

$$A(r - is) = (ar - bs) + i(-br - as) = (a - ib)(r - is)$$

which shows that $r - is$ is an eigenvector of eigenvalue $a - ib = \lambda_{k+1}$, completing the proof of (5.2.28).

EXERCISES 5.2

1. Prove that if v is an eigenvector of the matrix A of eigenvalue λ, so is av for any scalar $a \neq 0$.

2. Let $A = \begin{bmatrix} a & b \\ c & d \end{bmatrix}$.
   (a) Show that $\text{char}(A, t) = t^2 - (a + d)t + (ad - bc)$.
   (b) Write the condition (as a polynomial in a, b, c, d to be nonzero) for A to have two distinct eigenvalues.

3. Prove that if A is a real $n \times n$ matrix and $A = A^T$, then all eigenvalues of A are real numbers.

4. Let $A = \begin{bmatrix} 0 & \frac{1}{2} \\ -1 & \frac{3}{2} \end{bmatrix}$.

   (a) Compute the eigenvalues of A.

   (b) Approximate the eigenvalues of A by calculating $x^{(10)}$ from (5.2.21) with $x^{(0)}$ having both entries 1. [Use the program of Figure (5.1.5) with $B = 0$].

5. Let v be an eigenvector of A of eigenvalue λ. Prove that if $B = a_m A^m + a_{m-1} A^{m-1} + \cdots + a_0 I$, then v is an eigenvector of B. What is the eigenvalue?

6. Prove that for a real $n \times n$ matrix Q we have $Q^T Q = I$ if and only if $(Qv)^T(Qw) = v^T w$ for all n-vectors v and w.

7. Calculate all the eigenvalues and corresponding eigenvectors for the following matrices:

   (a) $\begin{bmatrix} 1 & 1 & 1 \\ 0 & 2 & 1 \\ 0 & 0 & 3 \end{bmatrix}$ (b) $\begin{bmatrix} 1 & 1 & 1 \\ 1 & 1 & 1 \\ 1 & 1 & 1 \end{bmatrix}$

8. Can zero be an eigenvalue of a matrix?

9. Let A be the 2×2 matrix of Example (5.2.10). Let $A_1 = A$ and for each k let $A_k = Q_k R_k$ be the Q-R decomposition of A_k and then let $A_{k+1} = R_k Q_k$. Calculate A_5. How close are you at this stage to an eigenvalue of A?

5.3   COMPUTATION OF EIGENVECTORS AND EIGENVALUES

Finding eigenvalues and eigenvectors of a matrix is a difficult computational problem. The theory (find roots of the characteristic polynomial for eigenvalues and solve the corresponding linear problem for eigenvectors) and the practical methods [the Q-R algorithm (5.2.27)] are genuinely different in their conceptual foundations. Unlike the situation in some of our earlier uses of program libraries, where we would envision the machine implementation of the theoretical solution procedure as being just a variation (forced by considerations of numerical accuracy and programming efficiency) of the theory, it is really not legitimate to imagine that the eigenproblem procedures we will be using are computing characteristic polynomials, locating their roots, and then row reducing for eigenvectors. This means that the user of these procedures must either study the numerical methods underlying the procedures—which, as noted, is a genuinely different topic in the eigenproblem case—or must be willing to assume that the procedures do what they are intended to do, and defer the study of the methods. We will adopt the latter course here. But it is hoped that the reader, like the calculus student who must accept on faith the assertion that the real numbers are complete, will ultimately have the opportunity to undertake the studies which establish the logical basis for the acceptance of methods they are adequately prepared to use, if not to rigorously justify.

We will study two FORTRAN callable procedures which yield eigenvectors and eigenvalues of matrices: a procedure called EISPAC, which in turn calls a selection of routines from a library called EISPACK, and a procedure called EIGRF, which is part of, and uses, a program library called IMSL. In dealing with eigenvalue/eigenvector problems, as we have seen, it is necessary to consider complex numbers and vectors with complex entries. There are basically two strategies for dealing with complex numbers in FORTRAN, and the two procedures we study, since they each adopt one of the strategies, will exemplify the positive and negative features of each.

One way to deal with a complex number $z = a + ib$ in FORTRAN is to reserve two storage locations, say A and B, to hold the real and imaginary parts, a and b, of z separately. If $w = c + id$ is another complex number whose real and imaginary parts are c, d, then we can compute $z + w$, zw, and z/w from the formulas:

$$z + w = (a + c) + i(b + d)$$

$$zw = (ac - bd) + i(ad + bi)$$

$$z/w = (c^2 + d^2)^{-1/2}((ac + bd) + i(bc - ad))$$

For example, to replace z by zw we put $ac - bd$ into A and $ad + bc$ into B.

This strategy (storing a complex number as a pair of FORTRAN real numbers) requires a bit of complication in programming, since we need to use the above formulas for arithmetic, but is is not hard to imagine how such complex arithmetic can be handled by some subroutines. The EISPAC procedure uses this strategy. There is a reward for the additional complications: it is possible, with this procedure, to use double precision on both the real and imaginary parts of a complex number. Since the eigenvalue algorithm involves a converging process, this additional accuracy can be important.

We will use the EISPAC procedure to obtain the eigenvectors and eigenvalues of a real N by N matrix stored in an array A of leading dimension LDA. The eigenvalues will appear in two N-vectors WR and WI [where $WR(K)$ is the real part of the Kth eigenvalue and $WI(K)$ its imaginary part: $\lambda_K = WR(K) + iWI(K)$], and the eigenvectors will appear in an N by N array ZP, with each column of ZP determining an eigenvector, according to the following scheme: if the eigenvalue λ_k is real, then the kth column of ZP will be an eigenvector v_k of eigenvalue λ_k. If λ_k is not real and has a positive imaginary part, then column k of ZP contains the real part of an eigenvector v_k of eigenvalue λ_k, and column $k + 1$ contains the imaginary part, so $v_k = ZP_k + iZP_{k+1}$. Then λ_{k+1} is the complex conjugate of λ_k and an eigenvector v_{k+1} with eigenvalue λ_{k+1} is $v_{k+1} = ZP_k - iZP_{k+1}$ [see (5.2.28)].

Under these assumptions, the procedure call looks like this:

(5.3.1)

CALL EISPAC(LDA, N, MATRIX ('REAL', A), VALUES (WR,WI), VECTOR (ZP))

where A is an N by N real matrix whose eigenvalues and eigenvectors are to be computed. On return, the eigenvalues of A are stored in WR, WI as

$$\lambda_k = WR(K) + iWI(K) \qquad i = 1, \ldots, N$$

and the eigenvectors of A are stored in columns $ZP_1, \ldots, ZP_N$ of ZP as

1. If λ_k is real then $v_k = ZP_k$ is an eigenvector with eigenvalue λ_k.
2. If λ_k is nonreal with $WI(K) > 0$ then $v_k = ZP_k + iZP_{k+1}$ is an eigenvector of eigenvalue λ_k and $v_{k+1} = ZP_k - iZP_{k+1}$ is an eigenvector of eigenvalue λ_{k+1}.

Using the EISPAC procedure is quite simple: we need to establish the vectors WR, WI and the matrix ZP, read in A, call the procedure, and write out the results. The input of A is standard. The establishment of WR, and so on, needs only the notation that *double precision* is expected, and is done with a declaration like

REAL*8 WR(15),WI(15),ZP(15,15)

To write the results is the only tricky business. The problem is to unwind the storage scheme used in numbers 1 and 2 of (5.3.1) to keep the eigenvectors of A in ZP. To do that, we will use an additional matrix ZI, and manipulate the results of the call to EISPAC so that for each k we have $v_k = ZP_k + iZI_k$. If λ_k is real, that is, if $WI(K) = 0$, then we want ZP_k as is, and $ZI_k = 0$. So we begin the manipulation with

```
      IF (WI(K).NE.0.0) GO TO 30
      DO 20 J = 1,N
      ZI(J,K) = 0.0
 20   CONTINUE
      GO TO 70   (70 is the end of a "K" loop; this is to get the next K)
```

If λ_k is complex, that is, if $WI(K) \neq 0$, then we have two forms of v_k. If $WI(K) > 0$, then we need ZP_k as is, and $ZI_k = ZP_{k+1}$. So, continuing in the program, we have

```
 30   IF (WI(K).LT.0.0) GO TO 50
      DO 40 J = 1,N
      ZI(J,K) = ZP(J,K + 1)
 40   CONTINUE
      GO TO 70
```

It remains to deal with the case $WI(K) < 0$. Then we need ZP_{k-1} in ZP_k (to be the real part of v_k) and $-ZI_k$ in ZI_k (to be the imaginary part): this is from the second equation in number 2 of (5.3.1), $v_k = ZP_{k-1} - iZP_k$. This we do as follows:

```
 50   DO 60 J = 1,N
      ZP(J,K) = ZP(J,K − 1)
      ZI(J,K) = −ZI(J,K − 1)
 60   CONTINUE
```

All these steps are done for each K from 1 to N, of course. When we write out the eigenvectors and eigenvalues, this will be done with appropriate labels. Here is a complete program [Fig. (5.3.2)]

Figure (5.3.2).

```
C     COMPUTES EIGENVECTORS AND EIGENVALUES OF N BY N MATRIX A
C     USES EISPAC
C         FIRST CARD N
C         NEXT CARDS N BY ROWS
 1000     FORMAT('0')
  120     FORMAT('0 MATRIX A OF SIZE ',I2,2X,'BY ',I2)
  130     FORMAT('0 EIGENVALUE NUMBER ',I2)
  140     FORMAT('0 EIGENVECTOR NUMBER ',I2)
          REAL*8 A(15,15),WR(15),WI(15),ZP(15,15),ZI(15,15)
          DATA LDA/15/
          READ(5,*) N
```

Figure (5.3.2) (continued).

```
        WRITE(6,120) N,N
        WRITE(6,1000)
        DO 10 I=1,N
        READ(5,*)(A(I,J),J=1,N)
        WRITE(6,*)(A(I,J),J=1,N)
10      CONTINUE
        CALL EISPAC(LDA,N,MATRIX('REAL',A),VALUES(WR,WI),VECTOR(ZP))
        DO 70 K=1,N
        IF(WI(K).NE.0.0) GO TO 30
        DO 20 J=1,N
        ZI(J,K)=0.0
20      CONTINUE
        GO TO 70
30      IF(WI(K).LT.0.0) GO TO 50
        DO 40 J=1,N
        ZI(J,K)=ZP(J,K+1)
40      CONTINUE
        GO TO 70
50      DO 60 J=1,N
        ZP(J,K)=ZP(J,K-1)
        ZI(J,K)= -ZI(J,K-1)
60      CONTINUE
70      CONTINUE
        DO 90 I=1,N
        WRITE(6,130) I
        WRITE(6,*) WR(I),WI(I)
        WRITE(6,140) I
        DO 80 J=1,N
        WRITE(6,*) ZP(J,I),ZI(J,I)
80      CONTINUE
90      CONTINUE
        STOP
        END
```

The strategy of storing the real and imaginary part of a complex number separately and then programming complex arithmetic in terms of real and imaginary parts is not the only way to handle complex numbers in FORTRAN. Actually, FORTRAN has the capacity to handle complex arithmetic, as long as the complex variables are explicitly declared. Complex numbers are read and printed as pairs of reals: if $z = a + ib$, then z is read or printed as $z = (a, b)$. The procedure EIGRF in the IMSL library which we will now discuss uses this FORTRAN complex arithmetic. This will only yield single-precision eigenvectors and eigenvalues, but they will be stored in FORTRAN complex form, so we can do additional operations on these numbers or vectors.

We will use EIGRF to obtain the eigenvectors and eigenvalues of a real N by N matrix stored in the array A of leading dimension LDA. The eigenvalues will be stored in a complex N-vector W and the corresponding eigenvectors in the columns of the complex array Z of leading dimension LDZ. Here is the procedure call:

(5.3.3)

CALL EIGRF(A,N,LDA,IJOB,W,Z,LDZ,WK,IER)

In (5.3.3), IJOB is an integer parameter, which we set to 2 to get both eigenvalues and eigenvectors (other choices solve associated problems), IER is an integer which reports certain errors in the computation process: IER $\neq$ 0 means some of these errors have occurred, and WK is a real vector of length at least N^2 used as a move area by the procedure. The first entry $WK(1)$ will contain something called the "performance index" which is a sort of measure of reliability of the results: if it is less than 10, the results are good, between 10 and 100 just OK, and poor if $WK(1)$ exceeds 100.

Using EIGRF is very simple: we reserve space for W, Z, A, WK, read A, call EIGRF, and write the results. The only novelty is declaring W and Z to be complex; this is done in a declaration like

COMPLEX W(15),Z(15,15)

A program using EIGRF now follows [Fig. (5.3.4)]:

Figure (5.3.4).

```
C     COMPUTES EIGENVECTORS AND EIGENVALUES OF N BY N MATRIX A
C     USES IMSL PROCEDURE EIGRF
C         FIRST CARD N
C         NEXT CARDS A BY ROWS
C         SEE IMSL MANUAL FOR PERFORMANCE INDEX AND IER
 1000     FORMAT('0')
  120     FORMAT('0 MATRIX A OF SIZE ',I2,2X,'BY ',I2)
  130     FORMAT('0 EIGENVALUE NUMBER ',I2)
  140     FORMAT('0 EIGENVECTOR NUMBER ',I2)
  150     FORMAT('0 PERFORMANCE INDEX ',E10.3)
  160     FORMAT('0 IER= ',I4)
          REAL A(15,15),WK(255)
          COMPLEX W(15),Z(15,15)
          DATA LDA/15/
          DATA LDZ/15/
          READ(5,*) N
          WRITE(6,120) N,N
          WRITE(6,1000)
          DO 10 I=1,N
          READ(5,*)(A(I,J),J=1,N)
          WRITE(6,*)(A(K,J),J=1,N)
```

Figure (5.3.4) (continued).

```
10   CONTINUE
     IJOB=2
     CALL EIGRF(A,N,LDA,IJOB,W,Z,LDZ,WK,IER)
     DO 20 I=1,N
     WRITE(6,130) I
     WRITE(6,*) W(I)
     WRITE(6,140) I
     DO 30 J=1,N
     WRITE(6,*) Z(J,I)
30   CONTINUE
20   CONTINUE
     WRITE(6,150) WK(1)
     WRITE(6,160) IER
     STOP
     END
```

So far, no advantage has been taken of the fact that EIGRF is working in FORTRAN complex arithmetic. We shall now do so.

Recall that in studying the homogeneous iteration equation (5.2.19), which was the motivating equation for the eigenvalue problem, we need to express our start vector as a linear combination of eigenvectors as in (5.2.20). That is, we have the matrix A with eigenvectors $v_1, \ldots, v_k$. We want to express an arbitrary vector b as a linear combination of $v_1, \ldots, v_n$: so, we seek the (unknown) scalars $x_1, \ldots, x_n$ such that $b = x_1 v_1 + \cdots + x_n v_n$, or, in matrix form,

$$(5.3.5) \qquad \begin{bmatrix} v_1 & \cdots & v_n \end{bmatrix} \begin{bmatrix} x_1 \\ \vdots \\ x_n \end{bmatrix} = b$$

Now the matrix $[v_1 \cdots v_n]$ in (5.3.5) is exactly the matrix in Z after EIGRF has been called for A. Thus (5.3.5) is the matrix equation

$$(5.3.6) \qquad Zx = b \qquad \text{where } x = \begin{bmatrix} x_1 \\ \vdots \\ x_n \end{bmatrix} \quad (\text{to be solved for } x)$$

This is exactly the type of equation we considered and solved in Section 2.4 via the LINPACK program listed in Figure (2.4.4a), using the procedures SGECO and SGESL to find the $L - U$ decomposition of Z and solve (5.3.6) using back substitution. These procedures are not applicable directly to Z, since Z is complex. However, LINPACK *does* contain versions of these procedures to deal with the case that Z is complex: they are called CGECO and CGESL ("C" for complex) and they are used just like the "S"-prefixed procedures are. Since complex FORTRAN arithmetic is being used, it is necessary to regard x and b as complex also, and so declare them.

Modifying the program in Figure (5.3.4) to solve (5.3.6), then, is just a matter of appending an appropriate version of the program in Figure (2.4.4a) to (5.3.4): we use U for the complex vector to hold x in (5.3.6) and B for the complex vector to hold b (when we read b into B, we assume b real so we do not need any special formats for the entities). If Z happens to have zero reciprocal condition number, we report this by saying that "the eigenvectors are dependent," since the columns of Z are the eigenvectors of A. The program now follows:

Figure (5.3.7).

```
C     COMPUTES EIGENVECTORS AND EIGENVALUES OF N BY N MATRIX A
C     EXPRESSES B AS LINEAR COMBINATION OF EIGENVECTORS
C     USES IMSL PROCEDURE EIGRF
C        FIRST CARD N
C        NEXT CARDS A BY ROWS
C        NEXT CARDS B BY ENTRIES
C        SEE IMSL MANUAL FOR PERFORMANCE INDEX AND IER
 1000    FORMAT('0')
  120    FORMAT('0 MATRIX A OF SIZE ',I2,2X,'BY ',I2)
  130    FORMAT('0 EIGENVALUE NUMBER ',I2)
  140    FORMAT('0 EIGENVECTOR NUMBER ',I2)
  150    FORMAT('0 PERFORMANCE INDEX ',E10.3)
  160    FORMAT('0 IER= ',I4)
  170    FORMAT('0 RCOND= ',E10.3)
  180    FORMAT('0 THE INITIAL VECTOR B')
  190    FORMAT('0 THE COEFFICIENTS OF B AS A LINEAR COMB OF EVECTORS')
  200    FORMAT('0 THE EIGENVECTORS ARE DEPENDENT')
         REAL A(15,15),WK(255)
         COMPLEX W(15,),Z(15,15),U(15),B(15)
         INTEGER IPVT(15)
         DATA LDA/15/
         DATA LDZ/15/
         READ(5,*) N
         WRITE(6,120) N,N
         WRITE(6,1000)
         DO 10 I=1,N
         READ(5,*)(A(I,J),J=1,N)
         WRITE(6,*)(A(I,J),J=1,N)
   10    CONTINUE
         IJOB=2
         CALL EIGRF(A,N,LDA,IJOB,W,Z,LDZ,WK,IER)
         DO 20 I=1,N
```

Figure (5.3.7) (continued).

```
        WRITE(6,130) I
        WRITE(6,*) W(I)
        WRITE(6,140) I
        DO 30 J=1,N
        WRITE(6,*) Z(J,I)
30      CONTINUE
20      CONTINUE
        WRITE(6,150) WK(I)
        WRITE(6,160) IER
        CALL CGECO(Z,LDZ,N,IPVT,RCOND,U)
        WRITE(6,170)RCOND
        T=1.0+RCOND
        IF(T.EQ.1.0) GO TO 90
        WRITE(6,180)
        WRITE(6,1000)
        DO 40 I=1,N
        READ(5,*) B(I)
        WRITE(6,*) B(I)
40      CONTINUE
        CALL CGESL(Z,LDZ,N,IPVT,B,0)
        WRITE(6,190)
        WRITE(6,1000)
        WRITE(6,*) B(I),I=1,N)
        STOP
90      WRITE(6,200)
        STOP
        END
```

EXERCISES 5.3

All computations are to be done with both the programs of Figure (5.3.2) and Figure (5.3.4).

1. Calculate eigenvalues and eigenvectors for the matrix of Example (5.2.10) and reconcile the calculated answers with the ones obtained in the text.

2. Repeat problems 1 with Example (5.2.12).

3. Repeat problem 1 with Example (5.2.11).

4. Repeat problem 1 with problem 7(a) of Exercises 5.2.

5. Repeat problem 1 with problem 7(b) of Exercises 5.2.

6. In the answers to problems 1 through 5 can you tell any difference in accuracy between the two programs?

7. Let $x = 10^{-7}$ and $A = \begin{bmatrix} 1 + x & 1 \\ 0 & 1 \end{bmatrix}$. Compute the eigenvalues and eigenvectors of A. Can you tell any difference in accuracy between the two programs?

5.4   SOME HOMOGENEOUS MATRIX POWER MODELS

The basic homogeneous matrix power model has the form

$$(5.4.1) \qquad\qquad x^{(k+1)} = Ax^{(k)} \qquad k = 0, 1, 2, \ldots$$

where A is an n by n matrix and $x^{(0)}, x^{(1)}, \ldots$, are n-vectors. We regard $x^{(k)}$ as representing the state of a discrete time linear system at time k, and A as representing the transition from time k to time $k + 1$. Equation (5.4.1) can also be written in the form

$$(5.4.2) \qquad\qquad x^{(k)} = A^k x^{(0)}$$

emphasizing that the various states of the system over time are determined from the initial state $x^{(0)}$ and the transition matrix A. In (5.2.21), we saw the implications of the theory of eigenvectors and eigenvalues for (5.4.2) were as follows:

(5.4.3)   If A has eigenvalues $\lambda_1, \ldots, \lambda_n$ with corresponding linearly independent eigenvectors $v_1, \ldots, v_n$ and if $x^{(0)} = a_1 v_1 + \cdots + a_n v_n$, then

$$x^{(k)} = a_1 \lambda_1^k v_1 + \cdots + a_n \lambda_n^k v_n$$

To use this theory in applications, we proceed according to the following pattern: The *given data* are the transition matrix A and the initial-state vector $x^{(0)}$. To analyze the system (5.4.2) we *seek to find*

The eigenvectors and eigenvalues of A.

The expression of $x^{(0)}$ as a linear combination of eigenvectors.

From these two groups of information we can then use (5.4.3) to analyze (5.4.1). In this section, we will study three types of systems modeled by (5.4.1): growing populations, expanding economies, and linear difference equations.

A.   Populations.   Prior to the arrival of *homo sapiens* in North America at the end of the last glaciation (about 11,000 years ago), the Great Plains were occupied by large herds of large mammals (bison, antelope, etc.). By studying the present-day remnants of these herds, we have a good idea of their natural reproduction and growth rates. Furthermore, we can estimate, on the basis of direct fossil evidence and on the basis of inference from measurements of the amount of range land necessary to support the present-day animals, the size of the prehistoric herds. We also know how a human population of nomadic hunters and gatherers will grow, when there are no environmental limits, and how many animals will be required to feed individuals in the population, on the average, per year. What we want to study is the effect of introducing a small group of humans into North America and the interaction of the human and animal populations.

The most convenient method for population studies to to divide the population into groups of approximately the same age, called *age classes* or *cohorts*, such that the basic population–dynamic factors—survival and reproduction—are constant for that cohort. Assuming that we are interested in an annual census of the population, the simplest division would be into three cohorts:

Newborn (those still dependent on direct parental care).

Juvenile (the free-ranging but not yet reproducing).

Adults (those individuals capable of reproduction).

(In the case of the prehistoric herding mammals, the newborn would be of age from 0 to 1 year, the juveniles from 1 to 2 years, and the adults from 2 years on.) It would also not be unusual to have a fourth class of postreproductive adults, although this is not relevant to our animal study. And in the case of populations subject to close scrutiny, such as a contemporary human society or a herd of animals on a ranch, many more subdivisions into cohorts are possible. The important property of the division into cohorts is that, for the analysis intended, it must be possible to assume that all individuals in each cohort have the same probability of survival and rate of reproduction. Finally, we are going to assume, for each in formulating the study in matrix terms that, except for the last one, *each cohort has the same length in years*. This assumption may require us to regard some biologically natural cohorts as being subdivided into a number of smaller cohorts with the same reproductive and survival factors, but it will not cause any serious problems. The formal form the data take is the following:

(5.4.4) Population Growth in Age Classes. A fixed time interval T is specified. The population is divided into n cohorts $C_1, \ldots, C_n$ such that

Individuals of age 0 to age $< T$ are in cohort C_1.

Individuals of age T to age $< 2T$ are in cohort C_2.

$$\vdots$$

Individuals of age $(n - 2)T$ to age $< (n - 1)T$ are in cohort C_{n-1}.

Individuals of age $\geq (n - 1)T$ are in cohort C_n.

Each individual in cohort i survives an additional T years (and so advances to cohort $i + 1$ if $i < n$) with probability p_i. Each individual in cohort i produces q_i new individuals in T years (and so adds q_i new individuals to cohort 1). We use $x_i^{(k)}$ to denote the number of individuals in cohort C_i after k time intervals of length T have elapsed.

The data in (5.4.4) can be used to describe the transitions in the population from the kth time interval to the $(k + 1)$th: since each individual in cohort i contributes q_i new individuals to the population, we have

$$x_1^{(k+1)} = q_1 x_1^{(k)} + q_2 x_2^{(k)} + \cdots + q_n x_n^{(k)}$$

Since individuals in cohort C_i have to come from aging from cohort C_{i-1} (or staying in cohort C_n) we have

$$x_2^{(k+1)} = p_1 x_1^{(k)}$$

$$\vdots$$

$$x_{n-1}^{(k+1)} = p_{n-2} x_{n-2}^{(k)}$$

$$x_n^{(k+1)} = p_{n-1} x_{n-1}^{(k)} + p_n x_n^{(k)}$$

These can all be written in matrix form.

(5.4.5) In the notation of (5.4.4), let

$$A = \begin{bmatrix} q_1 & q_2 & & \cdots & q_n \\ p_1 & & & & \\ & p_2 & & & \\ & & \ddots & & \\ & & & p_{n-1} & p_n \end{bmatrix} \qquad x^{(k)} = \begin{bmatrix} x_1^{(k)} \\ \vdots \\ x_n^{(k)} \end{bmatrix}$$

Then $x^{(k+1)} = A x^{(k)}$. As we can see in (5.4.5), population growth in age classes is modeled by the iteration equation (5.4.1).

For our example of prehistoric animal herds, we set up the model as follows:

(5.4.6) $T = 1$ year, $n = 3$ cohorts:

C_1 (newborn), ages 0 to 1.
C_2 (juvenile), ages 1 to 2.
C_3 (adult), ages 2 and above.

Only adults reproduce, at a rate of 0.4 newborn per adult per year (a herd of 100 animals—50 male, 50 female—will have 40 calves born annually.) We assume 65% of the newborn survive to become juveniles, 78% of the juveniles survive to adults, and 92% of the adults survive to live another year. That is:

$$p_1 = 0.65, \qquad p_2 = 0.75, \qquad p_3 = 0.95$$

$$q_1 = 0, \qquad q_2 = 0, \qquad q_3 = 0.4$$

In terms of the matrix version (5.4.5), we have

$$A = \begin{bmatrix} 0 & 0 & 0.4 \\ 0.65 & 0 & 0 \\ 0 & 0.75 & 0.95 \end{bmatrix}$$

Since the age–class population growth model can be described (5.4.5) in terms of the basic homogeneous matrix power model, we can apply the eigenvector analysis of (5.4.3). In (5.2.23), we saw that if the eigenvalues of A were such that $|\lambda_1| > |\lambda_i|$, $i \geq 2$, then (5.4.1) reduced to the approximate equation $x^{(k+1)} = \lambda_1 x^{(k)}$ for large k. This means that each age cohort is (approximately) changing by the factor λ_1: increasing (if $\lambda_1 < 1$), static (if $\lambda_1 = 1$), or decreasing (if $\lambda_1 > 1$). So we can take the matrix A of (5.4.6), examine its eigenvalues, see if there is a maximal one and, if so, see that changes according to this factor. And the program of figures (5.3.2), (5.3.4) will supply those eigenvalues for examination.

We also want to incorporate into our study the effect of the human hunters on the prehistoric animal herds. We will assume that our human population doubles every 25 years (this is an annual growth rate of 2.8%) and that on the average each person eats 2.7 adult animals per year. These are very crude assumptions: we are not dividing the human population into age cohorts, nor are we making assumptions about the varying consumption rates among those cohorts. To include this data in our model (5.4.6), we add a new measure $y^{(k)}$, the number of humans after year k. The equations become, then:

$$x_1^{(k+1)} = 0.4x_3^{(k)}$$

$$x_2^{(k+1)} = 0.65x_1^{(k)}$$

$$x_3^{(k+1)} = 0.75x_2^{(k)} + 0.95\left(x_3^{(k)} - 2.7y^{(k)}\right)$$

$$y^{(k+1)} = 1.028y^{(k)}$$

In matrix form, these become

$$
(5.4.7) \quad
\begin{bmatrix}
0 & 0 & 0.4 & 0 \\
0.65 & 0 & 0 & 0 \\
0 & 0.75 & 0.95 & -2.565 \\
0 & 0 & 0 & 1.028
\end{bmatrix}
\begin{bmatrix}
x_1^{(k)} \\
x_2^{(k)} \\
x_3^{(k)} \\
x_4^{(k)}
\end{bmatrix}
=
\begin{bmatrix}
x_1^{(k+1)} \\
x_2^{(k+1)} \\
x_3^{(k+1)} \\
x_4^{(k+1)}
\end{bmatrix}
$$

or $Ax^{(k)} = x^{(k+1)}$, where A is the 4 by 4 matrix of coefficients of (5.4.7) and $x^{(k)}, x^{(k+1)}$ are the population 4-vectors.

At the end of the glacial era, there were about 37 million adults, 10.1 million juveniles, and 11.3 million newborn in the mammal herds in North America. Suppose 100 human hunters then cross into North America from Siberia. We are thus assuming, in (5.4.7), that

$$
x^{(0)} =
\begin{bmatrix}
37,000,000 \\
10,100,000 \\
11,300,000 \\
100
\end{bmatrix}
$$

From (5.4.7), in the version (5.4.3), we can predict the size of the herd 1000, 2000, and 3000 years later, that is, compute $x^{(1000)}, x^{(2000)}, x^{(3000)}$ (see Exercises 5.4).

We are considering here a two-species population where one preys on the other. In general, we can study a population by means of (5.4.4):

(5.4.8) Population Growth in Predator–Prey Populations. A fixed time interval T is specified. The prey population is divided into n cohorts $C_1, \ldots, C_n$:

C_i: individuals of age $(i - t)T$ to age $< iT$ $(i \neq n)$.
C_n: individuals of age $\geq nT$.

The predator population is divided into m cohorts $D_1, \ldots, D_m$:

D_1: individuals of age $(i - 1)T$ to age $< iT$ $(i \neq m)$.
D_m: individuals of age $\geq mT$.

An individual in C_i survives an additional T years with probability p_i and produce q_i offspring in those T years. Similarly, an individual in D_i survives with probability r_i and reproduces s_i offspring, and, in addition, consumes

d_{ji} individuals from cohort C_j. Let $x_i^{(k)}$ be the number of members of C_i and $y_i^{(k)}$ the number of members of D_i after k time intervals of length T have elapsed. Then

$$x_1^{(k+1)} = q_1 x_1^{(k)} + \cdots + q_n x_n^{(k)}$$

$$x_2^{(k+1)} = p_1\left(x_1^{(k)} - d_{11}y_1^{(k)} - d_{12}y_2^{(k)} - \cdots - d_{1m}y_m^{(k)}\right)$$

$$\vdots$$

$$x_{n-1}^{(k+1)} = p_{n-2}\left(x_{n-2}^{(k)} - d_{n-2,1}y_1^{(k)} - \cdots - d_{n-2,m}y_m^{(k)}\right)$$

$$x_n^{(k+1)} = p_{n-1}\left(x_{n-1}^{(k)} - d_{n-1,1}y_1^{(k)} - \cdots - d_{n-1,m}y_m^{(k)}\right)$$

$$+ p_n\left(x_n^{(k)} - d_{n,1}y_1^{(k)} - \cdots - d_{n,m}y_m^{(k)}\right)$$

$$y_1^{(k+1)} = s_1 y_1^{(k)} + \cdots + s_m y_m^{(k)}$$

$$y_2^{(k+1)} = r_1 y_1^{(k)}$$

$$\vdots$$

$$y_{m-1}^{(k+1)} = r_{m-2} y_{m-2}^{(k)}$$

$$y_m^{(k+1)} = r_{m-1} y_{m-1}^{(k)} + r_m y_m^{(k)}$$

These can be put in matrix form as follows: Let

$$(5.4.9) \quad x^{(k)} = \begin{bmatrix} x_1^{(k)} \\ \vdots \\ x_m^{(k)} \end{bmatrix} \quad y^{(k)} = \begin{bmatrix} y_1^{(k)} \\ \vdots \\ y_m^{(k)} \end{bmatrix} \quad z^{(k)} = \begin{bmatrix} x^{(k)} \\ y^{(k)} \end{bmatrix}$$

$$A = \begin{bmatrix} q_1 & & \cdots & q_n \\ p_1 & & & \\ & \ddots & & \\ & & p_{n-1} & p_n \end{bmatrix} \quad B = \begin{bmatrix} s_1 & & \cdots & s_m \\ r_1 & & & \\ & \ddots & & \\ & & r_{m-1} & r_m \end{bmatrix}$$

$$D = \begin{bmatrix} d_{11} & \cdots & d_{1m} \\ \vdots & & \vdots \\ d_{n1} & \cdots & d_{nm} \end{bmatrix}$$

$$C = \begin{bmatrix} A & -D \\ 0 & B \end{bmatrix}$$

Then

$$y^{(k+1)} = By^{(k)}$$

$$x^{(k+1)} = A\left(x^{(k)} - Dy^{(k)}\right)$$

$$z^{(k+1)} = Cz^{(k)}$$

Thus the population-with-predation model also is in the general form of a homogeneous matrix power model.

Examples of population models are considered further in the exercises at the end of this section.

B.   Linear Economies.   We have previously examined economies from the standpoint of meeting external demands (Section 2.3B) and from the standpoint of setting prices to achieve desired levels of operation (Section 3.2C). Both of these were essentially static situations. We now turn to a dynamic study, where we include economic growth in the model.

We assume an economy divided into n sectors, with $x_i^{(k)}$ representing the total dollar value in sector i for year k, $1 \le i \le n$. Typical sectors will be industries of various types, agriculture and its divisions, raw-material production and recovery, labor, and accounting sectors such as capital, government, and so on. As the years go by, we expect changes in the various sectors: an expanding population increases the labor supply; with luck, technological advances increase the productivity of that labor allowing surpluses to be directed into other activities, while the increased population requires an expansion in agriculture to feed it, and the increased production puts heavier demands on raw materials. The linkage between sectors over time can be very complex: raw materials, like oil for example, may be initially expensive, become cheaper as production methods become more efficient, and then become expensive again as the limits of the finite supply start to be approached. However, we will make the simplifying assumption that *the sectors are linked by linear relations*: for example, in the oil case, that production rises in a fixed proportion to demand, and in the case of labor that there is a constant rate of expansion in the work force. Such an assumption is reasonable over the short term, and leads to a model of the form $x^{(k+1)} = Ax^{(k)}$, where $x^{(k)}$ is the vector with entries $x_1^{(k)}, \ldots, x_n^{(k)}$, and A is the n by n matrix expressing the linear relations linking the sectors in the economy.

We will formulate these notions precisely below. First, however, an additional comment on the linearity assumption: the typical questions asked of economic models such as we are describing is a forecast of rate of growth or decline. For the economy as a whole, this is best described by the dominant eigenvalue (5.2.23) when there is one. It may take a large number of iterations for the dominant eigenvalue to actually dominate in the sense of Eq. (5.2.23). So we have the anomaly: the model's assumption of linear linkage is only valid in the short term, while analysis via dominant eigenvalues is only valid in the long term. Thus we must remember in this analysis that the predictions from these models are long-range forecasts assuming static relationships, when in fact the relationships will be changing. In a sense, we are using the long-range future potential as a measure of short-range future activity.

To return to precise formulations:

(5.4.10) A Linear Iterative Economy. The economy is divided into n sectors. $x_i^{(k)}$ is the total dollar value in sector i for year k, $1 \leq i \leq n$. Let b_{ij} be the dollar value contributed to sector i by \$1.00's worth of activity in sector j annually, $1 \leq i, j \leq n$. Let c_{ij} be the dollar value that must be inputted by sector j from sector i annually to produce an increase of \$1.00 in the total value of sector j that year, $1 \leq i, j \leq n$. Let

$$x^{(k)} = \begin{bmatrix} x_1^{(k)} \\ \vdots \\ x_n^{(k)} \end{bmatrix} \quad B = \begin{bmatrix} b_{11} & \cdots & b_{1n} \\ \vdots & & \vdots \\ b_{n1} & \cdots & b_{nn} \end{bmatrix} \quad C = \begin{bmatrix} c_{11} & \cdots & c_{1n} \\ \vdots & & \vdots \\ c_{n1} & \cdots & c_{nn} \end{bmatrix}$$

We assume that the entire value of each sector is available for use each year. If there were no costs (i.e., $C = 0$) then the passage from year k to year $k + 1$ would cause each $x_i^{(k)}$ to be increased by $b_{ij}x_j^{(k)}$ from sector j, $1 \leq j \leq n$, so we would have $x^{(k+1)} = Bx^{(k)}$. If there were only costs, the passage from year k to year $k + 1$ would cause each $x_i^{(k)}$ to be diminished by $c_{ij}x_i^{(k)}$ dollars by sector j, $1 \leq j \leq n$, so we would have $x^{(k+1)} = x^{(k)} - Cx^{(k)}$. Combining both processes, we assume that all the increases are made first and then all the costs charged, giving $x^{(k+1)} = Bx^{(k)} - Cx^{(k)}$ or

$$(5.4.11) \qquad x^{(k+1)} = Ax^{(k)} \quad \text{where} \quad A = B - C$$

The matrix A in (5.4.11) is the simple difference of costs and production. It is formulated in terms of the matrices B and C to make the examples easier to express. As with most economic models, a realistic analysis of a complex contemporary economy would require a very large number of sectors. In order to have a small-scale example to deal with, therefore, we will consider a scheme for space colonization, namely, mining an asteroid. This plan is designed to mine, refine, and ship a refined iron product from an asteroid whose mineral composition is sufficiently iron enriched to make this scheme profitable. The asteroid also contains silicon, oxygen, and water ice. The silicon will be employed to manufacture photovoltaic cells, which will be the project's primary energy source. The oxygen, mostly in the form of iron oxides, will be liberated in the iron refinement process. The water ice will be melted and recovered as liquid water also as an artifact of the refining process. Because of the asteroid's low gravity shipping the refined iron out and importing additional mining equipment is simple and cheap. Because of the quantities involved, however, it is not cost effective to import either the solar cells or any food, water, or oxygen necessary to support the humans running the project. It is, however, also cheap to bring in new human residents, and their living quarters, as the project expands. (The actual mining crew will rotate on and off station.) We will speak, thus, of increasing the crew size over time.

To describe this model in the terms of (5.4.10), we have the following data.

(5.4.12) An Asteroid Mining Project. The economy is divided into six sectors:

1. Agriculture: hydroponic algae culture producing food for the human crew.
2. Energy: electrical energy produced by locally made solar cells.
3. Manufacturing: processing the mined product to produce refined iron, free oxygen, liquid water, and silicon photovoltaic cells.
4. Mining: excavating and mechanically preparing (by crushing and sorting) the raw material of the asteroid.
5. Labor: the human work crew, operating highly technologically advanced mining and manufacturing equipment.
6. Export: the refined iron product (total value shipped to date).

These sectors are linked as follows:
Contributions from $1.00 unit of activity:

From Sector → To Sector ↓	1	2	3	4	5	6
1	100	0.05	0.1		0.05	
2			2			
3		0.45		2.7	0.70	
4		0.45			0.20	
5	1	0.05			0.05	
6			5			

Costs per $1.00 unit of activity:

By Sector From Sector	1	2	3	4	5	6
1	0.10				0.25	
2	0.02	0.01	0.50	0.35	0.25	0.30
3	0.05	0.10				
4		0.02	0.15			
5	0.10		0.15	0.25	0.10	0.05
6						

These two tables are the matrices B and C, respectively, of (5.4.10). Their difference is the matrix

$$(5.4.13) \quad A = \begin{bmatrix} 90.9 & 0.05 & 0.1 & 0 & -0.2 & 0 \\ -0.02 & -0.01 & 1.5 & -0.35 & -0.25 & -0.30 \\ -0.05 & 0.35 & 0 & 2.7 & 0.70 & 0 \\ 0 & 0.43 & -0.15 & 0 & 0.20 & 0 \\ 0.9 & 0.05 & -0.15 & -0.25 & -0.5 & -0.05 \\ 0 & 0 & 5 & 0 & 0 & 0 \end{bmatrix}$$

The project is then modeled by Eq. (5.4.11). The possible future of the project is examined in Exercises 5.4.

In general, when we have an economy modeled by (5.4.11), we can apply the analysis of (5.2.21) and (5.2.23): the first of these gives the forecasts for the economy in year k in terms of eigenvectors and eigenvalues, while the second shows the year-to-year change, approximately, for the case where a dominant real eigenvalue λ_1 exists. In this latter case, the economy approximately expands by a factor of λ_1 annually (if $\lambda_1 > 1$), contracts by that factor (if $\lambda_1 < 1$), or is static (if $\lambda_1 = 1$).

C. Linear Difference Equations. The examples we consider in this section are purely mathematical, although they do have applications in some other contexts. Suppose we have a sequence of numbers $f(1), f(2), f(3), \ldots,$ one for each positive integer p, defined by the following equations:

(5.4.14)

$$f(p + 1) = \alpha_0 f(p) + \alpha_1 f(p - 1) + \cdots + \alpha_n f(p - n) \quad \text{for} \quad p \geq n + 1$$

$$f(1) = b_1, \qquad f(2) = b_2, \ldots, \qquad f(n + 1) = b_{n+1}$$

The most famous example of such a sequence is the Fibonacci sequence $1, 1, 2, 3, 5, 8, 13, \ldots$, constructed according to the rule

$$f(p + 1) = f(p) + f(p - 1)$$

$$f(1) = 1, \qquad f(2) = 1$$

It is, of course, a trivial matter to compute the value of $f(p)$ in (5.4.14), for any desired p, by computing the values $f(1)$, $f(2)$, and so on, successively up to p. To predict the values of $f(p)$ for large p, or to study their changes, however, is more complicated. What is needed is a closed form of $f(p)$; that is, a direct functional expression of $f(p)$ as a function of p which does not require computing prior values. Such an expression follows from a matrix formulation of (5.4.14).

(5.4.15) Let the sequence $f(p)$ be specified by (5.4.14). For $p \geq n + 1$, we have

$$\begin{bmatrix} f(p+1) \\ f(p) \\ \vdots \\ f(p-n+1) \end{bmatrix} = \begin{bmatrix} \alpha_0 & \alpha_1 & \cdots & \alpha_n \\ 1 & & & \\ & 1 & & \\ & & \ddots & \\ & & 1 & 0 \end{bmatrix} \begin{bmatrix} f(p) \\ f(p-1) \\ \vdots \\ f(p-n) \end{bmatrix}$$

which we can write in matrix form as

(5.4.16) $\qquad x^{(p-n)} = Ax^{(p-n-1)} \qquad (p \geq n + 1)$

Since then

$$x^{(0)} = \begin{bmatrix} f(n+1) \\ f(n) \\ \vdots \\ f(1) \end{bmatrix} = \begin{bmatrix} b_{n+1} \\ b_n \\ \vdots \\ b_1 \end{bmatrix}$$

we have from (5.4.16) that

$$x^{(k)} = A^k x^{(0)}$$

or

(5.4.17) $\qquad x^{(p-n-1)} = A^{p-n-1} x^{(0)}$

Equation (5.4.17) can be analyzed by eigenvectors and eigenvalues using (5.2.21). If A has eigenvalues $\lambda_1, \ldots, \lambda_{n+1}$ and corresponding eigenvectors $v_1, \ldots, v_{n+1}$ and $x^{(0)} = a_1 v_1 + \cdots + a_{n+1} v_{n+1}$, then (5.4.17) becomes

$$(5.4.18) \qquad x^{(p-n-1)} = a_1 \lambda_1^{p-n-1} v_1 + \cdots + a_{n+1} \lambda_{n+1}^{p-n-1} v_{n+1}$$

Now assume that the first entry of v_i is w_{1i}, $1 \leq i \leq n+1$. Then reading off first entries in (5.4.18) gives

(5.4.19)

$$f(p) = a_1 \lambda_1^{p-n-1} w_{11} + a_2 \lambda_2^{p-n-1} w_{12} + \cdots + a_{n+1} \lambda_{n+1}^{p-n-1} w_{1,n+1}$$

$$(p \geq n+1)$$

This is, of course, a closed-form formula for f.

For example, consider the sequence

$$f(p+1) = 3f(p) - 2f(p-1) \qquad p \geq 2$$

$$f(1) = 1, \qquad f(2) = 2$$

In matrix form (5.4.15), this becomes

$$\begin{bmatrix} f(p+1) \\ f(p) \end{bmatrix} = \begin{bmatrix} 3 & 2 \\ 1 & 0 \end{bmatrix} \begin{bmatrix} f(p) \\ f(p-1) \end{bmatrix} \qquad (p \geq 2)$$

$$A = \begin{bmatrix} 3 & -2 \\ 1 & 0 \end{bmatrix} \qquad x^{(0)} = \begin{bmatrix} 1 \\ 2 \end{bmatrix}$$

It is easy to compute eigenvectors and eigenvalues of A by hand. We find eigenvalues $\lambda_1 = 1$, $\lambda_2 = 2$, and corresponding eigenvectors

$$v_1 = \begin{bmatrix} 1 \\ 1 \end{bmatrix} \qquad v_2 = \begin{bmatrix} 2 \\ 1 \end{bmatrix} \quad \text{so} \quad x^{(0)} = 3v_1 + (-1)v_2$$

then (5.4.18) becomes

$$x^{(p-2)} = 3(1)^{p-2} v_1 + (-1)(2)^{p-2} v_2$$

and (5.4.19) becomes

$$f(p) = 3 - 2^{p-1} \qquad p \geq 2$$

More complicated examples are covered in Exercises 5.4.

EXERCISES 5.4

Use the programs of Figures (5.3.2) or (5.3.7) to do the calculations in these exercises.

1. (a) Calculate the dominant eigenvalue (and hence the rate of increase) for the animal herd of (5.4.6) prior to human intervention; and (b) compute the size of the herds 1000, 2000, and 3000 years after human arrival.

2. Two fish species, one of which preys on the other, inhabit the same territory. Suppose that the prey species is divided into three cohorts (ages 0–1, 1–2, and over 2) and the predator species into two cohorts (ages 0–1 and over 1). Assume that populations parameters (5.4.8) are given by:

$$p_1 = 0.5, \qquad p_2 = 0.7, \qquad p_3 = 0.75, \qquad q_1 = 0, \qquad q_2 = 10,$$

$$q_3 = 25 \qquad r_1 = 0.4, \qquad r_2 = 0.6, \qquad s_1 = 0, \qquad s_2 = 30,$$

$$d_{12} = 15, \qquad d_{22} = 8 \quad \text{and all other } d_{ij} \text{ coefficients are 0.}$$

Assume that in some year the prey species has 10,000 members ages 0–1, 6000 members ages 1–2, and 6000 members over 2, while the predator species has 2000 members ages 0–1 and 4000 members over 1. What will be the status of the population after 40 years? [use Eq. (5.4.3)].

3. (a) Calculate the eigenvalues for (5.4.12). Is there a dominant real one? (b) Suppose total dollar value in each sector in year zero is $1–10^5$, $2–10^4$, $3–10^3$, $4–10^4$, $5–10^5$, and $6–10^3$. What will be the dollar values in year 20? [use Eq. (5.4.3)].

4. A subsistence farming operation has been observed to consist of six sectors:

    1. Labor (supplied by the resident farm family).
    2. Grain.
    3. Poultry (for both meat and eggs).
    4. Livestock (milk cows and sheep raised for wool).
    5. Produce (vegetables and fruit).
    6. Sales (surplus wool and grain sold for cash).

The linkages are expressed in the following tables:
Contributions per dollar unit:

From To	1	2	3	4	5	6
1	0.05	0.40	0.50	0.40	0.30	0.20
2	0.30	0.02				0.10
3	0.10	0.20	0.60		0.10	0.10
4	0.10	0.20			0.10	0.10
5	0.15					0.10
6	0.01	0.04		0.10		

Costs per dollar unit:

By From	1	2	3	4	5	6
1		0.60	0.50	0.30	0.40	0.50
2	0.30	0.10	0.20	0.50		0.20
3	0.20		0.10		0.10	
4	0.20	0.10			0.10	0.20
5	0.10					
6	0.10		0.10		0.10	

Assume that in year zero the dollar values per sector are labor ($100), grain ($250), poultry ($200), livestock ($300), produce ($100), and sales ($25). Use Eq. (5.4.3) to forecast the values per sector in years 5, 10, and 25.

5. Find the closed form (5.4.19) for the solutions of the following difference equations:

(a) $f(p + 1) = f(p) - f(p - 1) + f(p - 2)$
  $f(1) = 1, \quad f(2) = 1, \quad f(3) = -1$

(b) $f(p + 1) = 2f(p) + 3f(p - 1) - f(p - 3)$
  $f(1) = 5, \quad f(2) = 4, \quad f(3) = 1 = f(4) = 2$

(c) $f(p + 1) = f(p - 4)$
  $f(1) = f(2) = f(3) = f(4) = 0, \quad f(5) = 1$

5.5 MARKOV PROCESSES

There are many systems deserving of, and amenable to, study by the methods of linear homogeneous discrete time iterative analysis whose long-range behavior is unpredictable. As an example, we can consider an atom being bombarded by a photon beam. Assume that the (quantum) physics of the atom allow it to be in just three possible conditions, or energy levels—low, medium, and high. A passing photon in the beam can miss the atom completely, interact with the atom by absorption, thereby raising the energy level, or interact with the atom by stimulated emission, thereby lowering the energy level. Also, left to itself, the atom can transition to a lower energy level by spontaneous emission. All of these events happen at random, although with fixed probabilities over a given time interval. What we propose to do is use these probabilities to describe the expected state of the atom after a large number of these time intervals. Obviously we can't hope to say which of the energy levels will actually be observed: these change at random. What we do is change our notion of "state" of a system. The three possible conditions of the atom we will think of as pure states, but we also want to allow states which involve mixtures of these pure states. Such a mixed state will be a triple (p_1, p_2, p_3) whose meaning is that the atom is in the first energy level with probability p_1, the second with probability p_2, and the third with probability p_3. Now it *is* possible to say that the atom is in a certain state after a large number of time intervals: this means that for subsequent observations the probability that the various energy levels are observed are the entries in this state. This example, which will be studied numerically below, is an example of the sort of random process that will be accessible to linear analysis. We now define what we mean by such a process.

(5.5.1). Markov Process. A Markov process is a system which can be in a finite number of conditions $C_1, C_2, \ldots, C_n$. In a given and fixed time interval T, the system undergoes random transitions from condition to condition. The probability that the system transitions from condition C_j *to* condition C_i in time T is denoted p_{ij} $(1 \le i, j \le n)$. We call p_{ij} the *transition probability* and the n by n matrix

$$P = \begin{bmatrix} p_{11} & \cdots & p_{1n} \\ \vdots & & \vdots \\ p_{n1} & \cdots & p_{nn} \end{bmatrix}$$

the *transition matrix* of the process.